# BELL IN THE TREE

# BELL *in the* TREE
## THE GLASGOW STORY

## EDWARD CHISNALL

MAINSTREAM
PUBLISHING

First published in Great Britain 1990 by
MAINSTREAM PUBLISHING COMPANY (EDINBURGH) LTD
7 Albany Street, Edinburgh EH1 3UG

ISBN 1 85158 293 2 (paper)

British Library Cataloguing in Publication Data
Chisnall, Edward H.
  Bell in the Tree
  I. Title
  823′.914 [F]

  ISBN 1-85158-293-2

Thanks are due to Wm Teacher & Sons Ltd, makers of Teachers Highland Cream Scotch
Whisky and established in Glasgow since 1830, for help and support in the production
of the radio series.

Typeset in Times Roman by Blackpool Typesetting Services Ltd, Blackpool.
Printed in Great Britain by Martin's of Berwick.

To my wife Margaret,
and my daughter Tabitha Jane.

Bell in the Tree is also dedicated to the figure
in brown who haunts my studio and looks over my
shoulder at three in the morning,
and the people of Glasgow wherever and whenever
they may be, travellers all.

Thank you also for help and additional
information to Gerry Slevin, Bill Murphy of Mossend,
John Ross, Eddie Friel.

*The time-traveller is Russell Hunter.*

# CONTENTS

# THE TRAVELLER'S SONG

Back lanes and grey ways, wynds and courts,
Thin ruins spread like shadows,
Far below the century's footfalls
And the River's tides.

Wooden mansions driven into the stony hill
Like spikes to halt the flow of dreams
That wash down brook and burnside in
The hilly country.

Every moment of a thousand years a church,
A Cathedral, a great thorn points its finger,
While some tinker's ghost with spectral dog,
Seeks for a bed long covered up in
Layered glass, and time, clear and hard as glass.

Here on the valley shore that looked down
On the builders of continents, the makers
Of ships, and words, of death and
Softness in a thousand cramped spaces,
And lost causes, and flight, pounding things,
Here lamps open on the balconies,
One, and one, and one
Like stars locked in stone,
Or flowers in a basket of laughter,
Or willows drenching the aisles of the Autumn roads,
Or the long afternoon filled with a white light,
Or you on a tram, and me in a room,
And them in a house, all painted up to
The barriers of the grey and green city
In its island of green.

Miles away it ends where the air smells cold,
And the grass is rust,
And in the hump yards bobbing lanterns nod,
And overhead the planets pull and tug,
And sleepers walk, and blind men look at God.

And at the end of the edge where the fields are,
Beyond, far away, bells chime in distant spires,
Trees blossom in the groves,
Fish, like darting tongues of light fill stream and pool.
The morning. A Sparrow lives again and sings.

Edward H. Chisnall                    *Glasgow 1989*

# FOREWORD

SEVEN years ago, in 1983, when Glasgow was celebrating the bicentenary of the oldest Chamber of Commerce in Britain and that of the *Glasgow Herald* (not to mention our own tenth birthday!), Radio Clyde produced a series of short dramas broadcast each weekday with the title *The Bell in The Tree*. The series was widely acclaimed and won the prestigious gold medal at the New York International Radio Festival. Equally important, our listeners thoroughly enjoyed it and such was the demand for a written version of some of the stories we produced two paperbacks with the same title.

Most important of all perhaps, we realised in our various conversations with Edward Chisnall, that we had merely scraped the surface of his vast knowledge of out-of-the-way information about Glasgow's past.

In deciding our programme of contributions to Glasgow's year as European City of Culture, one of the first and simplest of decisions was to commission Edward Chisnall to write another 261 episodes which would be produced for broadcast. With the benefit of our experience in 1983 behind us, we also knew that many who would listen to the series, or indeed who might unfortunately not be able to listen, would welcome a book. In the new series we have introduced a guide, who, like Kilroy, was there. And in the book we have also harnessed Edward Chisnall's considerable artistic talents to provide the illustrations.

The result is a book that we at Radio Clyde are proud to be associated with and which we hope will continue to be enjoyed long after 1990. The history, culture and above all the characters of Glasgow should, after all, transcend any one year or celebration.

*James Gordon CBE*

*It takes more than one pair of shoes to walk back from 140 A.D. – 1,850 years of lang Scots miles ago . . . They call me The Traveller, and I've travelled them all, The Bell in the Tree will take you to the places I've been, and the folk who made them. Punters and princes, wars and weddings, people just like you and me, building and sailing, laughing and crying. There were wild adventurers and chronic dafties, rascals, saints, dreamers and inventors, and the uncounted thousands of men and women, who have left their mark on the stones and bones of the old town just by being there.*

*The road to modern Glasgow began when the Romans came, saw and stayed for a while. They built outposts in the badlands along the Antonine Wall at places like Kirkintilloch, Croy Hill and, before the ancient Picts and Celts demolished it in passing, the Clydeside fort of Cathures.*

THE sun glittered on the puddles the recent rain had left on the sandstone paving of the open courtyard. As he marched past the collonade, Claudius Sextus, hard-bitten centurion of the First Cohort of the Victrix, was a long way from his native Apulia. He sniffed unhappily. The land of the Scotii was almost as bad as Trans-Danubia or North Germany – wet, inhospitable and peopled by wild tribes who were at best thieves and at worst as warlike as any barbarians in the Empire. Claudius was an old stager and had seen the lot, but the policy of taking men from one part of the Roman dominions and sending them to the other end usually meant that you were sent to the parts that no other self-respecting Roman would, or could, reach.

These were the lands of the impenetrable Caledonian Forest, and apart from a brief stay at the naval signal station on the rock of ail Clyd further down the river Clyd, he had spent almost his entire tour keeping up the morale of men who were as wet and miserable as he was.

The Emperor Antonine had decided to build a defensive wall from Old Kilpatrick to Bo'ness on the Bodotria Estuary to the east, and the Governor of Britain, Lollius Urbicus, had decreed that each of the 19 forts had to force the unwilling tatooed locals to build both the wall and the 18-foot wide military road that ran beside it. The work was completed, but the attacks went on. Only this morning he had looked out from the battlements and seen the pallid sunlight glinting on bronze spear-tips in the woods across the river. The Scotii would never be civilized. Anyone who charged naked into battle with hair sticking up in great mud-covered spikes was not cut out to wear the toga or take part in settled trade. They brewed a drink which was said to make them invincible – it certainly made them think they were. Claudius had managed to get hold of some once and still remembered the suicidal tendencies the next day, and the hole in his leather armour where old Fortus had spilled some "Water of Life" before he fell off the table he had been dancing on.

And so they sat it out, the spike-headed Scotii licking their swords in the bushes, and the miserable Romans wondering what the Emperor could possibly want with a land that was given over to bears, beavers and wild men.

Claudius sniffed again and drew his linen sleeve across his upper lip with resignation. Today's visit by Quaestor Gambrinus from the Fourteenth Station at Cadder was a welcome break in the unrelieved boredom, even though he couldn't stand the man. Gambrinus was a dandy, appointed by a high-ranking uncle somewhere in Gaul. He was spending the shortest possible time in Caledonia and making it perfectly clear that he could go where and when he liked, even if the likes of the benighted Victrix had to slog it out in the middle of a cloud somewhere on the edge of nowhere.

"Why do you always have to STAMP everywhere, Claudius Sextus?" Quaestor Gambrinus was wrapped from head to foot in an enormous red woollen cloak, so that his pale aristocratic face looked like an afterthought sewn on the front of his broad-brimmed Lombardy hat. "I've had to leave a too-lovely hot bath and simply drag myself here in a sedan-chair," Gambrinus continued, drawling as if even the use of words was somehow beneath his dignity.

Claudius saluted smartly, his arm stiff, palm outwards. "Ave Gambrinus, Quaestor Imperat . . ."

Gambrinus interrupted him rudely. "Yes. Yes, man. I know who I am. This isn't Londinium or Rome. Just because some stylus-pusher in Deva . . ." He paused to put something in his mouth and continued, chewing as he spoke, ". . . somebody takes it into their head to relieve the Victrix with some beastly slingshot unit, the Baetisi. Then the whole thing is snarled up with a duplicate posting of that dreadful Hamii crowd. THEY burnt down a whole street of taverns in Eburacum . . . Who are the barbarians, eh? Tell me that . . . ?"

The Centurion waited politely to see if an answer was required, but, before Gambrinus could resume complaining and chewing at the same time, Claudius realised what the man had been saying. "Quaestor!" he exclaimed with growing excitement. "You did say . . . RELIEVING the Victrix. You mean we . . . we're going home . . . ?"

Gambrinus dug deep into the satchel beneath his cloak for another morsel of quail pâté coated with honey. Finding nothing, he looked up, frowning. "Didn't I just say so, man? Contain yourself, Centurion . . ." He took a step backwards.

Claudius stood to attention sheepishly.

"In the name of Fortuna and Mithras," Gambrinus said, forgetting to drawl. "How dare you embrace me? Where's your Roman discipline?" He narrowed his eyes and smiled at Claudius. "Perhaps . . . later . . . ?"

Claudius, having saluted the official hastily, was a good soldier, and knew when to retreat.

"The Quarter-Master thought I had been at the local fire-water again when I asked him for a stylus and wax tablet," Fortus protested. "I didn't tell him it was because you wanted to dictate your story. Wouldn't do for that kind of rumour to get about."

They were standing by the barracks window looking over the long sweep of the hill down to the river, cleared except for a few bushes, to prevent sneak attacks by the locals.

"I've killed a few savages on a good day," Claudius replied apologetically. "I've patrolled every 37 miles of this wall too, so write it down for me, Fortus, since I never knew how. I won't take it back with me. I'll leave it here. Maybe somebody will find it years from now when this damned wall is forgotten."

Fortus sat down on the bunk and looked at his friend doubtfully. "If you say so, Claudius," he said, scratching the tablet with the pointed stylus experimentally. "Well . . .?"

Drawing himself to attention in front of the window, Claudius took a deep breath. "Well what?"

"Well start it then," urged the old soldier.

"I Claudius," began the Centurion . . ."I Claudius of the way fort at Cathures in the land of the Caledonians, Centurion of the Twentieth Valeria Victrix, farmer from Apulia . . ."

The two figures crouching in the undergrowth stared open-mouthed up at the long, low barracks buildings and the figure framed by the window.

"Ma woad's runnin' in the rain, so it is," said wee Liam, known to the tribe as Liam alone because of his worse than usual attention to personal hygeine.

"Shut it, youse," his brother Lug replied, cuffing him across the ear absently. "I'll gie ye mor'n woad in a meenit, so ah wull."

Liam was determined. "They'll see us, Lug. Would we noat be better gettin' a joab, like bein' a slave or somethin' . . . ?"

Lug turned and looked at his weaker sibling patiently. "Ur you aff yer heid?" he asked. "And get yer spikes oot ma eye. Stop yer greetin' and when it's proper dork Lug'll get ye a nice pair o' sandals or a good fryin' pan or somethin'. The Romans aye leave somethin' behind them. Clothes, a jug or twa, a wall . . . dead careless so they are."

*There was a time when the hills where Glasgow stands today were covered with a dear, dark green, murky, bracken-filled forest. Its shadowy dells and thickets were full of Druids, dryads, dolmens, wild beasts and wilder Welsh-speaking heid-bangers. I remember wading across the Clyde, the "Clyd" it was called then, in the year 425 A.D. – 1,565 years before this morning's milk. There were only a few fisherfolk about, living in tiny wattle huts clustered about the ford. Some of them were refugees from the Saxons and Northmen, who were working very hard at burning and pillaging everything they could lay their large, hairy hands on. Anyone travelling more than a pebble-throw from their hearth stone was taking their head in their hands, as we still say in Glasgow.*

*It took a lot of nerve to come to a land where unwary citizens were stuffed in wicker cages and set alight, just to make things go better in the New Year: nerve, a rugged resistance to rheumatism, and faith. Saint Mungo, our own Saint Mungo, had plenty of those things when he arrived by the Clyde. He built his Church or "Glas" and set about converting the wild Clydesiders to Christianity, a process which some people say is still going on. Mungo was a friendly chap, in fact his nickname "Cu" which means friend, stuck. So "cu" built his "glas" . . . and it's still there, in a place called GLASCU!*

THE blue wood-smoke that was too lazy to curl its way up through the hole in the roof lay like a hazy blanket in the air, filling the gaps in the twigs and ferns that poked downwards from the roof-tree of the hut. Little tongues of fire darted fitfully upwards from the sooty hearth stones huddled in the middle of the earth floor. A constant drizzle of water dripped down from the branches, where the hut roof sloped back to meet the upward sweep of the banks of the Clyd.

"I'm fair sick to death o' fish," Gran wheezed from her favourite spot by the fire. "Salmon... salmon aw' day. Nothin' but salmon..."

Her daughter Maeve thumped a huge fish down on the shiny tree-stump that served as a table and scraped her precious iron knife on a smooth stone. "Fish is good for ye, Gran," she observed stolidly, splitting the glistening carcase with the ease of long practice. "It's our living. There's that many traders comin' past here in the summer it keeps us frae starving like we did after the Rathsmen burnt us oot of the rigs at Perdyc Inch."

"It didny stop the bairn dying at Samain!" Gran hunched her thin shoulders towards the sputtering fire.

"Och, there's anither on the way," Maeve observed philosophically, depositing the inside of the fish on the growing mound at her feet.

"Anither mouth to feed," Gran replied bitterly, rocking backwards and forwards as she sat, knees drawn up to her bony chin. "And see that man of yours..." she refused to let go. "He eats enough for... for ten!" She silently counted the number with her fingers as she spoke. "If he was half of the half of a man your father and your brothers were before the raiders took them..." She broke off and lapsed into a fit of reedy coughing.

Maeve rounded on her angrily. "Mither!" she blazed to the defence of her husband. "He's out there like as not in the Clyd right up to his oxters the now! Just to give us, give YOU, a living."

A gust of wind and rain blew across the floor of hut. The fire hissed in protest.

*13*

"Sean, draw that cloth shut when ye come in!" Maeve protested as the hard-pressed Sean elbowed his way through the narrow entrance to the hut.

"Look what I've brought you." He held out his day's catch apologetically.

"There's mair salmon in that daft river than watter, so there is," Gran observed tartly. "See . . . afore my guidman Tingmoot was killed stone deid and they chopped his heid aff . . . he knew how to look after his family proper, and here we are . . . anither on the way . . ."

Sean looked at her sharply, then at his wife. "There's no' . . . no' another breadsnapper comin' is there?" he demanded. "Have you been sayin' your prayers to Belenos and the Wood Gods, Maeve?"

Maeve busied herself with some loose eyes. "I don't know how it can have happened, darlin'," she muttered. "I've tied the right herbs round ma neck every night."

Gran snorted sardonically but said nothing.

Sean's angry reply was drowned out by a cacophony of howling, woofs and staccato yelps from outside the lean-to. Another burst of cold air and icy wet was accompanied by an inrush of dogs of various shapes and sizes. The small cauldron of tepid water beside Gran was knocked over amid a flurry of wet paws and unkempt tails.

"Fang! Wolf! Jinty! Get tae Hades oot o' here by Belisama, and..." Sean stopped short as he turned and saw the tall stranger looking through the open doorway.

"Could you give me shelter for a while, friends?" The voice was firm but pleasant.

The dogs stopped bristling, swallowed their low growls, and sat looking at the stranger expectantly.

"Sit!" Sean said to the hounds unnecessarily.

The stranger laughed. "It seems they are," he said. "Do you think I might also? I have come a long way. Don't be afraid, I mean you no harm."

"Who's afraid?" demanded Sean aggressively. "What dae ye want?"

"A little shelter, a little rest... my friend."

"His... his name's Sean," Maeve spoke, sensing something in the stranger that she had not met before. "Are you just yerself?"

The man smiled again, a warm smile that seemed to cast a light across a face lined and tired but full of hope. The fire blazed up and crackled merrily amongst the stones. "No." The stranger walked quickly into the hut. "No, lady, Sean. There is another."

Sean took a halting step backwards and reached for the fish-knife. "I knew it!" he shouted. "There's more of ye! Get back or I'll give ye... THIS!" He brandished the knife threateningly.

The stranger held out both his hands palm upwards. "Do not be afraid," he said quietly. "My companion is also a fisherman, like you. His name is Jesus."

14

"Aye well, he's not fishing here. This is my bit," Sean replied sullenly, keeping the knife pointed at the cowled figure.

"My friend fishes for men, not salmon."

Gran chuckled by the fire. "That would make a change."

"You'll not get round me that way," Sean countered. "Who said you could come in here? What's your name?"

"I am the friend of Saint Servanus. My name is Moncu."

The fire cast dancing shadows on Moncu's brown robe.

Sean sneered. "Ahh..." he said. "Wan of thae Christians. Well, Moncu, we've got Gods of oor ain in this house, good wans. They look after us, see!" He paused, "Er... see your Gods...?"

"Only one," Moncu replied.

"Aye, well, maybe that would be enough," mused Sean, rubbing his chin with the back of a grimy hand. "Can your... God, do anything about weans?"

"Yes, baptise them."

"What does that mean when it's at home?" Sean snorted.

"It means," replied Moncu, scratching one of the dogs behind the ear absently, "...that they too can become fishers of men."

Maeve stepped forward, wiping her hands on her ragged skirt. "Would you... could you... baptise my bairn that's on the way?" she asked softly.

Sean took hold of her elbow. "That's not the kind of help I mean," he said, his eyes glaring.

Maeve shook him off. "Hold your tongue, Sean. The new bairn will need a friend as well as a father." She looked closely at the tall stranger. "Won't he... MUNGO?"

*15*

*When the Monday morning motorway traffic is down to a crawl for six miles and a milk tanker has collided with a cornflakes lorry near the Burrell Gallery, it's worth remembering that there was a time when there were no roads in Glasgow at all. For all that, traffic could still be bad, with ox-gangs – huge wagons pulled by teams of eight oxen – struggling into the city by the half-dozen.*

*Glasgow was a city then, of course. A papal Bull in 1172 had called it a "Civitas" which means city, and with almost 3,000 inhabitants how could they be wrong? Glasgow Fair was a going concern after 1190 when King William the Lion gave fat old Bishop Jocelyn a Charter to hold fairs weekly and an annual fair in July.*

*But back to the traffic . . . in 1195, 795 years of Monday mornings ago, the muddy track that ran up the Great Eastern Way – modern Duke Street, and once a Roman road – was full of mules and wagons loaded down with goods from foreign parts, like Flanders and France, England and even . . . Edinburgh.*

MORE like a small wooden castle than a wagon, the great wain rumbled and squelched painfully up the hill past the Ladywell. Wheels that could have stood in for the Round Table at Camelot splashed over pot-holes and through rivers of grey mud, as eight bedraggled oxen strained and sweated in their yokes to pull the leviathan up the brae and then down the High Street to the Glasgow Fair. Small dogs yapped and nipped at the stolid beasts toiling into the busy market town. The driver, perched high in front of the canvas arch that tented in his store of goods, applied his thonged whip with a will, whistling through yellow teeth.

"Soon be there, my girls!" He spat high in the air and snapped his whip among the flies clustered around the ox-gang.

"That us noo, Davie?" A thatched mop of red hair crowning a cavernous yawn was thrust out of the gloom at the back of the wagon.

Davie the driver stared ahead woodenly. "No' yet," he replied sourly. "Had enough rest have ye, Rory?"

Rory scratched the back of his head energetically.

"Nothing like a good sleep at yer work," Davie said.

Impassive as the eight great beasts in the cloud of clegs in front, Rory yawned again and smiled toothlessly.

"Och, yer right, Davie,"he yawned, his jaw making a cracking sound."The back of the wagon's warm as the sheep the wool came affa, from . . . wherever they call the place."

Davie sniffed. He always sniffed before showing off his knowledge of current affairs. "Ghent, Flanders, Broogies . . . aw' thae towns away south of Scotland."

"Never been abroad maself," Rory stared blankly up at the high cirrus clouds making ripples in the morning a mile above the valley.

"You've been to Edwinsburgh!"

"Aye, right enough." Rory thought for a moment, his face screwed up as if in pain. "See those bogs down from the castle . . . terrible bad for all kind of flies, so they are. I don't know how the Edwinsburgers can stand it!"

"Och, they're all right," Davie cracked his whip again. "Clegs don't bite other clegs," he added with relish.

Rory nudged him in the ribs with a bony elbow. "Some whale though, eh?" He winked slowly, a picture not unlike a cow backing out of a haystack.

"Where?" Davie looked about him doubtfully. The trees of the Black Frairs' orchards nodded in the wind, a sea of fallow silver below the dip and rise of the long shadow of the Cathedral.

"Not here," said Rory, exasperated. "Not here," he added for emphasis. "Over therr. . . Stirling, ya mug!"

Dawn broke in the back of Davie's brain. "Awww . . ." he smiled. "It certainly was. Big as a house. Big as twa or three, maybe. That's a town for ye, Stirling. Ships, whales, wimmen. Smells a bit, though," he added thoughtfully.

Rory sniffed deeply.

Davie rounded on him. "Not me! Stirling!"

Rory changed the subject tactfully. "You get sick of travelling the world, so ye dae."

Ahead of them the sky darkened momentarily. Great crowds of corbies, black rooks from the woods above the Garngad and Springburn hills to the north, were wheeling and diving in a solid mass. They swooped over the wagon and Davie and his companion heard one harsh dark "Crrroakkk" before they turned and resumed diving and weaving their black wings in and out, a patch of night sailing across the morning sky.

"There's more'n . . . ten," observed Rory, counting on his fingers.

"That's the Hangingcross," Davie lowered his voice and made the sign against the evil eye, " . . . where they string up the smoorers of bairns and the lassieknappers."

"And burn the witches," added Rory with relish, licking his lips.

Davie cracked his whip solemnly. "Ye know, Rory," he mused. "You can always tell you're getting into Glasgow when you see the deid bodies coming over the hill . . ."

Dogs barked and chased their tails. A juggler tossed brightly coloured cloth balls or slim bottles high in the air where they glittered briefly, before tumbling head-over-heels back into the outstretched fingers of the laughing man. Brats mewled and women puked; the Northumbrian pipes, squeezed tight under a tinker's arm, wailed with the gusto of a newborn jig, thrust unwilling into the world. Friars, mendicants, pickpockets, both amateur and professional, white-faced young girls with cheeks like roses and ankles spattered with mud, vendors selling black bread, ripe herring, twists and bunches of ribbon and fustian cloth . . . it was 1195 and Glasgow Fair was in full swing.

Bishop Jocelyn strode proudly through the throng, a ship of state, bald as a turnip.

"Make way for my Lord the Bishop," cried Friar Anselm desperately, lifting up the hem of his surtout as he scurried after his portly master.

Oblivious, Jocelyn sailed ahead, cleaving a path through the multi-coloured

citizenry. "You are in fine voice today, Anselm!" he grinned as the little man caught up with him and stood, panting like a rabbit. "A far cry from your cell on Oronsay!"

His words were drowned out by a frenetic skirl from the tinker's chanter.

"What did you say, my Lord?" asked Anselm breathlessly.

"Oronsay, man," Jocelyn replied tartly.

A wistful look came into the grey eyes of the diminutive friar. "To be sure, there were no gypsies and mountebanks there, Lord Bishop. Only the skua and the tern."

Hardly less in girth if not dignity than the Bishop, a birdwife approached the pair, cages and bundles hanging from her round shoulders, stuffed full of feathered panic. "Good larks for your table, My Lords," she said.

"Off you go, woman!" Friar Anselm drew himself up to his full four foot two. "My Lord the Bishop is not concerned with kitchen matters."

"And what about yourself then, master?" she replied pleasantly. "I've a good brace of widgeon."

"You mean, pigeon."

The woman grinned, full cheeks and an acre of freckles. "No, bless you. Cushat. Doos. Ye do ken doos, don't ye? I've some good fresh speugs and all."

"Woman, Blessed Saint Mungo breathed life into the sparrow," Bishop Jocelyn looked down at her good-naturedly, while Anselm tugged at his robe. "Be still, Anselm," Jocelyn rounded on his secretary. "This is our Congregation. Saint Columba was the Dove of the Church and Saint Kentigern was . . ."

"There's no harm in selling deid birds, or live wans is there, Lord?" enquired the birdwife with a frown. "A great lord like you would know."

Bishop Jocelyn expanded visibly and beamed, glowing like an apple in the firelight. "Honest trade is indeed . . . honest, my good woman. Honour God and his Saints and, er, perhaps . . . you might have a fair capon about your person?"

"Aw," the birdwife looked desolate. "I'm sorry, Lord. No capon or chicken. Just doos. Fair doos . . ."

*18*

*The Bonnie Bonnie Banks of Loch Lomond . . . now there's a name to conjure with and the place to be on a summer's day. Half an hour's drive from the middle of Glasgow and there's Ben Lomond, Rowardennan, purple heather, all on the doorstep of the highways and byways of old Second City land.*

*It was more than a mere step away before cars and coaches, of course, 727 years ago in long-ago 1268. I happened to be out that way late one afternoon. I was travelling, you might say I still am. I was leaning against a tree thinking deep thoughts and eating a stale piece of cheese. It was like eating an old friend. The cheese and I had come a long way together. Just along the track that led to the village of Balloch I saw some rough-looking customers with huge axes strapped on their backs. They didn't look as though they were in the mood to pass the time of day or help out a travelling man, except perhaps with the toe of their iron-shod boots, so I "vanished". After the first few centuries you learn how to vanish very effectively, believe me!*

*These lads had huge beards, some of them so long that they were tucked into their belts, along with a rather nasty assortment of knives, daggers, swords, and other unpleasant bits of sharp iron. They were dragging a boat across logs towards the loch. It seems like yesterday, more than 265,000 yesterdays since I saw those Vikings on the banks of Loch Lomond . . . !*

IF the seagulls of Kerrera sound had heard of Santa Claus they would have thought that Christmas had arrived, but then it was April and the men swarming on the decks of 200 black Viking drakkars in the bay had never heard of Christmas either.

The tent overlooking the bay was warm and stuffy, even though the charcoal in the bronze brazier in the centre had been cold for an hour or more. Ragnar stuck his head gingerly round the tent flap and peered inside. "Sire?" he enquired softly. "King Haakon? The Toiseachs of the Islands are here!"

The energetic snoring that had been going on under a pile of rather tired-looking furs in the corner ceased abruptly. "Whhaa . . . Who?" said a reindeer pelt sleepily. Bear, deer and beaver hides stampeded limply to the floor as the great King Haakon, last of the Bloodaxe Reavers staggered to his feet. "Odin's blood! What is it? What's up?" he demanded, turning suddenly and colliding with the tent pole.

"All's well, my Lord King," said Ragnar soothingly, striding into the tent. "The Chieftains of the Scottish Isles have come at last."

King Haakon adjusted his shirt and sat down on a pile of shields with a clank. "This must be played carefully, Ragnar my boy. We must impress them with our might," he sneezed, "and terror."

Ragnar looked affectionately at the ageing King, remembering fondly the monasteries they had sacked in their youth. "Two hundred dragon-prowed drakkars fill the bay, Lord King, aye, and near 2,000 Vikings stand ready. We shall 'impress' the islesmen. No doubt of it."

A twinge of rheumatism dug its bony fingers into Haakon's thigh and he stretched his legs stiffly.

"Are you well, my Lord?" Ragnar watched anxiously as the pain flickered across his master's face.

*19*

"Well enough." Haakon stood up with determination. Bring me my mail hauberk and the belt with the gold lilies I picked up in, where was it . . .?"

"Somewhere in France, my Lord," Ragnar replied rummaging amongst the clothes and booty piled at the back of the tent.

Pain struck the old Viking again, "Damn you!" he cried out. "Fafnir's Scrotum and Sigurd's Sandals! Bring the lot, Ragnar."

There was an unceremonious clatter.

"Try not to drop my sword again, Ragnar," said Haakon patiently.

Ragnar knelt in front of the greying giant, "'Brainbiter', Sire. Your ancient blade."

Haakon took the sword and felt its weight. Strength seemed to pass out of the handle and along his arm like a neap tide rushing up a narrow fiord. "These Scots are ripe for alliance, Ragnar. We have fought back and forth over these islands. When we refused to sell the Western Isles to Alexander III he ravaged Skye and Mull. He has driven the Western Lords into our hands. With the help and knowledge of these Toiseachs we will take back the West, and the South, and whatever else the Scots leave lying about." He grunted and breathed in as Ragnar buckled his sword belt about his waist. "You know, Ragnar," he continued as he was dressed. "We have the King of Man, the Earl of Orkney. Strathclyde is as good as in ours and . . ."

There was a ringing clatter at his feet.

"'Brainbiter', your ancient blade, Lord," said Ragnar meekly, lifting the sword from the ground and holding it up, taking care not to notice the slight shake in the old Viking's hand.

An armada of gulls and ducks bobbed up and down contentedly on the red gold waters of the evening loch. The last light touched the top of the ben and the deep cloven valley was filled with blue and the faint smell of woodsmoke. Somewhere, far off, a dog was

barking, the sound carrying across the still waters of Loch Lomond like a message from the morning, a waking, getting-up sound, not part of this world. This was an evening place where forest and moor and mountain were composing themselves for sleep. The first stars shone faintly above although the sky was still blue. Near at hand little waves lapped over pebbles, lazily, almost out of a sense of duty.

"Time to come in now, my darlin's," Meg shepherded the cackling hens towards the croft door. "Now, Jenny," she scolded, knowing them all by name. "Just you let Teeny alone. You're too rough!"

The baby began crying inside the low cottage and Wee Jeemy, Meg's only son and, at four, her pride and joy, next to the baby, ran up to break the news.

"I know. The bairn needs feedin', I'll be there directly," she forestalled Jeemy's eager tongue. "Your dad'll be home from the loch soon and we'll all have some bread and fish for oor tea.''

"But Mammy . . .!'' Jeemy tugged at his mother's skirts insistently.

"Now, Jeemy. Leave me be, will you! I've to see to the chickens first. We must look after the beasts before ourselves.''

Jeemy was not to be told. "Mammy!'' he whined. "Mammy!''

Meg planted her hands firmly on her broad hips and looked down at the tiny face. "He's got his father's nose right enough, poor soul,'' she thought. "What is it?'' she demanded in a fair imitation of anger.

"Mammy,'' Jeemy said. "Is this Dad noo? There's a boat comin' down the loch. More'n twa boats. Big wans. Black wans.''

"That's fine,'' she smiled indulgently. "C'mon now, my chickens. In ye go.''

"Mammy,'' girned the mite, "Bonnie boats. Bonnie stripey sails with animules on them.''

Meg looked over her left shoulder and up the long waters of the loch streaming with darkness. "Oh Holy Christ!'' she screamed. "Jeemy! Get the bairn!''

"Mammy! Me no can lift ma wee sister,'' complained her son.

"Oh Christ,'' said Meg again. "I'll get her then.'' She ran into the croft.

Jeemy watched the ships approach with interest. "Look Mammy!'' he cried as his mother ran back with the baby. "Here's big men comin' with flyin' birdies stuck on their heids!''

"Run!'' Meg screamed, pushing him roughly in the small of the back so that he stumbled. He looked at her questioningly. "Run! RUN!'' She took his hand and dragged him heedlessly towards the all too distant woods.

"What's wrang, Mammy?'' Jeemy bubbled, stumbling along. "Tell us!''

"It's Vikings,'' gasped Meg. "Vi . . .''

A tall, bearded figure stepped out of the woods ahead, smiled and leaned casually on the haft of a great axe.

*21*

*Glasgow people have been caring for each other for a long time. There were hospitals almost 1,000 years ago, but not what we would understand as hospitals today – no wards and nurses, scanners or prescriptions. Hospitals or hospices were a cross between old folks' homes and prisons. At best they gave the old and the poor a roof over their heads. At worst, there was St Ninian's Hospice near the Gorbals.*

*Provand's Lordship is more properly known as the Preceptor's House of the Hospital of St Nicholas in Glasgow. It wasn't built until 1471 – 21 years before a wee Italian called Christopher Columbus discovered the West Indies, but that is still in the future, so far as these stories are concerned.*

*Many years ago, but still a few years after 1350, which was at least 640 years ago, I found myself in a place called a "Lazaret". That was in France and you might well ask what I was doing there, but, as you know, I travel a bit and I like to keep my eyes open, as well as keep my head down if there is a revolution going on, which there was at the time. This "Lazaret" was a sort of hospital, and Glasgow had one not unlike it in the Middle Ages . . . the leper colony in the Gorbals. The poor souls had to carry a badge by law and wherever they went they were made to ring a bell so that folk would know when they were coming. They were allowed to beg, but doors tended to shut and heels vanish up closes whenever the bell-ringers turned down the end of a street.*

*On the other hand, there was the hospice up by the Cathedral. It was near the Girth Burn where you could claim sanctuary if the soldiers were after you for some misdemeanour or other. It was run for old men, and well ahead of its time. The unfortunate thing was that Glasgow being a small place, everybody got to know everybody else before long, unless, of course, they didn't want to know . . .*

HORNED Shambal, sneering Gorveg and winged Horbeth leered over the city of Glasgow, sloping down the hill like a ribbon of dusty silver wrapped in straw, 300 feet below. Red-gold in their sandstone newness, Shambal's horns made an ideal perch for a matronly pigeon looking for a roost, and the first nests in the history of the Cathedral began to flourish behind the leers and grimaces of new-born gargoyles. Devils all, they clustered together as if for warmth in the chilly spring air, staring silently at the tiny figures under the white leaden sky.

Some citizens trudged up and down the High Street, others pushed or pulled hand carts through the crowd, thronging the humped wooden bridge on the distant river. Two old men sat on a bench in front of the hospice near the Cathedral. A hooded figure shambled up the hill towards them.

Auld Ure stared at the dry earth in front of his feet. "Aye. They're still at it, Cunninghame," he wheezed without looking up.

Sounds of hammering and sawing, mingled with the protesting whine of rope, drifting down to the hospice from the scaffolding surrounding the Cathedral spire.

"Stop whisperin'!" Cunninghame drew his shawl about his ears and sucked the ends of his whiskers. "What are you whisperin' for?" he demanded.

Auld Ure took a deep breath and began again. "I SAID . . ." he began. "Those boys are still making a fair racket up at the building of the new Old Great Kirk!"

Cunninghame spat thoughtfully. "Canna hear what you are saying for the racket those builders and masons are making up at the Catheydral." He nodded, agreeing with himself. "When I was a boy there was never any of this . . ." His voice was drowned out by the sonorous clanging of a great bell. A flock of birds rose screaming from the ragged landscape of the half-built tower.

"Ach! They stop soon enough for the noon bell!" Auld Ure replied. "Coming doon or going up it looks the same."

"Eh?" Cunninghame cupped his bony hand against a shawl-covered ear. "Whit?"

"The tower," Auld Ure nodded towards the jagged crown of the uncompleted spire. "Looks the same if it's half fallen down or half going up. Funny that."

"That's the noise stopped now," observed Cunninghame, not in the mood for philosophy.

Losing track of his own train of thought Auld Ure turned to his friend. "Move over a bit," he said. "There's enough room on this bench for four. How are ye, auld yin?"

Cunninghame scuffed his toes in the dust. There was a glint in his eye. "You saw me when ye scraped yourself out of your bed this morning," he said crossly, ". . . and I'll 'auld yin' you. You're near 50 yourself. You and the rest o' us, 12 auld men living on Bishop Muirheed's charity."

"There's not many reach 50 right enough, and I've still got two teeth and my ain hair. Charity!" he snorted speculatively.

"No living without it," replied Cunninghame.

Auld Ure rubbed his eyes. The smoke of 30 chimneys drifted straight upward before being caught by the wind and spread out like a shawl of mist above the slopes and crooked gables of the skyline surrounding the Cathedral precinct. "Right enough. Best hospital in Glasgow. Leek and brose, and mutton once a month in the summer."

"Better than begging, asking alms from foreigners and gentry."

They looked up together as the frantic sound of hoof-beats echoed up the cavernous Drygate. Scattering loafers and fishwives, a tired-looking horseman raced along the narrow street. His mount was flecked with foam and wild-eyed, and the rider looked drawn and dishevelled. Watchers on the castle walls saw his approach. The great portcullis was raised and he thundered into the courtyard without a pause. The wooden teeth of the gate rumbled down.

"King's messenger," observed Auld Ure without emotion.

"He would be, if we had a king," Cunninghame examined the cloudy marks on the back of his hand. "I remember when we had a king. I saw him, more than once."

"The King's in prison in England, and I hear," Ure paused and looked about him, "there's no money for a ransom. I keep my ears to the ground, ye know."

Cunninghame coughed in agreement. "By God," he said with feeling. "See if I was younger again . . ."

"Aye." Auld Ure nodded, remembering.

"Aye," Cunninghame echoed, the one word expressing decades of adventure, and regret. "Aye," he added for emphasis.

Auld Ure looked across the square at the soldiers pacing back and forwards on the battlements. The fitful sunlight caught the tip of a spear and it twinkled, like a shooting star on the edge of mortal sight. ''Nae wonder,'' he added, taking refuge in philosophy again.

''This is the best hospital in Glasgow,'' Cunninghame said firmly.

''The only wan,'' Auld Ure said with emphasis. ''Thon Ninian's Hospice in the Gorbals . . .'' He lowered his voice. ''That's a Charnel House, so it is.''

''House of the Dead,'' Cunninghame wheezed with relish. ''All dead, all gone.''

''Christian duty though. It's charity, mind you.''

The sun gave up its unequal struggle with the clouds and passed into a shadowy country rising up beyond the Cathkin Braes. A chill wind flowed across the earth and around their feet and with it, from the direction of the Cross, its origin out of sight, came the slow, thin ringing of a hand bell.

''I think, maybe, we might go in now,'' Cunninghame observed, a hint of nervousness in his voice.

''Don't want the vapours, do we?'' Auld Ure agreed hastily.

The bell-ringer rounded the corner.

With more haste than speed, the two old men rose and went back into the hospice, closing the door firmly behind them.

The hooded figure, his face hidden beneath a tall, pointed cowl, stood still as a carved gargoyle. His ragged gown was clasped together at the shoulders by an oval badge. A bell hung silent in bloodless fingers. He stared at the door of the hospice for a long time before shambling off. ''Cunninghame . . . Ure! Don't you know me?'' he asked the wind. The clank of his bell was drowned out by the Cathedral, chiming the hour for the masons to return to their building and carving, high above the dusty ribbon of the little city.

24

*A man called Alexander Seton was once thrown into prison in Prussia for refusing to reveal the secret of the Philosopher's Stone. What's that, you ask? Nobody knows. There used to be a kind of Gretna Green of Science somewhere on the border between black magic and chemistry. Its name was alchemy, and Scots both high and low from the king himself to lowly punters hidden away in dark attics lit by the greenish light of bubbling retorts searched unceasingly for the secret of turning lead into gold . . . The strange substance that was rumoured to perform this miracle was called The Philosopher's Stone, the Alkahest, and many other names besides.*

*Poor old Seton, one of the greatest alchemists and magicians ever to conjure his way around Auld Scotia and most of Europe, claimed he had found this mysterious stuff. A red powder, he said it was. He even showed me some once, a little pile of scarlet dust like cayenne pepper in a gold box. Poor Sandy.*

*There were others, all over Scotland, variously called charlatans, mystics, chemists – they were, and they still are. There used to be an alchemist called Willie Skinner in Kelvinbridge here in Glasgow. He lived in a flat lit by gas and numbered among his accomplishments the lost art of making a seagull's skull transparent, and also producing "Quick Gold" out of lead. I saw some of that as well, before he died in the late 1970s. Then there were alchemists like Hermes McCann, a bit before Willie Skinner's time. Hermes was busy round about 1410 – 580 years into a Scottish past brimfull of compulsive chanting over steaming cauldrons and twisted coils of glittering glass. Alchemists never became rich men, but it wasn't for want of trying in their own peculiar way.*

THE broken crocodile had lost an eye, but none of its sense of occasion as it spun lazily in the warm air rising from the do-it-yourself athenor. The little furnace glowed and crackled, sending its currents of warmth up among the dried herbs hanging from the sloping attic rafters. The fire blazed up and something with a surprisingly intelligent face scuttled into the far corner of the gable and huddled in the shadows, muttering to itself.

Hermes McCann, tossing his head to one side to keep a wayward lock of reddish-brown hair out of his eyes, stooped over his pestle and mortar and pounded manfully. He was making magical paste. A copy of *The Investigation of Perfection* by Geber lay beside him, open at page 25, and he twisted round, wiping some stray liquid off the well-thumbed page with his elbow. "Shaun!" he called out without looking up. "Shaun! Get up here. I want you . . . NOW!"

A hand appeared at the top of the ladder that led back down to Spreull's Land, Glasgow, and the rest of planet earth. "Coming, Master Hermes," replied a reedy voice. "I was just down at the . . ."

Hermes cut him short. "I'm not interested. You be 'just at' whatever it was in your own time." He looked over the top of his square-rimmed glasses at the dusty figure clambering up into the attic. "This is the Great Art, boy," he intoned. "The Great Work!"

Picking up a pair of long-handled pliers he crossed to the furnace and lifted a shallow metal bowl from its resting place among the glowing coals. Carrying it back to the work-table, Hermes set it down gingerly on a rickety tripod and added a few drops

of something yellow and sticky from a thick little vial. A cloud of sweet, oily smoke blossomed upwards as the contents of the bowl hissed and bubbled ominously.

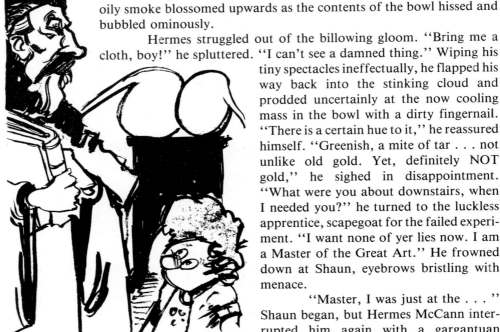

Hermes struggled out of the billowing gloom. "Bring me a cloth, boy!" he spluttered. "I can't see a damned thing." Wiping his tiny spectacles ineffectually, he flapped his way back into the stinking cloud and prodded uncertainly at the now cooling mass in the bowl with a dirty fingernail. "There is a certain hue to it," he reassured himself. "Greenish, a mite of tar . . . not unlike old gold. Yet, definitely NOT gold," he sighed in disappointment. "What were you about downstairs, when I needed you?" he turned to the luckless apprentice, scapegoat for the failed experiment. "I want none of yer lies now. I am a Master of the Great Art." He frowned down at Shaun, eyebrows bristling with menace.

"Master, I was just at the . . ." Shaun began, but Hermes McCann interrupted him again with a gargantuan sneeze. The stuffed crocodile spun in the draft and grimoires turned their pages helplessly. "Er . . . What was the question again, Master?"

The temperature in the cluttered attic dropped several degrees and the old alchemist regarded his apprentice with a basilisk stare. "Where . . . were . . . you!" He separated the words with care, like plum-stones, sucked dry and lined up one by one on the edge of a plate.

"I was . . . was delivering the remedies you sent me with to the apothecary in the Saltmarket, Master," Shaun stammered. "He says he will need more by the morra. There's a plague of runnin' rheum in the town with the east wind. He's got it himself. His face was running out of his heid, so it wis!"

"Is there indeed and was it?" sniffed Hermes, a dry tickling at the back of his throat. "And where's the money for the last lot? Have you been dawdling with the other apprentices? There's a deal of idle boys damaging the work-yards at the back of the Saltmarket. I hope that you have no truck with them? I have a sign that will tell me if you lie," he added threateningly.

"Naw, Master. It wisny me!" Shaun backed away.

"Wasn't you . . . what?"

"Breaking rigs and kale-yards, Master. I ken that the boys are just allowed archery as a recreashoon, so I dae."

"Well see that you do what is proper. I have enough on my mind. And the apothecary wants more physik!" Hermes sneezed again. "That I, Hermes McCann . . ." – he paused to wipe his nose on the cloth – ". . . that I, Hermes McCann," he continued, drawing himself up to his full four foot two, ". . . should stoop to making physik to stop up the noses of Glasgow. They should doctor themselves. 'Physician heal thyself,' I always say. I canna be bothered with it . . ." He threw the rag down and bent over another open book, turning the pages with a respectful care. Retrieving the rag, he attempted to wipe his precious spectacles again, peering through the smeared glass with his nose almost touching the page. "If only I had a better ink," he muttered to himself. "The Greater Clavicule of Solomon ibn Razir is but a scribble beside this work of . . ." Hermes screwed his face up like a prune to stifle the explosion building up at the back of his nose, ". . . work of truly Alchemical Magery," he continued, the cataclysm under control for the moment.

"What is it yer readin', Master?" Shaun enquired, standing on tip-toe.

His master readjusted the streaked glasses on the end of his nose and assumed the expression of someone who has been given a mortal insult. "This, boy?" he sniffed. "These are my own writings, my own record of the Great Work's progress." His voice sank to a conspiratorial whisper. "You must never reveal that I, we, are on the very brink, teetering on the nub, as it were, of distilling the Philosopher's Stone, turning base lead into gold. What do you think of that?"

Shaun looked up at the round, earnest face, full of excitement and more than a little sooty. He was very fond of the old man, but Shaun, the backside hanging out of his trousers and his left foot tingling where some of the last, failed, elixir had dropped on it, was a realist. "We havn'a got any lead, Master," he said.

The master closed the book dolefully. "Well, perhaps not. But mark me well . . . as soon as I make gold I shall buy all the lead in Glasgow."

"If you say so, Master," Shaun agreed quickly. "And," he added, changing the subject hopefully ". . . the fish merchant is no' very far!"

"What has the price of fish got to do with Magery? Details! Don't bother me with details. Now we are in funds, go straight back to the apothecary and buy, buy . . ." he ticked off the list on his fingers, "Gum of Araby, Aquae Fortis . . ."

Shaun looked up at the rafters, where patience dwelt, along with, perhaps . . . something else. "Very well, Master," he agreed, sighing with resignation. "Do you want me to see if I can steal a herring in the Gallowgate for our tea?"

Something rat-like scuttled into another dark corner above and settled down to wait until the old man was alone again.

*What's a "Tripos?" Well, there were three of them anyway, the subjects you had to study at the University, or the College, as they called it when I was wee, whenever that was . . .*

*In 1450 Glasgow was busy and thriving, trading in wool and pelts, hides and herring. The city's horizons were widening and her Bishop was proud of his thriving town on the banks of the Clyde. In that year, 540 years of missed lectures and summer holidays ago, Bishop Turnbull persuaded Pope Nicholas V to issue a Bull or decree, founding the University of Glasgow. In the Charter, Glasgow was praised as a place of mild air and plenty, which it certainly was, and still is, as everyone knows.*

*The "Auld Pedagogy" in the Rottenrow was the first classroom, and the college buildings proper were begun in 1459. The Regents, the teachers, taught all the subjects to both poor lads, with just a bag of meal or some beans to keep them going, and the sons of the gentry. They shared the same slates, chalk, talk and classes. The theory was that everybody was entitled to an education . . .*

*The only true measure of time is the changing of the seasons. Men die, centuries are unwritten, castle walls and tumult are swept away by the tide that paints the land green every spring, and each year the earth is split by uncounted fingers reaching for the new sun.*

FAITHER stooped and picked up an unusually large stone, tossing it high into the bracken. Meg's broad flanks, steaming a little in the early morning light, rose and fell like a ship at sea as she waded on up the meadow. Faither behind, Meg in front, they trudged on, each bound to the other in the lengthening furrow. The horse started as a hare broke cover and raced away up the bank towards the sheiling. The door of the rough stone cottage opened, and a figure walked carefully down the slippery hillside and across the broken earth towards him.

"Faither!" the young man called out, waving. "Hold up, will ye?"

The horse and the man stopped together and looked round.

"Well, lad?" he found another stone and tossed it away. "Look at that sky." He straightened stiffly. "There's mair rain to come, and a frost in the low park tonight if I'm a judge." He smelt the air knowingly. "I can smell it aff the water."

"I've just come to say goodbye," said the boy awkwardly. "It's time."

"That's fine, Will," Faither replied. "You've said it." He looked up at the gathering clouds. "The air's full of it. Mair to come right enough."

"Did you not hear me?" asked his son quietly.

"It'll flood the Mentieth, more'n like. The kine will need driven up the hill before we finish these furrows."

"Father, I'm away down to Glasgow." Will tried again, ". . . to the College."

"'Father' now, is it?" The old man looked at him sharply. "I don't suppose you could drive the kine up the brae before you go, son? Would you do that for me?"

Will sighed and patted Meg's great head. "We've been over that 100 times," he replied without looking up.

"Oh?" His father nodded sarcastically. "A hundred is it? Fours and fives used to be good enough for this farmland. Well, Will. College at last, is it? You'll make a good clerk for the Bishop or some Lordling, like as not."

"Can I have your blessing, then, Fath . . . Faither."

The old man looked at the fresh-faced boy, his broad shoulders, his long, sensitive fingers. The eyes were sea-grey, like his own, and just as determined. "Have you got your bag o' meal?" he asked at last.

"Yes, Faither, I have that." Will turned to go.

"Wait up, son," his father took him by the elbow. "Take that meal I grew for ye, and take my blessing on it and you tae."

"Faither . . ." Will began, but horse and man had already moved off, ploughing their straight furrow into the morning.

Apart from a sleepy ostler and two chickens, the courtyard of Lennox Castle was quiet and grey in the still of the morning. As the light grew, the castle came to life. Kitchens were scrubbed, stables cleaned, an insolent falconer whipped and the rubbish of the previous evening's meal cleared away. The Earl of Lennox and his Bailiff were deep in discussion, seated in the embrasure of the great window that looked out across the home lands. In the distance a ploughman and his horse plodded through the pools of late mist lying in the hollows.

The Bailiff raised his voice in outrage, pointing to the sheaf of papers in his hand. "But, your Grace," he protested. "The turning of good farmland to pasturage must be stopped. These villeins must be overseen like hawks."

The Earl, a thin-faced man with a high forehead and fine grey hair, nodded solemnly. "Indeed, John. That's truth. There have been too many changes. Changes for the worse." He nodded again, agreeing with himself. "If I had to depend on bond of manrent from inferior chiefs I would starve." He picked idly at the cold chicken in his hand. "You're right." He gestured towards the low hills with a drumstick. "We need to have eyes and ears everywhere."

"Father?"

The Earl half-turned to see his son standing beside the empty fireplace. Servants were scraping the still-glowing ashes of logs and coals into iron buckets. His son stepped forward. "What is it, boy?" the Earl demanded testily. "I've business to attend to."

"You asked me to tell you when I was ready," his son Robert said apologetically.

"Ready? What for?" Earl Lennox looked down, preoccupied with the papers in front of him.

"To leave sir, for the University."

"What? Oh yes, the schooling. Now . . ." He stood up and looked up at his son. "Remember what both your mother and I said to you last night. Learn some Latin, but don't come back a priest!"

John the Bailiff winked at Robert and raised an eyebrow.

"Here." The Earl held out a purse of coins. "I have no illusions," he said. "I

expect your mother has already given you some gold, and that both hers and mine will soon be gone, but remember who you are and what you are.'' The coins jingled as the boy took them from his father. ''. . . and don't spend them all in the same tavern!''

His son tried to say something but the words wouldn't come.

''Now be off,'' said his father, turning away and staring out of the window. ''. . . AND don't take my best roan.''

''Well, John,'' the Earl smiled solemnly at his Bailiff as the boy clattered out of the great hall. ''I hope Glasgow is up to it . . . !''

''Would one of you gentlemen open that window?'' asked the Regent desperately, as 80 student bodies crowded into the narrow room. ''We must let a breath of air enter upon our discourse together with Virgil!''

Will leaned across and nudged his companion. ''Stuffy,'' he nodded towards the tutor and smiled.

''Very,'' Robert agreed with a grin. ''Where are you from?''

''The lands of Lennox,'' Will replied openly, ''. . . and you?''

''Lennox as well,'' said Robert. ''In a manner of speaking . . .''

# OVER THE SEA TO GLASGOW  *1493* A.D.

*Everybody has heard of the "Auld Alliance" with France. In fact the continental connection between Scotland and Europe goes back 1,100 years to the days of Charles the Great, Holy Roman Emperor, and the legendary Scottish King Actaius, who united against their common enemy, the Saxons.*

*As Glasgow grew, so did its trade with lands that seemed more familiar than the kingdom south of the border. A year after Columbus discovered America in 1492, and while the mortar was still setting in Provand's Lordship, the oldest house in Glasgow, built in 1470, little trading ships not much bigger than the Iona ferry were heading out of the Clyde for foreign parts. They sailed to Antwerp, Amsterdam, Hamburg, up the Seine to Paris, laying life and limb on the line and at the masthead to bring home salt, glass, brandy; exporting herring and salmon and cloth. In fact, Glaswegians are amongst the oldest Europeans in Europe . . .*

*Antwerp, the port of Europe, was built on the edge of the Age of Exploration. Everybody was doing it, the Dutch, the Flemish, the Portugese, the Genoese, the Spaniards – sailing, finding, and colonising; merchants and half-pirates, the brave and the foolhardy. Trade flowed down the Scheldt to Antwerp and into the heartlands of Germany and northern France. Like sleepers awakening to their own birth, the European lands were becoming kingdoms, and the kingdoms nations. Cities and ports from Venice to Marseilles, Oporto to Antwerp, all round 200,000 miles of European coastline, were sending out their carracks and cogs and dromons and barges to trade and take and adventure.*

*Within a few years a new world would be found and conquered. Diaz to the Indian Ocean in 1487; Cabral to Brazil by mistake in 1500; Cabral again to China in 1514, Cristoph Colon or Columbus, also on his way to China, ended up discovering the West Indies, although he never actually set foot on the continent called after another explorer, Amerigo Vespucci.*

*Glasgow was also awakening, with a fleet of ten ships. Sometimes hiring from English ports, the Clydeside merchants were dealing with Flanders and France, sowing the seeds of a unique European connection that was to last 1,000 years.*

ANTWERP, the port of Europe, a Renaissance city carved and gilded, filled with the sounds and smells of every land yet discovered, and a few that were not. Antwerp, flowing with gold, where the Guild of Beggars was almost as strong as Paris. Antwerp, city of a hundred thousand souls, of countless chimneys, storks, roofs like the points of unnumbered wooden mountains, city of stately pinnacles and crumbling alleys, and, amongst the forest of masts bobbing in the harbour, a few Glaswegians.

Tam jumped out of the way as a man, seated in a cart, propelled himself round the corner with clogs on his hands. He dodged aside to avoid a thief, hardly more than eight years old, pursued by a butcher with a meat cleaver, several dogs and a couple who looked as though they might be trying to pick the butcher's pocket as they ran. An almost spherical monk ambled past on a tiny donkey. The friar looked as if he had four thin legs, all with a cloven hoof at the end. A scowling soldier, his round helmet sitting like an upturned bucket on his head, pointed a wicked-looking pike at the mêlée, clearing a way for a haughty-looking young man on a haughty-looking horse. Things were fairly

*31*

quiet for a weekday morning in the streets leading to the port of Antwerp.

Tam reached the docks where the *Scouti-Aulin* was moored, wedged between a carrack from the Levant and a fairly ordinary barge from Bruges. "Master, sir!" he called out, peering down into the hold of the little boat. "Are you there, Master, sir?"

A bull-like head supported by a thick neck was thrust up from the bilges. "It's yourself, Tam," said the Captain, with the air of a man used to making statements that were accepted without question. "Did you see him?" he demanded, staring up at the weedy figure teetering on the edge of the dock. "Come aboard, man. You'll fall in if you tip your toes over the water like that."

Tam steeled himself and jumped down on to the narrow deck. "I'm awfy sorry, Captain Hugh," he said in a rush, clearly believing that the bad news was best first. "I just couldn't get any sense out of the man at all. He said we hadna' got the right paper, or something, near as I could understand . . ."

Captain Hugh levered himself out of the reeking depths with his elbows, a tree uprooting itself, and glared at his Mate. "For pity's SAKE Tam!" he glowered. "See those merchants in Glasgow? They have nae idea what it's like trying to talk plain with furriners that canna understand guid clear Scots! My God! Have I got to go mysel'?"

A passing seagull, not sure if an answer was expected or not, perched on a sack of salt and waited.

"Well, you see, Captain Hugh," Tam continued anxiously. "The man disna' speak Flemishland talk, or anything."

"The man clearly speaks something, you dunderheid!" the Captain roared, "What is it then, French, Alleyman, Spanic, English even, for any favour . . .?"

The seagull felt ignored and flew away, complaining loudly.

"It sounded like nothing on this earth to me, Captain. I think, but I couldna' swear to it, it was meant to be English, but it was aw' Greek to me."

"God help us," groaned Captain Hugh. "He's no' a Greek is he?"

"No, Captain," cowered Tam. "I think he's from Bretonland, but mebbe no' . . . he certainly IS the Harbour Master, no doubt of it."

Captain Hugh narrowed his tiny eyes. "Well, 'mebbe no' is no good to me. Still . . . if the man is Breton, then maybe he has the Gaelic."

Tam looked even more flustered. "But I canna' . . ." he began.

Captain Hugh pulled his Mate towards him by a generous handful of jerkin. "Listen, Tam, you wee Sassenach," he spat the words out. "You get back there and speak to the man again. Tell him, TRY and tell him, that the salt is bought and paid for and we want the tide this week. Use sign language, dance a jig if you want, but don't you dare come back here without a release of lading." He paused and drew breath. "Well? What are you waiting for?"

He released his hold on Tam's clothing and the little man bounced backwards, almost fell into the hold, and steadied himself against a sack of salt. "I will, Captain Hugh. I'm on my way." He scuttled across the deck, leaped on to the harbour-side, and vanished into the heaving, glittering, smelly noon-time crowds.

"See furriners . . .?" Captain Hugh clambered back down into the hold in disgust.

The great warrior sleeping on Arran's mountains was covered in a shroud of mist as the *Scouti-Aulin* beat northwards into the gale. Captain Hugh wiped the salt spray out of his eyes with broad fingers. "Tam!" he screamed into the wind. "Get those rabandis tight to the fender-cleats."

Tam, the words torn out of his mouth and thrown away, shouted something in reply.

"We're riding lower and lower with that damp salt. We'll be lucky if the *Scouti* makes Erskine."

"I'll be down the now!" Tam's words penetrated to the deck through a hole in the gale's wrath. "We . . . we're going awful heavy, Captain," he said as he struggled through the spray towards the Master, clutching at the slippery rope that ran along the deck.

"Are you frightened, Tam?" asked the Captain stolidly.

"A bit . . . bittie, I am, aye."

Captain Hugh smiled and blinked the water out of his eyes. "We'll make a sailor of you yet, man."

The river that would one day give birth to navies raged and fumed, tossing the tiny ship about. Squalls hid the land and the distant bend in the river that led to the home port.

"What . . . what'll happen if we GO DOWN!" Tam shouted as the little ship tilted violently then righted itself.

"The price of salt will go up a farthing," replied the Captain.

*In 1538 – 452 years ago, give or take a few pages – a good read could cost about £5,000 in today's money. I didn't need a book, because I had one already, a present from a female admirer. I helped her escape from Cromwell's spies about 400 years past. The lady's gift wasn't a lot of good to me for a long time. I'm going to tell you something I haven't told anyone since about 1800 . . . I didn't learn to read until 1793!*

*The first printing started up in Scotland when James IV, a real king, gave a "patent" to Andrew Myllar or Millar and his friend Walter Chapman. Chapman was a merchant, but Myllar, a bookseller, had learned the craft of printing in Rouen in France – romances, poems by Dunbar, legends of the Saints, and the old Scottish Liturgy, were peeled off the presses at irregular intervals. Printing was a slow process in those days, with individual letters being clamped together in a frame and wedged tight by strips of wood or lead called "furniture". Pages were printed one at a time, and when a Bible might contain over 1,000, it was still almost as quick to copy it out by hand, the method used since the days of the Roman Empire. By the 1500s the Romans were as far in the past as James IV is from us today.*

*While there was no official printer in Glasgow at this time, as the seat of the Bishops, it was a place where the printed word was alternately encouraged and feared. One problem was that hardly anybody could read. Anyway . . . 480 summers ago books were a very new thing. An 18-year-old poet called Kennedy was burned for Reforming principles, in spite of the reluctance of Gavin Dunbar, Archbishop of Glasgow. People in higher places thought the best thing you could do with books and troublemakers was burn them.*

THE clear silver sound of a trumpet rang out across the City of Glasgow as the sun appeared obligingly above the east port gate.

Archbishop Dunbar, having risen at six for prayer, had been hard at work in his study since before seven. There was a lot of paperwork to deal with. In front of him were piles of papers and parchments, bundles of documents and records, yellow scrolls tied with ribbon and bearing the seal of his office. A forest of quills, like the tail of some fabulous bird diving through a hole in the table, sprouted beside his elbow. A thick book lay open in front of him. The fire crackled in protest as it found some stones among the coal brought from the Gorbals last evening.

The Archbishop stirred restlessly and rubbed his eyes. Smoke and candlelight were not the ideal illumination for reading crabbed Latin script at eight o'clock on a winter's morning. The printed page in front of him was altogether clearer.

"John . . .?" he asked, without looking up.

Brother John rose from the chair he had been dozing in at the back of the room. "Yes, Lord Archbishop?" he said with a start. He jumped again as the book was closed in front of him with a bang.

"This is a hymnbook for the Devil, John." Gavin Dunbar sat back, stretched his legs, and stared at the carvings on the ceiling.

"Indeed it is," the brother agreed hastily, perched on the edge of his chair. "Can I get something for you, My Lord?"

The Archbishop, Prince of the Church and nobody's fool, stared at the closed book and read the future. "I had hoped that the art of printing would defend the

*34*

orthodox, John,'' he said, still directing his eyes upwards. Is there nothing that the Reformers cannot turn to their own uses?''

Brother John rose and walked across to the table. He began to arrange the chaos of papers solicitously. ''May we not print against them, My Lord?''

Dunbar shook his head and smiled.

''But . . .'' Brother John began.

''There are no 'buts' in Heaven.'' The Archbishop turned his piercing stare on his secretary. ''Bishop Elphinstone thought we might use the printing press against the Reformers, as did I . . . then. Andrew Myllar and Walter Chapman were sound enough. Their *Legends of the Saints* is a fine work. Damn it all to darkness, John!'' he thumped his fist down on the book and the quills fell off the table, scattering in the fireplace. ''These Precepts,'' he pounded the book again as Brother John bent to pick up the smouldering feathers. ''These Precepts,'' he continued, ''pretend to be Holy Writ.''

''The printers have already produced . . .'' John broke off, peeling a piece of melted quill from a plump finger. ''Sorry, My Lord. They have already printed those gypsies Henryson and Dunbar . . . poetry, and Kennedy. He deserves death, deserves to be burned,'' he added with a sneer. Standing up, he wiped the ash off the knees of his surtout.

''The floodgates are open.'' The Archbishop ran his finger along the spine of the book thoughtfully. ''Yet, burning . . .?''

''We can be thankful that few can read, Lord Dunbar.''

''A few is more than enough when it comes to these rabble-rousers and levellers.'' He pointed to the thick tome in front of him. ''See this, John?''

''Indeed I do, My Lord.''

''This is not a book . . . no, don't look at me strangely, man. It is a stone, rolling downhill. I fear that it is already going too fast to be stopped and will sweep us all away.''

''We must print 'stones' of our own, then,'' said Brother John, frowning.

''Perhaps.'' The great Archbishop shivered. ''Stoke up the fire, would you? The chill in the air pains my feet.'' He lifted the book with difficulty and held it out to his secretary in both hands. ''And make a blaze out of this,'' he said.

Brother John took the volume and almost dropped it. The metal clasps glinted in the light of the embers in the grate. ''It is very beautiful, my Lord.'' John ran his fingers over the gold tooling on the cover.

''The jacket is not the man,'' replied Gavin Dunbar. ''Burn it, John. In the hottest part of the fire, mind.''

The kitchens of John Stewart of Minto, Lord Provost of Glasgow, were as hot as Hades in a heat wave. Cauldrons bubbling and steaming, venison roasting on a spit as one

35

urchin turned the handle and another basted the meat, stewing, boiling, frying, the air was thick with a miasma of appetising smells, together with the odour of wood smoke and sweat.

Purry Lamont, the understairs tweeny, pressed into service in the kitchen to deal with a large and succulent sea-cat, was a gossip of some accomplishment. She was practising her art as she pounded manfully at the porpoise steaks, beating the meat with a wooden mallet until it was tender as veal. "So I said to him, that he said to her that it wisny me told them what she said to us," she declared, punctuating her words with thumps and bangs.

"Oh aye. You have got to nip that in the bud," Sadie, her companion agreed, splitting a leek with relish.

"So. There he was!" Purry left off punishing the deceased porpoise and looked at Sadie expectantly.

Sadie nodded emphatically and trepanned a turnip with surgical skill. "Who's 'He'?" she asked.

"See you?" Purry clicked her tongue as only a tweeny can. "Minto! The Provost hissel'. I had to haud back the laughter in ma mooth, so I did."

"But what was he daein', Purry?" Sadie enquired with renewed interest.

Purry laid aside her wooden hammer and blew a lock of reddish hair away from her face. "Daein'?" she said with a shriek of incredulity. "The Provost of Glasgow, him that is goin' to eat this very meat," she prodded the battered steaks with a grubby finger. "Himself," she continued, "was standing there in the middle of his big room daein' . . . POETRY!"

"Away," replied Sadie with awe. "You mean stories and that?"

"Aye. He had a big fat book in his hands."

"What's a . . . book?" Sadie was genuinely puzzled.

"You know," Purry waved her hands in the air impatiently. "Wan of those things the Priest tells ye the lesson from in the Kirk."

Sadie laughed. "Don't be saft, Purry. Even I know that's called readin'. There's nobody in Glasgow can do that 'cept the Church and them."

"It's true. I saw it," Purry was hurt.

Sadie laughed again. "Never," she smiled the maddening smile of those who are convinced they are totally, utterly right. "The Provost of Glasgow . . . talkin' like a book? That's like saying ye need to learn your letters to scrap trenchers and wash dishes!"

# THOU SHALT NOT SAY "I DO" *1583* A.D.

*It's easier to tie the knot today than it was in the reforming days of 1583 – 407 years of walking down the aisle ago. You were not supposed to spend more than one shilling and sixpence, about fifteen pence, on a wedding, and you had to recite a lot of scripture before being allowed to say "I do", never mind the first kiss. It was worse than passing your driving test at the second attempt. I'm single at the moment . . . I CAN do a hill start.*

NOT since Sommerled the Mighty had marched past to do battle with King Malcolm in the fields outside Paisley had there been such a fuss by the road to Inchinnan. The track made a dip and a sharp turn by the duck pond, near where Sandy Heggie got run over by a carriage while he was sleeping in the middle of the road. Tucked into the lee of the brae stood a long croft, low, thatched, and on one particular Sunday in 1583, full of bother.

Wee Mona just would not stand still. "Oh Mither! Are you sure positive that I look my very best for him?" Her fine hair, full of the mousey highlights of an overcast noontide in medieval Scotland, shook with agitation.

"Mfff . . ." her long-suffering mother tried to agree and not to swallow a long preen, simultaneously. The Scots, internationally famous for rolling their "R's" have practised this form of speech training for centuries. "Mfff . . . Mona darlin'," she said again, successfully curling her tongue around the offending object. "Yer bonnie as May, Mona. It's me that's supposed to be a-fuss on your wedding day. There now." Mither stabbed a flounce like a fencer. "That'll not come apart so easy." She stood up with a groan, eyes level with her daughter's waist. "Oh, yer fine and slim though, waist like a straw, so ye have, my darlin'." She began to sniff. "I only hope that ruffian that will soon call himself your husband has some respect for ye." She wiped her eyes on her plump little arm. "Let me see you!"

"I'm standing right in front of you, Mither," Mona pulled at her frock to emphasise the fullness of her hips, ". . . and Benedict's a lovely man, so he is. Hardly any spots ata'. Cares for me, so he will."

Mither busied herself with some invisible speck on her daughter's sleeve. "Remember what I've told ye about men," she said, lowering her voice as if agents of the male race were hunkered in the darkness of the ingle or lying, large lugs downwards, among the damp thatch sweeping low above their heads. "Keep yer man happy. They like to get their own way. Just let him do what he wants. There's a fair shortage of men these days what with all the wars and that, and there never were many that were worth anything. Do something nice with rabbit as well. They like a bit o' beast with the kale and brose. I've showed ye how, anyways . . . !"

"Oh, Mither! I'm not a wean anymore!"

"You're 16, my wee Mona, and your a wean until . . . until . . . You'll always be my wee lamb pet, Mona darlin' doll!" She flung her arms about her large daughter and almost succeeded.

"It's afternoon, Mither," Mona shook herself free. "Watch my blouse".

Mither took a step back and looked affectionately up at the Inchinnan Amazon, her pale face warmed by the pink of her cheeks. She had been pinching them for days. "If only yer poor faither had not been carried off by God with the bowel-hives . . . and

then, gettin' the bloody flux on top of his bowels was a cruel stroke for a man of his promise, so it wis. Best muck-raker and ploughman for miles, so he wis. He would have so loved to see ye off on yer wee road across life.''

Mona took hold of her mother's shoulders firmly. "I'm not going anywhere. I'm just gettin' married. Lots of people do it. So don't start on about Dad again. It was a merciful release him gettin' taken afore it spread up to his heid. At least he could sing tae the end, Mither!"

Mither burst into floods of uncontrollable tears. The real reason for her bitterness was having to live in a damp lean-to for 20 years, abject poverty, and a singular lack of anything to eat. But love and marriage, brief and inevitable, made a fine excuse. "That's better," she sighed. "A good greet does ye good. It's as well yer poor Dad was tooken, so I'm thinking. With this new rule we canna even sit with the men in the Church. Still, it's gettin' late. I wish THEY hadna' made it afternoons only for marriages on a Sunday.''

Mona was already on her way to the door.

Mither followed slowly, muttering to herself, ". . . and you have to repeat your Ten Commandments, your Confession of Faith, your Lord's Prayer . . ."

"Aye, Mither, off by rote." Mona opened the door.

Mither waddled after, sobbing a little. "If'n you don't, my precious, the Meenister will not marry you to thon, whatever his name is."

"Benedict, Mither," Mona was already outside.

"Oh wait!" Mither rushed back inside the croft. She re-emerged carrying two milking stools. "The new ruling again, Mona. Women have to bring their ain seating to Kirk. I near forgot. Could you not marry somebody with quality?"

Mona snatched a stool from her and strode ahead angrily. "He's my man, Mither, not a piece of dirt that fell off a plate, so don't tell me what to do when I've a tongue in my head, and can hold my own when any wee . . ." The words trailed off into the distance.

"Oh, my wee vulner-apple Mona darlin'," Mither hirpled after her along the lane, the wooden stool tucked under her arm. "I only hope you can look after yourself like I have . . ."

The body of the Kirk at Inchinnan was a solemn place. The atmosphere was serious, and even the coughing and subdued murmuring of the congregation had an air of finality and a lack of humour about it. Predestination made someone drop a book and another to snore, furtively. Outside several lawless gannets, unaware that fundamentalism stalked the plains and rigs of Alba, swore and nipped and soared in the empty Sunday skies above the Clyde estuary.

MacFadzean the Meenister glowered at the couple contemplating holy and, undoubtly, sexual union as well. It would be all right so long as they didn't enjoy it. Favouring them both with a basilisk stare he began: "We are gathered here in the sight of God and his Elders tae witness the betrothal and solemn marriage of Benedict Russell . . ." He paused. "Answer in the affirmative, man!"

Benedict looked up, one of those who always finds the answers to difficult questions written on the ceiling. "Aye, sir."

MacFadzean lost his train of thought. "Tae . . . tae . . ." He fumbled with the papers stuck in the heavy Bible in his hands. "Mona Middop," he said with triumph, deciphering his own handwriting at last.

"Oh aye, sir," Mona answered eagerly.

". . . of the Parish of Inchinnan," MacFadzean continued remorselessly, "this Sunday of March in the Year of Our Lord 1583 . . . Benedict Russell. You will now satisfy this Convocation of Elders that you have the Ten Commandments." He tapped his foot rythmically like a bandleader. "Begin!"

Benedict looked hopefully at the distant ceiling. "Right." There was a pause. "Right," he said again. "Oh aye," his face brightened. "Thou shalt not . . . not . . ."

". . . shalt not remember?" asked MacFadzean coldly.

"I've got it now, Reverend," Benedict grinned hopelessly. ". . . cover thy neighbour's ass, nor his oxter, nor anything that was thy neighbour's. Thou . . . thou shalt not cover . . . neighbour's wife . . . er, that's not it . . . adulterate, steal," he spread the fingers of his hand. "How many was it again? I just need a little . . ."

At his side Mona dissolved in floods of tears. "Oh, Benedict," she wailed.

MacFadzean's eyebrows joined, shook hands, and turned to ice. His nose reddened and milk curdled in Bogferry Yetts two-and-a-half miles away. "There can be no marriage if ye don't know your Scriptures," he thundered. "I see from the record before me that you have spent more than the permitted one shilling and sixpence on this buffoonery, this tomfoolery, this Godless sham, with no more thought than a jade or harlot of Babylon! Get you gone baith from this Kirk! How can you be a proper husband if you don't know about stealing and murder and adultery . . .? OOT! BAITH O' YE!"

Mona wept, Mither bawled and Benedict, keeping his own counsel, winked at an elfin creature sitting demurely at the back of the Kirk on her own milking-stool.

*The main thing I remember about going to see a doctor in 1597 – 393 years of headaches and hangovers ago – is that it was not a very good idea unless you were desperate.*

*Wee Semmit was desperate, probably because a big barrel fell on his head, or so his boss Rab Toner thought at first, but it was his leg that brought things to a head, so to speak. It had come off. Leg, not head, by the way. No anaesthetic, no soothing words and blurring vision as the white socks flop sideways out of control and they wheel you off to the theatre. A jug of brandy and a bang on the jaw were the tools of the anaesthetist's trade in the good old 16th century, if you were lucky.*

*There was a man around Glasgow at that time who had a particular interest in surgery, wee chap with a big beard and black hat, curly sidelocks and a way of talking with his hands. He used to be seen about the High Street. Always giving money to beggars he was. Must have been an intellectual. He came from York or Europe, or something. His name was Doctor Lowe and he wrote a book about surgery and accidents, the very first one in Scots . . . Never read it myself. Never needed to, thank God . . .*

**B**ARRELS full of many a life-story stood in solemn ranks in the long shadows of the upper attic of Vintner's Hall. Sweat pooled in the small of Rab Toner's back as he strained on the guide-rope and pulled the jib towards the door. The "door" was 45 feet above the hard cobbled ground and he shifted his feet inside the leather cleats, reassuring himself that they were comfortably riveted to the inside of the hoisting-frame. The block and tackle gear complained and juddered as the 300-quart tun of wine rose by fits and jerks towards the distant mouth of the attic and the straining figure of the time-served overseer. Rab let out a little slack and pulled manfully.

A thin voice floated up from the street below. "It's working its way out, Master Rab," the voice cried, the sound of youth and anxiety mingling with the creaking protest of the hoisting machinery.

Keeping a careful hold of the end of the rope Rab leaned towards the opening and its dizzying drop. "What's that you're sa . . .?"

Before he could complete his question, there was a sharp whiplash and the ends of the torn hemp struck him a stinging blow across the forehead, narrowly missing his left eye. A distant scream was cut short by a splintering crash.

Rab knelt down and looked below. "For Jesus sake!" he said with awe. "Right on his HEID!" He sprang up and raced for the ladder. "Keep the heid, Semmit son," he cried as he scrambled towards the ground. "Yer all right, Semmit! Here I'm coming . . . !"

The multi-coloured sounds of the busy High Street floated up and through the open casement window. Phoebe Lowe stretched out, took hold of the catch, and drew the window closed. "There we are, Peter." She dusted her hands on her apron and looked round at her husband, and the sprawl of papers on his desk. "You'll get a sore head and a chill, sitting by the window without your shawl."

Doctor Peter Lowe ran his fingers through his beard absently. "What was that, Phoebe my love? Just a moment." He lifted one book and turned over another. "Pass me the Galen would you . . . the one with the open lock.'' An arthritic finger curved towards a pyramid of paper.

"This one or the thin one?'' She spluttered, "Why don't you let me dust in here? All these books and papers make a terrible . . .'' – she groped for the word – ". . . a terrible 'stour'.''

Peter Lowe looked up thoughtfully. "Stour? Now there's a new word. A fine word. Not a Yorkish or Yiddish one that.'' He picked up his pen, dipped it in the half-empty inkwell, and scratched a few characters on the flyleaf of a convenient volume. "Two 'O's, I suppose. On the OTHER hand . . .''

His wife put her arms around his neck and nestled her head against his, grey against black curls. " 'Rest' is a fine word as well, and so is 'sleep'. You will make yourself ill, you work so hard.''

Doctor Lowe kissed his wife's arm as it lay against his cheek. "I should be ill?'' he asked rhetorically. "Doctors heal themselves.''

His wife stood up and sighed patiently, "I am married to a mule, not a doctor, but I love my 'Doctor Mule'. As he knows. When will you finish your book?''

"You mean, when will I finish my NEXT book, Phoebe. It is finished, just now, before you came upstairs to fuss with the window. Here.'' He held out a thick bundle of papers to her and sat back, a twinkle in his grey eyes.

Phoebe Lowe turned the pages slowly. "I'm sorry, my love, I don't understand.''

Peter Lowe laughed and took the manuscript from her. "No, no. Not from the *back*. This is in Scottish, straight from the Latin, although these Scots Doctors of the University read Hebrew and Greek almost as well as I. This is a book on surgery so that they can heal themselves, as you would have me do.''

"They say we are welcome in Glasgow because we are the people of The Book.''

Peter Lowe rocked himself back and forwards in his chair gently in agreement.

'They are a strange people, these Glaswegians. For two zuzim they would cut each other's throats, I think. They fight like cat and dog among themselves, but strangers . . . to strangers they give the cat and the dog, and their friendship.''

Phoebe Lowe smiled. She didn't always know what her husband was talking about, but she had been taught that shared kindnesses between husband and wife were the best type of understanding. "And so you have written a book for our friends. That's nice, dear. Now, before another book should come and knock on your window you must have some soup.''

Fleming the Barber cast a practised eye over the pathetic bundle being manhandled towards him along the street. He stood aside to let the two men bring their comrade into his shop and closed the door after them discreetly.

41

"Over there lads," he gestured towards the stained wooden table in the corner. "Put him on there."

Semmit the bundle groaned weakly. "Ohya, mammy daddy," he said faintly.

Satisfied that the boy would not fall on to the floor, Rab Toner took the barber aside. "We thought it was his heid, Fleming," he said in a conspiratorial voice. "The heid's bashed, but that's no more than many get any day of the week. It's the leg. His leg's crushed awa' tae Hell."

Fleming the Barber, a former Dutch sailor with a talent for working quickly, crossed over and prodded the remains of the leg in his best table-side manner. "Achzo. Is bad!" he nodded thoughtfully. "But there is no better barber-surgeon in all the Clyde towns. I remember one like this many years ago, caught between two barges on the Scheldt." He reached behind him and opened a slim book of hand-coloured illustrations.

Rab Toner's eyebrows shot up. "For God's sake, man," he splutterd. "Yer not gonny cut the boy's leg aff with a book?"

Fleming licked his thumb and turned the pages. "Not a bit of eet. This is a new treatise on surgery and the butcher's arts by thon Glasgow doctor near the Cross. Now, page 42. First, sharpen your saw with a good water-of-air stone unt with the honed steel . . ." He paused. "Tell me?" he asked Rab. "I hope you are strong enough to hold him. I will be too busy reading and sawing to keep him from struggling."

# DON'T HANG AROUND HERE  *1605* A.D.

*It was a very good idea not to hang around where Glasgow's new Cathedral Precinct now is round about 7 September 1605 – 385 years of good going rammies ago. I came round the corner of the Drygate and found myself right in the middle of a first-lass riot. Lord Darnley's House was there at the time – it's been public toilets for 100 years – and the people were revolting all the way up the Bell o' the Brae and along the Rottenrow.*

*It was all over the head of a John McLellan, who was allowed to get away with murder if he agreed to become the town's hangman. This was never one of the more popular occupations in Glasgow, and he was hated worse than a barman who fills your glass from the drip tray. I wasn't very fond of him myself, since he was the reason I nearly got trampled like the bedsheets at Glasgow Green, by a charming, 18-stone washerwoman from the Calton. I also tore my coat on the handle of the pump at the Ladywell, and I've had that coat for 200 years, at least!*

THE damp stone chambers of Glasgow's jougs were not the happiest of places. It was a kingdom of echoes where the steady drip of water and the scampering of rats hurrying to a feast took the place of rain and wind. Its people were few and chosen carefully. There were beggars, caught red-handed pleading for life; there were thieves and pickpockets, kissing goodbye to the hands they were about to lose; there were murderers and smotherers of children, actors, tumblers and other general disturbers of the King's peace. In this Kingdom the only monarch was darkness, the only certainty punishment, which makes it very like the world outside. But this was definitely inside, dark, smelly, unpleasant, and while no one in their right state of mind would choose to go there, any would choose to go out. Only one had the choice. His name was John McLellan.

The turnkey's iron-shod boots struck sparks as he scuffed his way down the narrow passage to the cell. He turned a key like a small axe in the lock and swung the heavy door open with a creak. "McLellan?" he demanded roughly. "McLellan? Are ye in there?"

A bundle of chains and rags in the corner shifted slightly. "Naw. I'm out," said a voice.

"Just you watch yer lip . . ." The turnkey waded into the darkness of the cell and produced another key from the huge bunch hanging from his belt. "Haud still!" he demanded. "Do you no' want yer chains aff?"

McLellan cringed as the jailor lifted up his candle to the troublesome padlock. "That's bright as day," the prisoner complained, shielding his eyes.

"Shut it, you. Yer wanted," his captor replied dispassionately, dragging the unfortunate man to his feet. "Do as yer telt."

"But . . . but I thought it wisn't until the morra! No. Wait . . . !" McLellan's cries, punctuated by the scrape and spark of the turnkey's boots, faded into a hollow silence.

The mob seethed and heaved its way along the bottleneck of the Bell o' the Brae towards Provand's Lordship. The sound of breaking glass and hoarse cries of triumph mingled together as the mob surged along the alleys and wynds, in high

spirits, after blood in general and the sangre of one John McLellan in particular.

"Watch where you're goin'!"

I winced in sympathy as my elbow buried itself in an ample waist. Bouncing back from the collision I looked warily at the walking barricade. "Sorry, missus."

She relented and threw a large arm round my shoulder. "Och, yer all right, son. Great crowd, eh?"

A little distance away something was being tossed high in the air to cries of "Give him wan for me!" and "That's what we'll do to McLellan when we get him!"

I tried to wriggle free, but was held in a cuddle of iron. "Looks exciting," I nodded nervously. "What's happening? Are they going to Hampden?"

She drew me a puzzled look. "What's a 'Hampden', son? Never heard of that."

"I was thinking of another place, another time . . ."

She smiled toothlessly. "Furrin' are ye? Embrugh? Yer just in time for a rare show across the square."

"What's up then?" I managed to wriggle free.

She smiled and licked her lips with relish. "We are gonny get John McLellan, son."

I knew a McLellan once, but that was at Elder's Yards in Govan. Considering the fact that John Elder's great grandfather wasn't even born yet, this couldn't be him. ". . . er, McLellan?" I asked.

The lady looked up at me condescendingly. "You must be from Embrugh," she grinned toothlessly. "I'm talkin' about the McLellan that murdered an auld body in Camlachie with a post. Claimed he didn't know there was a nail in it. McLellan's been offered his freedom if he took on being hangman. The hale town has a perfect hatred for the man, so we dae."

I looked at her doubtfully. "You mean the hangman's a killer?"

"Yer not wrang, son, but it's the killer that's the hangman. It was just September there he took the job, no training or nothing! So we are going to get him and hang him hissel'."

44

I managed a rather weak grin. "Maybe he needed a job." The attempt at a laugh died like an English comic at the Glasgow Empire on a Saturday night.

She narrowed her eyes. "Are you tryin' to be funny?" I started to say that there was nothing funny about it at all, but was interrupted by more uproar and breaking glass across the square. "No way!" I managed to get in before being drowned out by the death-rattle of another window.

"No way where?" She looked puzzled. "Awww," she turned longingly towards the seething stramash. "That's me missing the best bits talking to you." She brightened visibly as the mob surged towards us.

A small, stocky figure, his face flushed with excitement of the chase, ran towards us. I tried to make myself as invisible as possible for a man in a raincoat in 1605. "Here!" he shouted. I wished that I wasn't. "Youse had better get up a close quick," he panted. "The Council boys have called up the sodgers from the Gallowgate Barracks. If ye get catched ye'll be fined £5 for annoying his GRACE the hangman. Nae money, and he gets to whip ye through the streets." He ran off in the direction of the Thieves Kitchen.

"Here, son," the woman took hold of a generous helping of my sleeve. "I've nae money. Have you?"

"I've just got my Transcard," I looked around for a hole big enough to jump into.

"What are you talkin' about?" she stepped back and was swept away by the receding mob tide as it scattered into the shadowy alleys and back-courts down the hill.

"I'm just travelling!" I shouted after her receding back. The sun broke through the clouds and glinted on the steel of approaching helmets and the tips of razor-sharp pikes. "I'm just a traveller!" I made myself scarce, hoping there would be no riots in the future. Some hope.

45

*If you have ever been down the Costa del Sol way and seen folk building houses in each other's gardens and up the sides of cliffs, you'll realise that planners are fairly new on the scene over there. Would you believe people used to ignore the planners in Glasgow as well? Like in 1606 – 364 years of compulsory purchases ago. The Baillies used to ride round the city checking up, and they were not very pleased with David Ramsay, a potter, who "contrair tae all good ordure", almost blocked the Saltmarket Gate with his busy shop, making and selling pots to replace those smashed by the gangs of louts who were "brekkin treis and destroyin' goods in yardis" at the time . . . town planners, vandalism, there is nothing new under the Hielan' Man's Umbrella.*

TWELVE horses stamped restlessly on the damp cobbles in the courtyard. High walls and buildings surrounded the echoing space. The top gables of the tenements leaned towards each other in an effort to shut out the rain-washed blue of the sky, and the rags of clouds drifted towards the green fields of Partick and the wide reaches of the Firth of Clyde.

Fairfax was red in the face. The tight belt round his riding-coat irked a generous shape that had seen a good many excellent dinners and beads of sweat ran down from his thinning hair and stung his eyes.

"May I be of some assistance, Fairfax?" The Lord Dean of Guild was too much of a gentleman to allow his amusement to be obvious. "Is there some small difficulty?"

Fairfax, puffing mightily and mighty proud, was in a huff. "Thank you all the same, Lord Dean," he replied stiffly. "I can mount this nag without aid, thankee." As he spoke he put his foot in the stirrup and began to lever himself into the saddle. The horse, like the Dean of Guild, considered itself something of a thoroughbred, swivelled a large brown eye and squinted back at its would-be rider with no show of emotion.

"Now the rain's away we have a fine day for riding the bounds," the Lord Dean attempted to change the subject tactfully.

"Verra fine, verra . . ." Fairfax tipped sideways slightly, tried to right himself, failed and toppled off his mount stiffly, like a puppet when the strings have been cut. He ended up in a disordered heap. The horse jingled its harness and snorted. It might have been laughing, but then again, it might not.

"Let me help you," the Lord Dean winced a little as he bit his lip.

Fairfax struggled to his feet. "I'll see to it myself, thank you all the same, Lord Dean . . ."

The Lord Dean of the Guilds of Glasgow was a kindly man, as well as being a fair horseman. "You've to nip them in the belly when you tighten the girth," he offered helpfully. "They're rascals, you know . . . puff out so the thing is slack and the saddle is pulled underneath when you, er . . . mount, so to speak." He pushed the saddle up and pulled the straps tight and Fairfax clambered aboard again.

"I have ridden before," Fairfax sat like an elephant on a glass table. "Hold still, you brute!" The horse decided to try a little dressage, lifting its forelegs and rearing slightly while swaying from side to side. Fairfax hung on grimly, digging his short legs into the ample belly of his mount. "I said HOLD STILL!"

"They know when you are not quite, er . . . ready." The Lord Dean stepped back apprehensively. "Mind yourself now, man. That mare will nip, if you rein the bit . . ."

## *46*

His good advice came several seconds too late as Fairfax yanked harshly on the bit. Man and beast pranced drunkenly off towards the wall in perfect disunion. Sighing, the Lord Dean turned to address the mainly mounted company. "Gentlemen! The Court of the Perambulation of the Marches of the Burgh of the City of Glasgow is in session . . ." He sprang deftly on to the saddle of a roan standing patiently beneath the arched gateway. "Let's forward then, gentlemen. Ride!" he called over his shoulder, cantering off. As the company progressed through the arch, the riders ducking to avoid the low carving on the keystone, the sweet sound of a horn being winded echoed around the courtyard and receded into the distance.

"Move, damn you!" Fairfax cracked his whip and was carried out of the gate at the gallop. He almost cracked his skull on the stonework, and cries of "NO! NO! Not that way . . ." could be heard vanishing down the narrow street, in the opposite direction from the stately progress of the Court of the Marches.

The yard at the back of Ramsay's Pottery off the Saltmarket was a paradise for stone-throwers. A large and rather splendid earthenware vase, until a moment ago high on a shelf under the overhanging roof, and monarch of all it surveyed, exploded in a cloud-burst of shards and bits of turned handle.

"Ohhh . . ya beauty!" Big Podger grinned with satisfaction.

Manky Dan pushed him roughly in the shoulder. "Here. You've had your shot, Podger," he complained. "It's me noo, so it is." He let fly with a carefully chosen pebble, smooth and rounded like a slingshot stone, a prince among chuckies. Another carefully thrown pot fell victim to a different kind of throwing, wasting its substance among the growing pile of broken ceramics in front of the unfortunate Ramsay's storage-shed.

"It's me noo, then," Big Podger reached for another handy missile. "That's us even steven, seeven each."

"Naw it's no," Dan objected mankily. "That ither wan was a chanty, no' a right jug ata', so it wisn't," he pouted spottily.

"Wisny," the Podger retorted, taciturn as ever.

"Wis SOT!" Manky Dan, a ferocious 11-year-old with acne and no seat to his trousers, stood his ground with dignity.

The great debate was interrupted by an anguished cry from the shadows of the storage-shed. "You black-dyed pig-swill . . ." roared a voice. "You sons of wall-eyed mule master's bastards!"

Big Podger was as quick on the uptake as any. "RIN!" he shouted, dropping the stone in his hand. "S'auld Ramsay . . .!"

"Make for the Saltmarket," Manky Dan yelled advice to his friend's retreating

back. He scampered down the long yard, almost tripped, recovered himself, and just managed to squeeze his ragged backside through the familiar hole in the fence, as the clutching hands of the irate potter clawed the air after him.

The Lord Dean of Guild, like Caesar staring across the Rubicon, sat mounted and thoughtful at the head of the company of the Court of the Perambulation. He was about to speak when a rather dishevelled figure cantered up from the opposite direction.

"Ahh . . . you are with us, Fairfax," he nodded formally to the new arrival.

Fairfax opened his mouth. His lips moved, but the only sound to emerge was a kind of strangled gasp.

"Indeed," replied the Lord Dean of Guild indulgently. "I will take that as an affirmative."

Fairfax was an odd colour. He sat painfully still and said nothing.

"Just look at Ramsay's Pottery," the Lord Dean continued solemnly. "Built near right across the Saltmarket Gate. An evil example. He had no permission to build this, no plan."

"Is this not him coming now, Lord Dean?" Fairfax nodded breathlessly towards an approaching figure whose face also seemed to be a rather unusual shade.

Ramsay the potter reined himself to an abrupt halt in front of the assembled horsemen. "What are you going to do about these apprentices stoning the work-places of honest folk?" he demanded angrily. "I have had more than any hard-working trader can stand, Your Honour."

The Lord Dean of Guild looked down at him coldly. "Ramsay, isn't it?" he asked with a basilisk stare. "Who gave you permission to plan a workshop on this site at the very gate of the Saltmarket?"

The pain in Fairfax's chest was now a mere dull ache. Breath and something resembling life had returned to his body. "Aye, indeed!" he chimed in dutifully. "Do you know who we are, man? We are the Bounders. Never mind the hooligans, mind the Bounders. You canna park anywhere you want to in Glasgow . . ."

48

*Glasgow is a nation of pet-lovers, or something like that, and 378 years before this morning's "walkies", in 1612, people were just as fond of their wee "Spots" and "Towsers" as they are today. This is a story of dogs, crime and punishment. The magistrates used to consider it merciful to nail people to a stick by the ear and give them a knife to cut themselves free whenever they wanted . . . ! Not so with butcher Richard Herbertsoun. He got jail and the stocks, and a dead dog to go with them. Afterwards, he was hounded out of town – and where do jokes like that lead? Sir Walter Scott wrote a book called* Kenilworth, *but in Glasgow it is usually known as . . . the doghouse.*

THE Burgh Court of Glasgow had witnessed many a high drama, and would look down its municipal nose at a good many more. It was also a popular source of entertainment, and the crowd were there for the show. If the Provost had had his way and looks could have struck the lieges with something sudden and fatal, there would have been a good deal less uproar than there was. "I will have ORDER in the Court . . . !" The Provost hammered manfully with his gavel to little effect, except to spoil the finish on his desk-top. "Order!" he screamed pathetically. The uproar subsided a little. "Shall we proceed, gentlemen?" The Provost nodded wearily to his left. "Baillie Moody?"

Baillie Moody gathered his long robe about him and scuttled forward. Moody was famous for taking several hours to answer the simplest question. Old and incredibly wrinkled, it was rumoured that he had served with six Provosts, seen more than fourscore of windfalls in the Blackfriars orchards, and kept a Chinese fish called a carp swimming around in a large jar in his parlour. It was not known what the carp was called. Moody advanced like a prune wrapped up in somebody's old curtains. He nodded to the Provost. "Thenk you, my Lord Provost," he replied nasally. "You are most gracious, and I . . ."

"Oh get on, man, or we'll be here all forenoon," the Provost nodded curtly and examined a stain on his waistcoat.

"Indeed. Just so, Lord Provost. Er, now, where was . . .?" Baillie Moody wrestled with the bundle of papers in his hands.

"The bit about the 'barbarous bangsterrie', I believe," the Provost supplied drily.

"Oh yes. Maist perspective of ye, Lord Provost, maist perspicatorous to boot. Right to the nub, the very nib as is your wont, Lord Provost."

The Provost was not a happy man. "Pray won't you complete the charge against the man Herbertsoun, Baillie Moody?" he pleaded.

Moody drew himself erect. "Stand up!" someone shouted from the back of the court. "He IS standing up," came the reply. Moody busied himself with his papers until the general merriment had died down. "As you please, Provost." He nodded towards the bench. The Provost buried his face in his hands. "Aye, weel," Baillie Moody continued, "I shall then continue. I will count it an honour . . ." He cleared his throat and sniffed loudly. "Here, tae wit," he began. "It is alleged that Dougald MacPhee, fiddler of those Highland parts did attempt to force a young damsel to . . ."

The Provost examined his waistcoat with renewed interest, hoping that the patience of Job might be stowed away in one of its many pockets. "That is the wrong

subject, Baillie Moody,'' he said slowly. ''That case was found 'Hard to be verifiet' yesterday morn and the idle vagabond is even now in the public stocks and tae be banished on pain of hanging.''

Moody leafed hastily through the chaos of papers both before him on the table and clutched in his fingers. He looked up in surprise. ''Why, that's right, Provost. That IS remarkable. I cannot remember such details.''

''Herbertsoun?'' asked the hard-pressed City father hopefully.

''Herbertsoun. OH! That Herbertsoun. Aye, here,'' Moody discovered a scrap of paper in a fold of his robe and began to read. '' 'That Herbertsoun did cause a maist grievous bangsterrie against another Fleisher to Trade name of James Watson and his beloved son.' ''

''Mister Moody,'' the Provost turned to the Baillie. ''Why, for any favour, must Watson's son be 'beloved'?''

''It seemed apposite to the aforementioned bangsterrie of grim proportions, Lord Provost.'' Moody stared up at the bench innocent as an octogenarian babe in courtroom robes.

It seemed the Provost was not going to add to the weary sigh that answered him, so Baillie Moody continued. '' 'On the 25th of January the Year of Grace Sixteen Hundred and Twelve . . . the said grievous stramash did disturb the lieges about their lawful gain and further, the very next day Herbertsoun did maist foully ding doon and murder Rover, the only beloved, er, the valuable hound employed, er, owned, er, used by Watson and son afore referred to in the initial summary', and so on.''

The Provost's eyebrows shot up in incredulity. ''He killed the man's dog? Why, for pity's sake?''

''It appears it was a great muckle beast, Provost,'' Moody replied.

''That is not a reason, man.''

''Well, it, Rover, I mean, him . . . the dug was necessary to bite tinkers, minkers, gudgies, actors and the like. It protectit the meats and ither lights . . . that's offal, Provost.''

The Provost said nothing.

''I have prepared a short speech in summation.'' Baillie Moody lifted a heavy bundle of documents from the table in front of him.

''And I, Baillie Moody,'' replied the Provost slowly, ''have kept a short temper in rein for near three oors.'' He banged his gavel on the desk. ''I deem the deid dog worth £40,'' he thundered. The assembled crowd had been listening to the exchange with a

50

mixture of awe and amusement. A gasp went up when they heard "£40". The Provost stood up, banging his gavel so hard that a button flew off his waistcoat. "Furthermore," he roared, the floodgates open at last, "I find the man Herbertsoun guilty as alleged. He is to be held in the jile till Monday 27th and put in the stocks. 'Rover', the same 'aforementioned', Moody, shall be laid across his feet for company. If Herbertsoun canna pay the fine he is to be lockit up again in the Tolbooth until he can . . ."

"Er . . . may I point out," Baillie Moody began helplessly.

"WELL!" The Provost growled with as much menace as the best of guard-dogs.

"Herbertsoun is already in the jile, and if he is in there already, how can he be put there if he canna pay?"

The Lord Provost sat down and looked upwards as if Moody had somehow flown up and was crouched among the rafters over his head. "Moody," he said quietly, "I have been dogged by your obstructive manner all afternoon. It's hot. I'm tired. My gout has returned with a vengeance, and . . ." – he sniffed deeply – ". . . and there appears to a rather strange smell in the Court."

Baillie Moody smiled helpfully. "Oh, that would be the evidence, Lord Provost. You never called for it so it was left in front of your desk down there."

"Evidence?"

"The corpus delecti, as it were, or perhaps, to be pontifical and correct as is required, the corpus cani, which of course, is Latin for 'deid hound', Lord Provost . . . that's dog-Latin, naturally."

*It was a date like any other date, filled with the bogles, glaistigs, warlocks and witches that lit up many a moonless forest glade with their goings-on . . . or so people seemed to think back in 1636 – slap in the middle of an era when Scotland seemed like a great cauldron full of all kinds of magic and halloween nastiness. Three hundred and fifty-four years before tonight's midnight, a poacher and his friend in the woods north of Glasgow found . . . well, you'll find out what they found in a minute . . . certainly something that would never happen today . . .*

FROM the woods of Sighthill the city of Glasgow was hidden by the descending sweep of the valley towards the river and the South. Only the needle of the Cathedral spire, its weather vane dark against the last light of the day, stood like Christ's lighthouse in the badlands as the great bowl of the valley filled with shadows. Somebody lit a lamp in an attic in the Rottenrow and the light glimmered fitfully through the branches of the trees about Garngad. Of the 4,000 souls on the edge of the wild the watchers on the hill could see no other sign.

Bron Zuill nodded with satisfaction, shouldered his pack and led his friend northwards, skirting the settlements of Cadder and Kirkintilloch, vanishing under the eaves of the forest into the darkness of the Campsies and the Lennox Hills. The two men picked their way through the tangle and the glens for an hour or more, Bron in the lead, and found themselves following the Kelvin where it flowed between the ancient Roman settlement at Bar Hill on the one hand and Kilsyth, a handful of twinkling lights on the foothills to the left.

"Is this us yet, Bron?" Zebby Aird was a townsman to the soles of his dark red hose. "I'm fair puggled. Do we need to come so far?"

Bron turned and looked at his friend, his face a lighter dark against the grey river. "Just about there," he said softly, pointing towards a looming mass of darkness on the ridge. "Up just a bit."

"Well I canna," Zebby stopped and leaned forwards, his hands on his knees. "All this fresh air's killin' me." He looked up. "That's it for me," he said stubbornly.

Bron ignored him, looked up at the sky, and sniffed. "In for a bit of rain, and the moon'll ride oot the wrack soon, or I'm no judge."

Zebby Aird stood up and moved his shoulders back and forward stiffly. "Listen to me, Neb . . ." he took a step forward and a twig cracked. In the dark night, with no sound but the sough of the wind in invisible leaves and the soft rushing sound of the river, the noise was like a musket-shot.

"Jesus!" exclaimed Bron, turning and taking him by the sleeve. "You'll have every roe from here to Fintry at the run, Zebby!"

"I CANNA," Zebby began loudly then sank into a whisper, ". . . canna see. You must have eyes in yer feet! Wh . . . whit was THAT . . . ?"

"It was a mavis, and the owl that started it aff," Zebby laughed quietly. "Yer a right fraidy cat, Zebby Aird. I thought you were desperate for a wee bit hunting?"

"I've a family's bellies that need fillin'. If I hadna' cast ma lot with the Covenant, and . . ."

Bron poked him in the ribs and gestured violently. "Shhhhh . . . t!"

The wind sighed in the darkness and the tree-tops waved their arms against the silvery sky.

"The wh . . . wind's gettin' up a bit."

"Shurrup!" Bron replied hoarsley.

"Don't tell us YOU'RE afeared o' the . . . Bron! You're hurtin' me!"

"I said . . . quiet, man!" Bron replied with surprising fierceness.

A light pattering sound began as the promised rain drummed its fingertips on the dark leaves.

Zebby peered about him nervously. "I . . . I don't like it here awa' frae the lichts o' the toon, but it . . . it's just the wind, Bron. Sure it is?"

Bron sounded puzzled. "There was something else. I'll swear I . . ." he paused. The sharp intake of breath was louder than the wind in the bushes. "There it is again!" he gasped.

"I canna hear nothing," Zebby shook his head. "There's no . . . Oh Christ . . . whit was THAT?"

A new sound had added itself to the night whisperings and sighings, a low ululation, faint at first, rising and falling like the tides of an underground sea. Something in pain.

"It . . . it's maybe a beast in a trap," Zebby stifled a sneeze.

"Aye, like as not," replied Bron doubtfully. "I think we'd better . . . go the other way . . ." He hurried off, crashing through the undergrowth in the lee of the Bar Hill.

"Are we no' going quiet like we were?" Zebby stumbled along, trying to keep up with his poacher friend.

"I'm not bothered," Bron said over his shoulder without looking back.

Zebby drew level. "At least we are getting away from the . . ." he began, panting, "from the . . . is that a LIGHT ahead through the . . . the trees there? It's . . ."

"It's red." Bron looked about him like a badger in a net. "It's fire. Who's lighting a fire in the woods in the middle of the night?"

". . . and it's winking on and off. Look. On and off."

"I can see that, ya dunderheid!" Bron stepped behind a large tree and stared towards the glare in horrified fascination. "I'm looking. It's not winking at all. There's folk . . . oh my God . . folk running round it."

"Aw mither!" Zebby wailed. "They're all naked as bairns in a bathtub." Something brushed past him, nearly knocking him into the tangled brambles and hawthorn on either side. It was Bron Zuill, going in the other direction. "Wait for me!" Zebby turned and raced after the vanishing poacher.

"Run, ya fool!" the reply floated back to him from the gloom of the forest. "Run . . . They've seen us! RUN! WITCHES . . .!"

The keening sound, a song without words, rose to a fever pitch. It seemed to vibrate through the earth. Branches dipped and danced in sympathy. Something

*53*

in the forest was wailing, adding to the hellish piping, the sound of animals caught in a trap.

The merry sound of bells echoed down the High Street. A group of urchins, the eldest at least five, ran laughing and skipping towards the Cross. A small dog of mixed parentage, one ear definitely larger than the other, scampered after them, yapping and joining in the dance. After the night's rain the sun glittered on windows and rooftops, the slates and shingles a twisting river of light ringing the city.

"Aye, fit like, monnie?" Jamie Barnes strode down the hill towards Johnny Gartshore, his perpetual grin directed towards the vanishing gaggle of bairns and their composite dog. "Grand day!" he continued expansively. "Fine after that storm in the night, eh? Thought the roof was coming in." He laughed hugely, the laugh of a man who enjoys good food, bad women and the occasional game of cards with a fellow cheat.

Johnny Gartshore looked preoccupied. "Oh, not bad," he said thoughtfully.

"What's up with ye, man?" He received a bone-jarring slap on the back. "Are ye well in yourself? Not coming down with nothing, I hope?" Barnes took a step back.

"No need to keep your distance. There's nothing up with my face. Birds'll swim the day you find me under the doctor."

Jamie Barnes grinned so hugely that it looked as if the top of his head was about to swivel off. "You are the joker, Johnny Gartshore. A right tonic, so ye are."

Gartshore flinched but the expected slap on the back did not materialise. "Have you seen that rascal Bron Zuill?" he said sullenly.

"Naw, can't say I hiv. How?"

Johnny Gartshore refused to meet his eye. "Oh, he was to give me somewhat he has for sale, or so he said. I was to meet him by the Tron earlier. Never came. Not like the man no' to come."

"He'll be in his bed still," boomed Jamie Barnes. "Best place with rumours of war. Lord Balmerino, whoever he is, done fer treason. Grand morning though."

"Still no' like Zuill," Gartshore persisted.

"Ach, life's too short. Enjoy yerself! C'mon up the hill and see the show," Jamie beamed benevolently at a passing horse and cart.

"Whit show's that?" Gartshore asked suspiciously.

Jamie Barnes's open face, as blank and welcoming as a page of next year's diary, shone. "Whit show?" he exclaimed with mock surprise. "They are burning some of thae witches, so they are!"

Johnny Gartshore brightened visibly. "Ur they now?" he said with interest. "I'll likely meet Bron Zuill up there then. He never misses the witches."

*I'm no philistine, but after 2,000 years I know what I like . . . especially pictures you hang the right way up first time. I used to have a painting somebody gave me when there were fields and orchards at Garscadden, nice picture with things you could recognise in it.*

*A map's a picture as well, you know, and when I came back from 1641 this morning I would never have found my way to Ingram Street if it hadn't been for that picture with all the coloured lines that shows the best trams, I mean buses, to get. In 1641, 349 years of waiting for some kind of transport ago, Glasgow had its very first picture of the city, a map, drawn by John Colquhoun. They gave him £1 for the job – about five pence in today's money . . . He was worth every penny!*

LATE morning in the back-court was like late evening in a ravine. The Rottenrow was a long chasm of wood and stone, except for the gentle rise of the green hill towards the Cathedral and the Prebends.

There were only two women standing in the tub of water. It could easily have held six. Their skirts were tucked up about their waists and the grey water squelched over feet and lapped about calves as they trod the linen rythmically.

"It keeps your heels fine and soft," said Sadie thoughtfully.

Nancy wiggled her toes against the smoothness of the wood. "Awayyy . . ." She tucked a hem of stray skirt into her waistband.

"Yer right, dear," Sadie nodded sagely. "That's just what I said myself."

"Awayyy . . ." Nancy shook her head compulsively. Hair like new minted gold in the firelight danced across her narrow shoulders.

"Aye," continued Sadie, encouraged. "And that Duke of Montrose is awfy good looking for a nob, so they say."

Rowan-red, the hair stirred a little in the breeze. "Awayyy . . ."

"That's right, Nancy dear," Sadie continued. "Ye need a body to give ye an ear when yer treading the dirty cambrics and nickers for yer bread. It's the sewing it together again that tak's the time. No' our job though, thank the Good Lord and all of Them."

"No' hauf half," Nancy looked up, and the sun filled her green eyes with light like a cup full of paradise. "Yer no' wrang," she said.

"That's what I like about you," Sadie added, tramping with gusto on a bubble of air. "Yer awfy strong in yer opinions. See some of the things you come away with . . . ?"

"Awayyy . . ." Nancy marched on, staying where she was.

Sadie looked up, narrowed her eyes, and stamped and squelched with frenzy. "Nancy!" she whispered. "Don't look round. Keep squashin' yer shirts, but . . . there's a MAN watching us!"

Softly, almost at the limits of human hearing, Nancy muttered "Awayyy . . ." and frowned down at the swirling water in the tub.

"He's up on the hill at yer back in behind the bushes at the Auld Pedagogy . . . oglin'," Sadie added with a mixture of disgust and excitement.

"Fit's he daein' with himself?" enquired the scarlet angel, her head bowed almost to her knees.

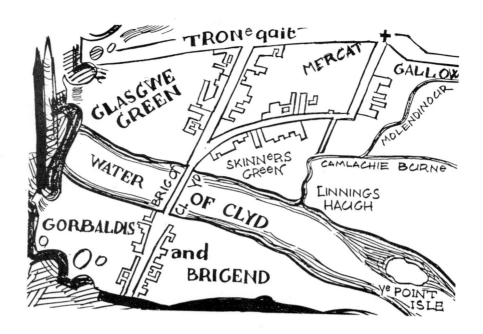

Sadie sounded almost disappointed. "Nothin'. Somethin'. I canna make it out right. It's oor knees, ye know. Knees can drive a man mad. The washin' just makes it worse."

"Is he still lookin'?" asked Nancy, not looking.

"Aye. Just lookin'."

"Maybe he's deid."

"Don't be stupid, you," replied Sadie with the categorical certainty of a geographer who knows the world is flat. "Deid men canna look at yer knees. How can he be oglin' wir knees if he's not in the land o' the living? Use your brain!" She let out a little cry, half a scream. "Oh! Oh!" she exclaimed. "Here he's comin' doon the hill. Has he no shame at aw', at aw' . . .!"

"We'll need to stie in the water," replied Nancy firmly. "If'n we don't he'll see wir bare feet!"

"He'll see mair than that!" Sadie let down her skirts and turned boldly towards the newcomer. "Here mister!" she said loudly. "Just you keep your distance. I'm a respectable woman, and so's she," she nodded towards the demure Nancy, whose head was still bowed.

The gentleman, or so he appeared to be from the cut of his long top jacket and the fine buckles on his shoes, slithered his way down the bank towards the two woman in the tub and dusted himself carefully. He had a large pad of white material tucked under one arm. A lace hankie protruded delicately from the other cuff. "Pray do not be alarmed, ladies," he said politely. "I'm just looking."

"Aye, we know ye are!"

"At . . . at wir knees," Nancy added boldly, still not looking up.

The gentleman threw back his head and laughed, dabbing at his eyes with his handkerchief. "Merciful heavens . . . I am most certainly not. Not!" he added for emphasis. A small copper pomander emerged from a side pocket and he held it up to his nose and sniffed. "Please be assured that I have no interest in, er . . . matters anatomical." He laughed again.

*56*

Sadie was taken aback. "How no?" she asked aggressively. "Whit's wrang with oor knees?"

"Bless us, Modom," replied the stranger, toying with a button. "I'll have you know that I am here on the business of the Town Council of Glasgow."

Sadie eyed him suspiciously. "Can they no' come themselves?"

The gentleman looked at her pityingly. "Modom," he said, holding the pomander closer to his nose so that his voice sounded even more affected. "I am, for my sins, a cartographer." He waited for a suitable reaction.

"Well don't confess your sins tae me!" Sadie had lived too long in an atmosphere of religious strife, battles and bloody uprisings, for the words "for my sins" to mean anything except terminal trouble. "Are ye a Papist?" she asked coldly.

The pomander returned itself to an invisible pocket. "A cartographer, Modom," drawled the stranger with vast patience, "is, for any favour, a maker of maps."

This sounded worse than Papism to Sadie, but she continued bravely. "What's 'maps', some kind of bonnet?"

The gentleman took a step forward, hesitated and stepped back again. "Maps," he replied, shaking his head slowly, "are the delineation of the outline of the land, fortifications, cetera . . . cetera . . . I have a commission from your good Burghers to limn the outlines of the City of Glasgow. First in their entire history, cetera, cetera . . . I am a humble limner." He bowed.

Sadie frowned. "Limb?" she let the hem of her skirt fall down into the water, completely hiding her legs. "Are you trying to talk . . . racy?"

The stranger took the white pad from under his arm and held it up in front of them. "This is a map," he said indulgently.

Nancy lifted her head and looked at the drawing. "Oh the bonnie!" she cried in delight. "Look at the picter with aw' the wee hooses and trees, Sadie. That's awfy good, mister."

The gentleman smiled, like all artists pleased by what appeared to be appreciation, even from those who don't know what they are talking about. "I have some small skill with silverpoint and the art of triangulation," he simpered.

Sadie looked disappointed. "So you weren't . . . weren't looking at us at aw'?"

The map-maker was enjoying himself. Two women standing in a tub of water was an audience by any standards. "I may, if you wish," he began, "draw you at your work."

"Awayyy . . ." squealed Nancy clapping her hands. "Write a picter of us?"

"Well just don't you bother yourself." Sadie put her arm protectively round her friend's shoulders. "If my man finds oot, when he gets hame from whichever war he's enjoying himself at the noo, if he finds out that some English nob's been drawin' 'maps' of my knees, I'll get belted and so will you, mister. Do you get the picture?"

*"Auld Ayr wham ne'er a toon . . ." as Robert Burns says, was unsurpassed in 1647 – 343 September weekends ago – as a beach and a busy port, and together with other towns along the coast like Irvine and Troon, as a refuge from the plague-ridden city of Glasgow. It is hard to describe the fear that the words, "Ye peste has cam' in tae the city from the south", conjured up. Panic, bonfires in the streets, doors bricked up . . . The good Doctors of Glasgow University took themselves off to the woods, the fields and even to a place that is unsurpassed to this day for, "honest men and bonnie lassies".*

A WARM wind hurried last autumn's leaves along the cobbles past the door at the end of the lane. It was a most unusual door. It could never open. The long white cross scrawled in chalk on the wall at the side may have had something to do with it. The ground floor windows were also not of the ordinary kind, clearly, since little light can penetrate an opening glazed with stone. The house was not empty. No one lived there anymore, yet it was not empty. Behind that brick door and those sightless windows, on the other side of the heavy walls, still as the furniture thick with dust and the silent corridors, there dwelt a visitor to Glasgow, a visitor who had paid many calls on the inhabitants of the strangely quiet city. The visitor's name was Plague.

Waves thundered against the shore in sympathy with the storm raging out in the Firth, passing round Goatfell, and moving on across the sea to the distant coast of Antrim.

Regent Mark shivered and drew his cloak tight about his ears. "It's a fine view, Montaigue," he shouted above the gale. "But the wind off the water plagues the bones!"

Montaigue grimaced, shaking a drip off the end of his nose. "And naught else will plague you but the air of Ayr, Regent," he shouted back. ". . . but we'll go back now if you will. The dunes between St John's Church and the Old Castle are perhaps a mite exposed for a townsman." He walked up the sandy rise. "If you look past the Craig you can see the light of some tradeship or other, going south," he called back, pointing. "I thinks she's a Galliot Ewer, German more like than Dutch."

Regent Mark stumbled after him. "Perhaps we could have a lecture on s . . . seaworthiness in your rooms in the B . . . Burgh, Montaigue? I would sooner see the light of a f . . . fire than a galleon."

"GallIOT, Regent," Montaigue corrected him. "More proper, she's a flat-bottomed coasting Ewer of the Elbe, also known as the . . ." The last of his words were torn out of his mouth and scattered across the water.

Regent Mark struggled on, pretending to listen. "F . . fine," he replied, only hearing one word in ten. "Is there any proper way to walk across this shifting sand?" For every step forward he seemed to take two back.

Montaigue drew level, still waxing lyrical about his distant sailing ship. "Quite a rare sight at this season. Now your Boier for instance, Regent. Your Boier's rigged with one gaff on the mainmast, and . . ."

"For pity's sake, man," Regent Mark took hold of Montaigue's collar and bawled in his ear. "May we go back now?"

"Aye. Indeed. Fine." Montaigue shook himself free and plodded forward. "This isn't Glasgow University, you know, it's Ayr beach. We must keep a sense of proportion, Regent. The sea is powerful good for a body."

Regent Mark trudged doggedly after him towards the rain-swept town.

The roof creaked ominously in the gale and water poured in torrents from the gutters of the wynds off the High Street of Ayr. Nearby, seagulls huddled for shelter in the ruins of the demolished Friaries and the fire in the iron grate of Montaigue's attic rooms glowed comfortingly.

Master Crawfurd, fingers ink-stained as ever, leaned forward and peered out of the vibrating glass. "What a night Regent!" he said and his reflection spoke too. "Black on black. The casement's awash."

Regent Mark, huddled by the fire, nodded in agreement but said nothing, staring deep into the glowing embers.

"I feel as if this study is under the water," said Crawfurd from the other side of the room.

"Come over here then, boy." The Regent half-turned. "There are many things to discuss. Leave the storm to its work, and we will do ours while we are able."

"We are as safe here as if we were on the moon looking at Glasgow through a telescope." The tall man, prematurely bald, but a "boy" to Regent Mark, sat down a respectful distance from the fierce heat.

"We have no need for Italian toys to understand the universe. We have our minds, sir." Regent Mark looked at Crawfurd witheringly over the top of his spectacles, rare, and thick as the bottom of a bottle. The Regent's pale eyes, watery from reading too many manuscripts by candlelight, regarded Crawfurd with a fishy stare.

"No doubt it is warmer on the moon, whole lands and peoples if Seigneur Galileo is to be believed," replied Crawfurd stubbornly. "Brain or machine, we have knowledge and reason as tools, Regent."

"We have nothing at all, young man, if the peste should cross the leagues from the city and find us huddled here by the sea."

Montaigue looked up from the table where he had been writing in a large leather-bound notebook. "Surely not?" he aked nervously.

"Who knows how the plague moves, M'sieu Montaigue?" the Regent cast a bleary glance towards the French scholar.

"Who knows indeed, Master," countered Crawfurd, "but surely we must assume we are safe. For a while at least."

Montaigue replaced his quill carefully in a glass inkwell. "Perhaps the rain will wash it away. That is my belief," he said.

Crawfurd stood up and began to pace backwards and forwards nervously. "No one, here, or on the moon, least of all we Doctors of the University and Learning, have the least idea. We must, however, give thought to the student body that has not returned home, but come to study in Irvine."

Regent Mark poked another log into the fire gingerly. "Every room in every house, every pallet of straw in the meanest barn is full of the body of Glasgow College tonight . . . and will you stop pacing, for pity's sake, Crawfurd?'' Crawfurd slumped into a chair across the table from Montaigue.

"The Doctors and students of Montpellier have gone to Bezier and Pezenas, and of Paris, deep into the Massif,'' the little Frenchman took up his pen and resumed writing.

"That's true, Master,'' Crawfurd turned towards the Regent. "Oxford has fled to the Welsh borders, or so I am told. It's like the end of the world.''

"I'm not a great believer in 'ends of the world', Crawfurd.'' Regent Mark moved closer to the fire. "Here I am, warming myself in front of sunlight stored in the form of wood. If it were coal, it would be heat from something made when the world was created, 4004 years ago . . . and our task is to store, preserve, and keep something against the day when this plague has gone, or is conquered.''

"I have heard of a new notion from Cordoba,'' said Montaigue, continuing to write as he spoke. "A most ingenious hypothesis.''

"I've had enough lecturing for one day, thank you, m'sieu.''

"Master Mark!'' Crawfurd scolded his superior gently.

Regent Mark sighed and looked at Crawfurd. "Pay no attention to an old man's testiness, M'sieu. I am rebuked by a man who was my student, and justly so.'' He winced at the heat of the fire, but stayed where he was. "And what is your 'notion', pray?''

"Well,'' said the Frenchman, warming to his subject, "using a magnifying glass, a follower of Averroes claims to have examined the blood of plague victims.''

"Preposterous! What has blood to do with disease?''

"Well . . .'' Montaigue continued, a true scholar and immune to ridicule. "He has seen in miniscule . . .''

"A map of Rome, perchance . . .'' Regent Mark laughed dryly.

"Not at all, sir. He has looked down on the blood of plague victims, from a great height, as it were, and seen . . . thousands of tiny plague devils.''

Crawfurd looked up with interest. "It is at least the germination of an idea, Master.''

"Germ nothing,'' snorted Regent Mark. "Germ rubbish more like. Now, if you have quite finished with philosophy for the evening, what are we to do about the plague . . .?''

61

*Three hundred and thirty-three years ago, in the long winter nights of 1657, the terrible cry of "fire" split the dark Glasgow nights all too often. Then a new sound was heard in the narrow wooden streets . . . the scoosh and gurgle of the town's first fire engine. I remember somebody describing it to me at the time as "an ingyne for casting watter oan land that is oan fire . . ." and that would have been fine. Except for the fact that it was houses not pieces of land that were burning, and the new machine, a big pump on four solid wooden wheels, couldn't manage to force the water more than ten feet in the air. There was no hose, just a long brass nozzle, and an awful lot of people in Glasgow, then as now, lived a fair bit higher in the air than ten feet . . .*

ALL over the old city of Glasgow, from the mansions of the lordly to the dens of the denizens, night-caps were being donned and bed-socks turned the right way round. The inhabitants of the great western metropolis of some 6,000 souls, the good and the not so good, were yawning on the brink of a Scottish dreamland. Some folk, of course, were just getting up, or had no intention of going to bed, but as their reasons for doing so were mostly suspect, if not distinctly dodgy, we shall draw a veil over this sprinkling of nocturnal Clydesiders and concentrate on the more or less honest majority about to clamber between the sheets. The residents of Peasie's Wynd, off Parnie Street, comfortably off and safely respectable inhabitants of the daytime world, were as honest and as "more or less" respectable as any. . .

Netta Drub watched her husband in the mirror as she combed her hair, wincing at the tugs. "Is it right shut now, Ian?" she said watching the night-shirted figure struggling with the shutters. "Give it a good bang."

With that special brand of mental telepathy that exists between couples who have been married for 20 years, "over-married" Ian called their state on the quiet, he chose that moment to give the shutters an almighty thump. "Ya b . . ." he said with feeling, stuffing his throbbing finger in his mouth to both ease the pain and seal in the language. "It's tight as a tinker's trousers," he said, turning.

"For heaven's sake, Ian! Have you no modesty?" Netta scolded, still watching the world through her looking-glass.

He looked down and coloured. "Sorry, my dove. It must have come undone while I was struggling to close the window for you."

"For us, Ian, us. The night wind is no respecter of persons, and it fair whistles down Peasie's Wynd and up my close when it has a mind to."

Ian sighed deeply and, crossing the room, sat on the edge of the bed and looked at his wife's round face reflected in the mirror.

"And I hope it is right shut, too" she continued relentlessly. "I've got a right crick in my neck from thae drafts. It was howling a gale through here last night. I never slept a wink."

Ian muttered something under his breath but his wife appeared not to hear. There was a moment's silence while he watched his toes wiggling, seemingly of their own volition.

"If you expect me to bring bairns into the world," Netta said suddenly, and the toes stiffened, ". . . bring bairns into the world in a room which might as well not have a roof . . ." she left the sentence unfinished but banged her hairbrush down with an air of finality.

"I'll hang a cloth over the windy if you like," replied Ian, clambering wearily into bed. "There's a spare coverlet in the kist." He blew the candle out and closed his eyes with a sigh. In the dim quietness of the room the couple drifted towards sleep.

"Ian?" Netta's voice snatched away the dream opening out before him. "Are you asleep?"

"Yes."

"Ian?"

"What is it?" he propped himself up on his elbow.

"There's a ringing in my ears," she turned over and looked up at his face pale in the gloom. "Can you not hear it?"

He held his breath and listened. Somewhere beyond the world of bed and bedroom, shutters, walls and windows, a handbell was clanking and clattering out in the street. "Oh, damn me, Netta," he complained bitterly. "They're not out already?"

"What out where?" she mumbled, sitting up. "Where are you going, Ian? It's the middle of the night."

Her husband was already on the other side of the room and lacing up his long white linen shirt as if his life depended on it. "It's just the start of the middle of the night," he replied without turning round. "I have to go. Remember!" he cut short his wife's cry of protest. "The engine I was telling you about last night in bed."

"It's the only engine you do talk about in bed," she said, lying down again and staring at the ceiling.

"Well then," he continued. "That new engine for casting water on land that's on fire."

"Here I was thinking I was going to be warm . . . for once. Do you have to go out? Come back to bed for a wee while. They'll keep your fire going for ye."

But Ian was already disappearing out of the door and running down the stairs. "Don't hold me back, Net, pet," he called over his shoulder. "It's my duty. Able

men from the Inntownswards. I'll be missed if I'm not . . ." The door to the street slammed and she could hear him scampering off across the cobbles and into the night.

"Very well then, off ye go" she said icily to the ceiling. "Any excuse . . ." Lighting the bedside candle for the warmth of its clear light, she was soon asleep again and snoring loudly.

"The lum was up" as they say in Glasgow, and a lot more besides, as Ian Drub hammered up the High Street towards the smoke and the toiling men. Glasgow's first fire engine stood in the middle of the road, its long brass nozzle directing a thin but steady stream of water towards the burning tenement. Romans and saints had once climbed that hill, knights and executioners, kings and pedlars had passed this way for nearly eight centuries, but there had never been anything quite like the fire engine. It stood

on four stout coach wheels and was a mixture of solid workmanlike Scots mechanics and theatrical decoration. The T-shaped pump handles sticking out on either side like wooden wings were being forced rythmically up and down by several pairs of willing hands, directing the Clyde water through a mysterious tangle of pipes and cylinders. Emerging at last in triumphant spurts it left a fine mist of water drops hanging in the air like a cloud about the heads of the toilers. Mixed together with the ''scoosh'' and ''gurgle'' of the flame-red engine, tongues of fire crackled greedily above and men ran backwards and forwards across the cobbles, carrying a variety of buckets of water to feed the beast. Somebody was shouting plaintively, ''It's no' goin' high enough!'', as Ian pounded up the street.

A big man, standing in the dark red shadows that leaped and danced back from the towering machine, turned towards him. ''Watch yersel'! The windy's comin' oot!'' He pushed Ian to one side and a rain of broken glass and blackened wood pattered about them as they covered their heads with their arms. ''Pump harder, lads! HARDER!'' The tall man shouted to his crew.

''It's a bad one, eh Sandy?'' Ian asked, trying to recover his breath. ''Sandy?'' he asked again, peering up at the smoke-blackened figure.

''Aye, it's me,'' replied Sandy, ducking as some nameless object, still partly alight, plummeted out of the glowing clouds above.

''. . . just getting into my bed,'' Ian wheezed, still breathing painfully. ''That's some soot you have on yer face.''

''This engine's worse than useless,'' Sandy wiped the sweat off his forehead with a grimy hand. ''It won't send the watter over ten feet in a jet. Glasgow tenements don't start 'till they are near ten feet aff the ground.''

''I think it's goin' oot itself,'' one of the men labouring at the pump gasped.

''Maybe just a lull. Keep pumping,'' Sandy urged. He turned to Ian. ''Nothing we can do anyways. Naebody burnt. The folk just ran down a few flights and jumped oot the windy.''

''Many hurt?'' Ian asked, clambering up beside his friend.

''Just that auld fishwife McGinty. Cam' oot the sterrheid windy like a rocket wi' her skirt in a bleeze and burst her leg when she hit the privy roof.''

''That's something to be thankful for, at least.''

A soot-encrusted figure like a burnt scone with trousers on hurried up to the fire engine. ''Sandy!. . . I mean Fire Mester . . . there's another bleeze,'' he gasped. ''Jist . . . jist down the road at Peasie's Wynd . . .''

Ian looked up, his eyes red in the reflected light of the new flames licking round the chimney-tops above. ''That's where I stay . . . Oh my Goad . . . the CANDLE . . . she fell asleep with it lit again. Sandy! Quick! Bring the engine . . .''

Sandy looked at the distraught Drub and put his hand on his shoulder. ''Now hold your nags, Ian,'' he said calmly. ''The only danger is in not keeping the heid. Anyway. I am Fire Master here.'' He turned and began to issue a rapid stream of orders as the water from the brass nozzle died to a pathetic trickle. ''Right, lads. That fire's near oot. Stop pumping, ya fools! Drub's hoose is up and all. Come oan. GET THAE WEDGES OOT! MOVE!'' He smiled at Ian, his teeth white against the blackened mask of his face. ''Dinna worry, man. My lads know what they are doing. Your fire will like as not be oot or the hoose burnt down when we get there.''

*Soap works and sugar-houses, 15 ships, one-tenth of Scotland's entire merchant fleet in 1668 – 322 spring tides ago – were based in Glasgow. At first a port called the "Wee Quay" at Cunningham in Ayrshire was used. After 1663 a fine new port was built at the Broomielaw with a fountain, a customs house and jetties made of oak taken from the Cathedral. The Custom House Quay was just about where Jamaica Street Bridge is today at the bottom of Union Street. It was put there because trade was picking up and the Glaswegians, never noted as stay-at-homes, were trying to establish colonies in the Americas. There was more than a little opposition from their southern neighbours furth of Hadrian's Wall, and that included the Spanish.*

THE girl's eyes sparkled as the company stamped their feet in time to the tune she was picking out on the flute. All the way back into the shadows of the main room of the Golden Ram, the worthy and the not-so-worthy of Cunningham laughed and clapped. Ginty Leckie stopped, adjusted her bodice, was helped down from the table by a sea of thrusting, willing hands, and accepted the mug of ale held out to her as a prize. She drained it without a pause for breath and there was more applause from 50 admirers.

"Thank God for small mercies," Jamie Ewing drained his own mug and stared sourly across the room at the circle of farmhands, tinks and sailors surrounding the well-built lass. Her cheeks were glowing like ripe cherries and the company were urging her to play another tune.

Shaun Twim grinned at his friend. "Not one of the world's music lovers, are ye, Jamie?"

Jamie regarded him darkly from beneath bushy eyebrows. "I canna stand music or any o' thae fancy arts, thank God," he grunted. "Give me the good solid planks of ma deck and a following wind. That's all. That's what I want."

"You'll doubtless get plenty of both if our scheme comes about." Shaun half-turned to watch the scenes of merriment by the fireplace. The landlord bustled across to the 17th-century fan club with three large tankards in each hand, smiling like a man who has not stopped making money all night.

"The scheme's the thing. That's why we are at the Wee Quay, so let's to it," replied Jamie dourly.

"Only for now." Shaun looked meaningfully at his empty mug. "There's the grand new Quay at the Broomielaw . . . a weigh house, a fountain! That oak they used from the Great Kirk is solid as . . . well, as oak, since that's what it is. We'll no' be coming all the way down here to Cunningham, will we?"

"Thank God for small mercies," said Jamie again, ignoring the empty tankard that was edging towards him. "We are as well down here for now. There's over many long ears in Glasgow. They'll not reach to Ayrshire." He leaned forward and stared woodenly at a point about two inches above Shaun's head. "Here," he whispered, trying not to move his lips. "Don't look round. See that lad in the corner, ill-favoured and with a long nose like a drookit ferret. DON'T LOOK ROUND!" He half-choked, trying to whisper and shout at the same time.

"How can I see him without looking?" Shaun favoured the suggested area with a quick glance and turned back. "Aye. What about him?"

Jamie spoke through his teeth, like a ventriloquist who has just been to the dentist. "Is he not one of Cambell's men? Him that masters the *Sunburst* and the *Nancy's Leg* that foundered yon time when they took a woman aboard . . . ?"

"Don't be daft!" Shaun waved the landlord over with resignation and pointed at the two empty mugs before him. "You'll be fighting with shadows next," he continued. "That lad's an orra loon or a tinkler's pot-mender mair like. See the cast in his eye and the muckle plukes. He's a landsman, or I'm no judge."

"Aye . . . well . . ." Jamie half-agreed, reluctantly. He folded back the small sheaf of papers lying in front of him. "We have enough here then. Charts, reports from those that have tried to settle, ephemera for moon and stars, a'thing needful for the venture."

"I've yet to be telt where," said Shaun, shaking his head as two brimming mugs were thumped down beside him. Jamie rummaged in his purse. "This time I'll fumble and you pay," said Shaun without much hope.

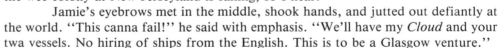

"Eh? Didn't catch ye?" Jamie looked puzzled.

"Aye. Right." Shaun gave a coin to the landlord who bit it speculatively and rushed off to fill another order. Shaun turned his attention to the papers. "Where are we going?" he asked again.

"Fairland," Jamie placed a brown spatulate finger firmly over a dot on the map.

"Oh?" Shaun sipped the froth on his beer and wiped his moustache with his sleeve.

"God's teeth, man!" Jamie thumped the map and a pool of ale spread across the Atlantic. "Fairland, I'm tellin' ye! Newfoundland's Isles. America!"

Shaun looked doubtful. "Weel . . . the wee colony at New Jerseyland is failing, so I hear."

Jamie's eyebrows met in the middle, shook hands, and jutted out defiantly at the world. "This canna fail!" he said with emphasis. "We'll have my *Cloud* and your twa vessels. No hiring of ships from the English. This is to be a Glasgow venture."

"But there's only 15 brig in the whole Glasgow port. We'll not keep it secret long enough to hold others out."

Jamie smiled. This was such a rare occurence that Shaun leaned back in his chair and nearly fell off. "I've got it all reckoned out. Three ships, 120 paying colonists, and in twa, maybe three year a high tide of pelts and furs. We'll be rich as Croesus, man!"

"Croesus never tried conducting business in Glasgow," replied Shaun dryly. "The English will keep us oot. Nae doot of it."

Jamie pointed at the chart again. Ultima Thule was now a brown stain. "Look at the chart!" he said. "There are 6,000 miles of coasts and bays, Shaun. We've sailed together afore. Are ye in or oot?"

Shaun looked at the wet world spread on the table and the area marked in bold

letters "uncharted," apparently already colonised by two cherubs and a coiled sea-monster. "In!" he said firmly, holding his hand out.

Jamie lifted his mug. "To our first sight of the Fairland Hill."

The music started again, this time accompanied by a fiddle, and Jamie winced.

"You're not just going to Newfoundland to escape the fiddling, are ye?" grinned Shaun, pushing his empty mug hopefully towards the scowling Jamie.

The *Cloud* dipped and waves broke across her prow, swirling across the deck. "Land! Land to starboard," the voice drifted down from the top-tree, swaying drunkenly from side to side as the little ship rose and fell in the wild water.

The bosun looked up. "Here we are at last, Captain Ewing," he said to the silent figure at his side. "We know that hill . . . eh?"

Jamie Ewing narrowed his eyes and peered into the gale. "Aye Bosun," he replied dryly, drenched to the skin. "Arran."

"Three weeks," the bosun continued with forced cheerfulness. "We've made good time from Stuart's Town, although those colonists were not so happy, leaving their wee settlement and all."

Captain Ewing shook his head. "They're failing, one by one. I tried to start a colony myself, ye know, Bosun. Sixteen long years ago . . . went the same way as these poor devils from the Carolinas."

"It's God's will, Captain. English and Spanish. We canna stand them all off." He clutched at the ratlines as the ship pitched violently.

"Well, Arran and then Glasgow," Jamie Ewing, steadied himself and made his way towards his cabin. "This is as fair a land as any. Keep her into the wind."

*In 1695 – 295 years before this morning's train from Waverley, or to, depending on which way you are going – there was already more than a hint of rivalry between the Capital in the east and Glasgow, known as one of the most beautiful cities in Europe and by the end of the 17th century as the Second City of Scotland. Edinburgh and Glasgow "fell out" over such things as fire engines or the quality of bread, and from such small beginnings are traditions and jokes about Morningside born. Together with this, Glasgow's sanitation policy meant that it was already becoming "smells better" than Edinburgh. There was also a greater rivalry which caused a few upheavals on Glasgow's four main streets in 1695. The proposals for a Union with England were generally disliked, but Glasgow's trade was stopped at every road block, toll-gate and foreign port closed by English merchants. Union was going to have to be accepted, together with a lot of broken windows, but Glasgow's merchants were determined to survive the upheavals AND that Glasgow should remain first among "Second Cities".*

*Enoch Crubbis was respected both as a man and as a window-maker. His workshop was a model of modern practice, and as soon as the horses were finished with it, his apprentices always had clean straw to sleep on beneath their benches . . .*

DAVID Deanside tilted forward delicately on his toes and watched the glass-cutter with admiration. "How do you know it won't shatter when you do that, Enoch?" he asked.

The tiny diamond in the cutting wheel squeaked in protest as Enoch ran it unerringly along the square sheet of laminated French flash. He slid the glass across the felt to the edge of the table, gave it a series of short, almost reverential, taps underneath, and a thin sliver parted company with the main body of the glass with a neat "snick". The edge was sharp, clean, and straight as the road to Damascus.

"Tricks of the trade," he smiled, resetting his half-moon spectacles on the end of his nose. "It's not quite as easy as it looks, Deanside."

"Not much call for coloured glass these days," said Deanside, standing back as the glass-cutter held the pane up to the morning sunlight. It filled with a deep luminous azure as the coloured layer caught the light and spread it out in every direction.

"None at all, man," replied Enoch, turning the glass gingerly in his hands and examining it for flaws. "This French is for the Merchants' House stairwell. Nice, isn't it?"

"What a blue!" exclaimed Deanside. "It's like a fire!"

Enoch put the pane down on the table with care. "Aye," he sighed. "There's a fire in every colour that has the sun at its back. That's two glasses, of course, Deanside. One laid on the other, plain then blue. All the way from Dijon in the hold of some ship or other."

Deanside looked over his shoulder cautiously. "Speaking of ships, Enoch," he said, lowering his voice. "There is a whisper that there is more than glass, shoes and such, coming to Glasgow among the French cargoes."

"Indeed. French cargoes you say!" replied Enoch boldly, taking his glasses off and peering at Deanside's round face as if it was a window.

"Not so loud, man!"

"Don't be so daft, man," replied Enoch Crubbis genially. "I cut fine window-panes. My walls are not made of glass, nor have they ears, neither . . . and you'll give yourself a pain in the neck nodding 'knowingly' at my apprentices like that. They were all born deaf." He turned towards a boy busily soldering lead. "Or they had better be . . ." Enoch added pointedly. "Aren't ye, Bill?"

Bill laid his hot iron aside on a decorated bracket and looked up. "Oh aye, Master Crubbis," he replied brightly. "What was that again?"

"Good laddie." Enoch Crubbis patted the boy's head affectionately. "Deaf as the floor. Now, Deanside. What exactly are you on about? You know I prefer plain talking."

David Deanside took hold of the glass-cutter's elbow. "You know this talk about a Union with the English . . .?" he began.

Enoch laughed loudly, a fine clear sound, like a crystal glass striking a decanter. "And pigs will fly about the Saltmarket. What about it?"

"They say," Deanside continued relentlessly ". . . that people are being stirred up by agents of the King. French agents."

"I take it that the 'King' you refer to is not our good King William?"

"You take me right in the bull, as you well know, Enoch Crubbis."

The glass-cutter picked up his spectacles and began to polish them. "There is a lot of bad feeling about an Incorporating Union with the English," he said. "I think that the . . ."

David Deanside interrupted him ". . . but French Jacobite agents, man. That will earn us nothing but the jail, or worse. The Merchants' House have written to the Town Council urging that rioters should be dealt with severely."

"They know which side their bread is buttered on," Enoch nodded sagely. "All this politics is good for my business."

"In what way . . .?"

"Lots of broken windows," replied Enoch Crubbis, picking up another pane of glass.

The moon was waning and the sun was in the house of Aries. The clock on the wall of the Council Chamber of the Merchants' House was certain of it, as the fine filigree of its hands swept across the painted heavens without deigning to touch them.

". . . and as for this growing rivalry between Edinburgh and our own fair city . . ." the speaker, Samuel Raeburn, was a man of substance, and his place at the head of the table was due more to the size of the available chair than his contribution to the proceedings.

Dougal Grant adjusted his wig and interrupted rudely. "It affects our business worse than the interference of English merchants, Raeburn," he said and lapsed into silence.

Raeburn controlled himself with difficulty. "There's no call for it," he

addressed the meeting, frowning in the direction of Dougal Grant. "Glasgow is now the Second City in Scotland."

"We have our pride," Grant added, greatly daring.

There were murmurs of agreement all round the long table.

Raeburn continued. "We find ourselves at a crossroads, gentlemen," he said, sitting back and thrusting his thumbs into his waistcoat pockets. "Playing one party off against another is one thing, but the trade of Glasgow cannot go west because of the English, and on the other hand, is stifled by the obstructions of our own folk and sister towns."

"We have survived worse than this," added David Deanside with an air of commonsense. "If we do not trade we do not eat, none of us, gentlemen . . ."

There was an embarrassed coughing and rustling of papers.

"So what is to be done?" someone asked from the far end of the table.

Deanside stood up. "I think . . . I believe Glasgow will prosper," he said solemnly, looking at each of the company in turn. "But a United Kingdom? I don't want it, none of us do, but we must ask ourselves, 'How can Glasgow best flourish?'"

"Will you ask the mob crying against the Union?" said Raeburn dryly.

"No, sir, I will not," Deanside rounded on him. "But I will say this. We'll ride the storm. We always have and we always will. Glasgow is a survivor of hard times, Raeburn. There will, more's the pity, be a Union, but if there are to be any 'Second Cities' in that Union, Glasgow shall be first among them . . ."

*The year 1699 – 291 years before this morning's charges at the Sheriff Court – was not a good time to tangle with the law in Glasgow. There was no slavery in Scotland, at least not the kind you read about on the statute-books, although there was a rip-roaring trade in slaves by Glasgow merchants, but that comes later. Anyone without a few coppers in their pockets, or those who had their hands in other people's, could rely on a first-class professional whipping, not to mention a hefty fine. If not, there was always the danger that somebody else might pay the fine for you. Why was this a danger? Liam, a tinker with very little in the way of "visible means of support" could tell you, and he's going to . . .*

THE Saltmarket was at its best. Dogs barked and weans howled. Maids picked their way among the stalls and loungers, endeavouring to hold their noses and their baskets of provisions at the same time. A dragoons officer, resplendent in scarlet and a moustache that was a regiment in itself, guided his horse none too gently past a small parliament of beggars. Clothes flapped out of curtainless windows and fish-sellers and butchers dusted their stock or reached for the pot of dye.

Tam stumbled and the jug of water he was carrying emptied itself joyfully on the already wet cobbles. A small stream added itself to the other nameless liquids coursing their way downhill towards the Clyde. Liam leaped at the wee boy and delivered an enormous, ringing slap across his ears.

"Ohhh . . . ya!" Tam fell back in confusion, almost dropping the now empty jug. "I wisny!" he cried plaintively. "It wisny me!"

Liam looked wrathfully down at his cowering assistant. "Do you . . . think I'm BLIN'?" he spluttered. "I'm not that auld gettin'. It wisna you pouring that watter, my life's flood, awa'! It was that lassie's ankles!"

Before he could knock the cowering Tam clear across the river he was interrupted by the approach of a tall, stately figure in a travel-stained cloak. "Is your water fresh, my man?" the stranger asked haughtily.

"Oh, er . . . aye," replied Liam, taken aback. "Here's my Seller's Badge. I've a right to . . ."

"I don't give a monkey's fig for your permissions," the man interrupted him. "I wish to purchase a mite of your water, provided it's not new-drawn from some pox-ridden pest hole."

Liam wrung his hands. "Oh no, indeed it is not, your worshipfulness." He stared at the would-be customer for a long moment.

"Well . . . and what are you looking at?" the stranger demanded aggressively.

"Oh, nothing at all, your honour, beggin' your pardon, sur," Liam looked shame-faced. "It's just that the great ladies, like your ain, no doot, are 'customed to send the weemin' to draw water, and . . ."

"If it flowed as fast as your tongue then I would no longer be a thirsty visitor to this plague-ridden burgh. Will you sell me some water or no?"

Liam hastened to his cask and began to draw a flask of water. "Indeed, aye," he stammered. "A thousand, thousand . . ."

"Not 1,000 pennies, I hope," replied the man, snatching the container from him and draining it in one gulp. "This whole town is full of thieves." He burped.

Liam out-grovelled himself and tied his hands in a knot. "Oh yes, quite so, sir," he agreed. "Terrible troubled times we live in. That will be twa pennies, your honourableness . . ."

"What? TWO?" The stranger spat at him. "You don't remember me, do you, you rascal?"

Liam recoiled in fright. "No, Master . . . er, when was . . .?"

The tall man took a step towards him and laid his hand on the hilt of his sword. "This very Tuesday morn past the week gone before Wednesday fortnight I had other occasion to visit this land of rogues on er . . . other matters. Your water then was but one pence."

Liam rallied. "Are you sure it was myself, my Lord?" he simpered. "It must have been Drobby Walter up the road a bittie and along the wynd there. He IS a thief. Yer far better buying at the honest traders."

The sword was already half-drawn. "You tinkers are all alike. In league with this Walter no doubt. I . . ." He paused, slid his sword back into its scabbard and peered beneath his cloak, like a great lanky crow examining its wing.

"Are you well, sir?" enquired Liam anxiously. "Would you like another drink of water. Free, like."

"Where is it?" demanded the bad-tempered customer, helping himself to a generous handful of the unfortunate Liam's collar.

"Where's what?" choked Liam, struggling. "Where's what, your worshipful . . .?"

"MY purse," yelled the man, shaking the tinker. "Where's my purse, you mongrel rat?" Waving Liam like a handkerchief he called up the street, "Watchman! Ho. Thievery!"

"Naw," protested Liam. "It wisny me!"

The Bridewell Prison had its reputation to think of. Damp ran down the walls in torrents, mushrooms grew in secluded corners, rats scampered playfully along the subterranean corridors, and the windows kept out more light than they let in.

Pat bent over anxiously and peered at the floor. "C'mon!" he yelled excitedly. "Come away. C'mon, Feemie! You kin do it."

O'Hare snorted scornfully and picked a bit of straw off his sleeve. "Feemie?" he said with disbelief. "Are you off your . . . well, I know you are, Pat, but why 'Feemie'? It's a bed-bug."

"Shurrupp," replied Pat with feeling. "Yer trying to put my wee Feemie aff.

C'moan!'' he yelled again, the cry echoing round the walls of the cell. "Yer in the lead!''

There was the sudden wet thump of a fist on stone, awful in its finality.

Pat turned to O'Hare. There were tears in the corners of his eyes. "Aww,'' he said with desolation in his voice. "What did ye have to dae that fur? Squashin' ma good flea at the winnin' straw. I've been feedin' her up for a week. All that trainin'. That wis wan of the great fleas, that wis. Poor wee sowel.''

O'Hare wiped something off the back of his fist and opened his hand. "Here's anither,'' he said.

With a sound like a muffled gunshot the bolts on the cell door were pulled back and the door swung open on rusty hinges. A figure was thrust forward into the cell without ceremony and the door slammed and bolted again.

"Aye, fit like, lads?'' said Liam, picking himself up and grinning.

O'Hare yawned and leaned back against the wall. "You and all, Liam,'' he said slowly. "It's like a hiring fair in here, gettin'.''

Pat looked up hopefully at the newcomer. "Do you want a wee race?'' he asked.

"Shut it you,'' O'Hare leaned forward and pushed the crouching figure over. "Do you want the same as yer champeen?''

"Champeen? Race? What are you on about, O'Hare?''

"This is Pat,'' explained O'Hare, examining his fingernails. "He trains bedbugs.''

"Got to do somethin' in here,'' replied Pat, sulking.

O'Hare studiously ignored him. "So what brings you tae the Bridewell, Liam? Bottom fall oot of yer bucket?''

Liam shook his head sadly. "The Magistrate says I was at the thievin', so I must have been. Canna pay the fine neither.''

"Oh never bother about the fines,'' replied O'Hare without looking up. "The ganger pays them for ye.''

"How do you mean?'' asked Liam.

Pat sniggered.

O'Hare looked darkly in the direction of the bug racer. "There's a good market for tinks and gudgie folk, women, and that, in the colonies. The ganger pays yer fine and off ye go, boyo. America, before ye even have time to train a flea . . .''

*1700 is a nice, round number. It was the start of a new century, and 290 years before the ending of this one. It was an age of bloodless revolution and bloody rebellion, of disunion, adventure and immense promise for Scotland in the wider world, and also, like a page torn out of the book of history, it was the time of the Darien Disaster.*

*The Darien Scheme and the events that followed it ultimately ruined a sizeable part of the nation of Scotland. Glasgow lost some £56,000, a vast sum in those days, including £3,000 invested by the Town Council. William Paterson, a former missionary and buccaneer, and the driving force of the Scottish East India Company, proposed two settlements, one on the Pacific coast of Central America and one in the Caribbean. The settlements were to be linked by a road, a meeting of the Atlantic and Pacific coasts centuries before the Panama Canal was dreamed of.*

*Things went badly wrong from the very outset. The local Indians were not over-enthusiastic about the trading goods the Scots brought – small caps, bibles, grey paper and the like – and the Governors of the English Colonies, acting on the orders of King William, gave the settlement of St Andrew in "New Caledonia" no aid. The first colonists abandoned the site. Two more ships arrived, and again, only a handful returned. In spite of warnings another fleet left Scotland, comprising the* Rising Sun, *the* Duke of Hamilton, *the* Hope of Bo'ness *and some smaller craft. When they arrived at the ruined and charred colony the Spaniards were already mustering against them. The new colonists decided to fight it out and the Scots attacked the Spanish at their settlement of Tubacanti, capturing it. The triumph was short-lived. The Spaniards and their Indian allies invested the fort of St Andrew and the Scots, weakened by hunger, held out for a month against both attackers and a hostile fleet. Eventually, with many dead and the attackers within a musket-shot of the walls, the Scots capitulated. They were allowed to march out with drums beating and colours flying, but the attempt to return to Scotland ended with three of the four ships sinking, 250 victims dying in the "middle passage" on the way to Jamaica, and another 800 dying when Jamaica was reached. Of a total of 2,800 emigrants, less than 800 fever-stricken wretches left Jamaica. Hardly any of them reached Scotland. These were the years of the Darien Disaster.*

GULLS wheeled and dipped over Port Glasgow, until recently "Newport Glasgow", built by the city fathers as an outlet for Glasgow Trade on the ancestral lands of Sir William Wallace, laird of Elderslie and Auchinbothie. The mud flats stretched out like a thousand glistening islands towards the deeper channel midstream, as the receding waters reached for the moon, and two small boys waded ankle deep in what was left.

Wee Doogie, sleeves and breaches rolled up, bent his shock of orange-red hair towards the water and called out. "Here's a good wan!" he shouted to Ruary, his friend, grubbing in the mud further along the shore. "Look at that yin!" Doogie called out excitedly. "There's gold oan it!"

Ruary waded across and snatched the driftwood from the smaller boy's grubby hand. "Ach . . . that comes aff . . . see?" He scraped the faded gilding away from the woodwork. "Nae good that."

"Gies it!" complained Doogie, trying to retrieve his prize. "Ye've broken it, so ye have. That was the best bit o' wid I've found in the tides aw' week. It's got a wee lion oan it and you've bursted it. Its crown's come aff.'' He began to greet and sniffle.

"Ach, ya wean,'' Ruary looked down at the wee boy haughtily from the distance between a seven and a six-year-old. "It's just rubbish that fell aff a ship,'' he said.

"That could have been tae America,'' Doogie jumped up trying to take hold of the wood, while Ruary held it up at arm's length.

"America? Huh. Some chance.''

Doogie leaped up helplessly, like a dog reaching for a stick. "Ma Da says there's a big colony to get startit at Dary . . . somethin','' he whined. "That could be aff a that and that.''

"It's Dareen,'' replied his tormentor with a professorial air and a fart. "I heard all aboot it when I wis gettin' Ma's ale syne. Dareen,'' he said again with conviction. "If'n this bit o' wid is aff a Scottish ship frae Dareen, then . . .'' he gloated. "Then . . . they are aw' DEID!''

Tears welled up in wee Doogie's eyes. "Naw they're NO!'' he screamed. "Gies it! It's ma lion!''

Ruary threw the driftwood far out into the water. He was proud of his ability to throw things away, proud of his knowledge that he was king of the seven-year-old bullies of Port Glasgow. The carved wood turned lazily over and over, landing in the fast flowing water with a soft "plash''. It sank, bobbed up again, and began to drift down towards the sea on the ebb tide.

"It's there if ye want it,'' Ruary goaded his sobbing companion. "IF ye can get it again, then why don't ye save it up with yer ithir bits, and when ye've got enough, build yer ain ship and sail away to Dareen . . .''

The stout door closed, shutting out the tavern noise of the Black Bull Inn on a Thursday night.

"Sit ye down, Walter,'' Robert Graeme looked up at the newcomer. "Sit ye down,'' he said again, nodding at the empty chair.

"Aye, a private room's better,'' Walter scraped the chair back and sat down with a sigh.

"Nae doot of it,'' Graeme drummed his fingers on the table-top. "I don't think any of us are in the mood for the idle chatter and banter we'd get oot there.''

"Am I early?'' Walter glanced at the empty chairs ranged around the room.

Graeme reached ponderously into his waistcoat pocket and extracted an enormous turnip watch. He opened the case with a "click'' and squinted at the enamelled face. "Early, Walter? Ye usually are,'' he replied, closing the watch with a flourish and returning it to his ample person. "Yer all right though. Ingram, Snoddy, Bogle and the rest will be down here directly. Then we can get to business.''

75

Walter snorted. He might have been laughing, but then again, he might not. "Business! There'll not be much of that from what I hear."

"Oh?" said Graeme with interest, lifting his restless fingers from the table and stroking his greying beard. "Some new intelligence?"

"No, nothing you haven't heard yourself, Graeme, just £56,000 worth . . ."

Graeme nodded gravely. "Aye, just," he said. "I think we need to . . ."

Before he could complete the sentence, the door of the private room opened again and the uproar and jollity of the tavern washed over them.

"I left word not to be disturbed . . ." Graeme began, stopping short as the dapper figure of William Snoddy entered, closed the door and crossed to the table.

"My God. You are a man on a short fuse the day, Graeme," he said, shaking the rain off his hat and laying it beside him. He turned. "Evening, Walter. Am I early?"

"We've done that," Graeme looked at him sourly. "The others will be here directly."

Snoddy nodded. "Aye, well, so . . ."

"Well, whit?" Graeme began drumming on the table-top with his fingers again.

Snoddy cast a meaningful glance to his right at the silent figure of Walter. "We might as well go over the matters in hand, even if the others are not yet here. Three's a quorum when you are facing disaster . . ." he laughed.

"There is no room at this inn for levity." Graeme's face was like a mask.

Snoddy forced a smile. "Do you know, there's an old saying, 'There is never a body too . . .' "

Graeme interrupted him rudely. "I know the body of the town merchants have lost thousands," he snapped. "The Town Council of Glasgow is itself out of pocket £3,000 and all you have to offer is 'sayings'."

Walter put his hand on Snoddy's arm and leaned forward. "We will get nowhere if we quarrel among ourselves, Graeme," he said softly. "It's 20 years now since the Privy Council first floated the notion of a Scots colony."

"1681," added Snoddy with an air of authority.

"That's right, Snoddy," agreed Walter, still looking Graeme in the eye. "1681. Since then we have been hounded out of New Jersey, burned out of the Carolinas and now little short of exterminated in Darien by the Spanish."

". . . and the English," added Snoddy.

"Darien was a disaster," Walter continued, "but think of those that have not come back, Graeme. How can we sit here in a tavern in Glasgow and talk about the cost . . .?"

*Scotland and England have been united since 1707 – 283 years. The Act of Union made our two countries one. It preserved Scots Law, the judicial system, the Church of Scotland, and guaranteed the Hanoverian succession in Scotland, opening a wide world to Scottish trade, and yet . . . when the commissioners of the two countries met in the Cockpit overlooking the green spaces of St James's Park it was to consider a Treaty which was being largely coerced, some would say "forced", on the Scottish Parliament and people. Scotland desperately needed the trade outlets that the Treaty would provide, trade outlets sabotaged over the previous 20 years and aggravated by the "Aliens Act" which declared Scots traders anathema and Scottish citizens aliens in England.*

*The Treaty became a reality. Certainly bribery was involved, the political norm in those days. The interests of the Hanoverians against Scotland's old ally, France, were also a factor. Scotland's National Debt was settled as a result of the Treaty, but more than half of that went to pay for the financial disaster of the Darien Scheme. The rest arrived in Edinburgh in the form of "paper guarantees".*

*Direct and immediate benefits to commercial centres like Glasgow did result, but however reasonable and balanced the assessment of what actually took place, the intentions of Scottish Lairds like Seafield and Queensberry were less than noble and it was a tragic end to "Ane Auld Sang" that told of 1,000 years of pride in war and national dignity.*

SMOKE curled lazily up into a sky that was as wide as a new world. Portsmouth basked in the heat of a late autumn afternoon – Portsmouth, New Hampshire.

Davis lifted his hammer and brought it down square on the glowing horse-shoe of iron. Picking it up gingerly with the tongs he dipped it in the tub of brine beside him, dropping it on the growing pile at his feet, and reached into the fire for another glowing bar.

A shadow fell across the anvil and he looked up. A tall Susquehanna Indian was standing watching him with an air of detachment. His proud face was impassive, dark as the shadows under the trees of the great forests that stretched outwards from the little settlement, clothing the vast mountains and valleys of the western seaboard of America. "You take for trade?" the Indian said, thrusting something towards the stocky little Welshman.

Davis brought his hammer down with a thud and sparks flew. "What?" he said, intent on his work. He beat the soft metal again, bending it round the former to make the shape.

"You take for trade?" the Indian said again, quietly insistent.

Davis disliked being interrupted. "What the devil?" he said, laying the heavy hammer on the anvil and wiping his hands on his apron. "What is it? What are you after? There's no drink at a smith's shop. Understand, chief?"

The Susquehanna looked puzzled, as if he had been asked why he was alive. "I have skins," he said with a slight frown. "I drink. I wash. No need for more. Here. I give you in trade for knife of hard wood . . . esanna . . . iron knife, I give you this pelt of silver cat. Very soft. Your woman pleased with you."

*77*

Davis cast a glance at heaven and scratched his ear. "If you want to trade skins, there's McCorquodale's post down the lane. I'm not giving you no knife."

"No?" the Indian looked through him.

"N . . . O!" said Davis emphatically, reaching for his hammer.

"No want hammer," replied the Indian quietly. "Want knife. Good pelt. You feel."

"You'll feel this in a minute," said Davis, picking up the hammer.

The Susquehanna had seen a hundred thousand buffalo on the move. Patience was his strong point. "I go," he said noncommitally. "Maybe I come back."

"Aye, that's what I'm afraid of," muttered Davis to his retreating back. The blacksmith cursed as he beat the iron and found that it had gone cold during the exchange.

"What was all that about?" asked Alec Spence, perching on the edge of the water-barrel.

Davis looked up and put his hammer down again with a sigh. "One of those Suskyhanna. Wanted a knife! If I gave him one it would end up in my back, or yours, Alec, like as not."

"Big lad though," Alec watched the tall figure stride regally down the leafy lane.

Davis turned and followed his gaze. The Indian looked back briefly and vanished over the rise. "He's a brave. Alec. Three feathers. That means he has killed a man for the tribe. Take the Abenaki, now. Four feathers for the same thing, two on each side."

Alec stared at the metallic scum on the surface of the brine barrel. "That's a ship in from home," he said.

Davis looked longingly at his hammer. "Where's 'home' when it's at home?" he replied sourly. "We are far enough here from everywhere."

"I thought you were a New Hampshire man?" Alec asked, standing up and dusting the seat of his pants.

"Indeed, Scotty, I suppose I am," the Welshman looked thoughtful. "Still think of Portsmouth as Maine, though. Hasn't been Maine since '68. You've been here a good five years. Still homesick?"

Alec sat down again. "Each year I tell myself 'just one more year'. I can't now."

"What do you mean? Somebody stolen Glasgow?"

Alec reached into his pocket and produced a carefully folded sheet of buff-coloured paper. "I got this off the ship new in."

"Lucky man," the blacksmith nodded in approval. "News from home."

"But I can't go back now," said Alec, re-reading the letter. He looked away. "If I do I'll be a stranger in my own land, just like that Suski you sent packing."

"For why man?" the little blacksmith put his hand on his friend's shoulder.

"I can't go home because they've sold it," replied Alec without turning round.

"In that case, boyo," the blacksmith spun him about with gentle force, "let me shake the hand of a fellow-American!"

Alec looked past him down the lane. "IF I am an American," he said, "then what is he . . .?"

"Crokdale no trade," said the brave, striding towards them. "You trade? Good pelt for your woman . . ."

It was a warm, late autumn afternoon. The rooftops were painted a pale gold by the westering sun and the imperial crown of the Tolbooth Tower seemed to float above the blue shadows that filled the streets, like the gilded ghost of a vanished age.

"Aye," said Spence, rounding the corner and colliding with Brodie. "Quiet day the day."

"Ye gave me a richt fleg!" exclaimed Brodie. "Give's ye palpitations, that. It's quiet right enough. Like the grave, after the carry-on last week."

"The riots?" Spence raised an eyebrow. "Everybody's staying out of the road. I'm just away in mysel'."

Brodie looked carefully up the High Street and down the Saltmarket. A solitary mongrel, unaware of the gravity of events, found a patch of sunlight in the middle of the deserted street and lay down. "They say it's what's needed, though," continued Brodie, keeping his eyes on the quiet horizon.

"What, to be declared 'Aliens'?" returned Spence. "I blame the Lairds, lining their ain pockets. Union!" he spat in disgust. "Our own Parliament wishing itself into oblivion."

"How's your lad?" said Brodie, changing the subject tactfully.

Spence brightened. "Alec? Oh, fine, fine, I suppose. I wrote him a wee letter three months ago. He'll have it by now, like as not."

"We'll be able to trade freely with the colonies," said Brodie.

"Aye, whose colonies?" Spence nodded and walked on. "I'm away, it's gettin' dark . . ."

# A SHAWL OF ANY COLOUR

## *1715* A.D.

*Glasgow tried to stay out of the Jacobite uprising of 1715, 275 long years ago. However, "It's an ill wind . . ." as they say, and in return for the 500 men the city sent to help the Duke of Argyll's army in September, we got 353 Jacobite prisoners in early December. Nobody really wanted these poor souls, least of all the City Fathers who had to pay for their upkeep in Glasgow Castle. A few were "allowed" to escape because it was cheaper. Jacobite and Government spies were thicker than clegs in a wet September, and the colour of a man's, or a woman's, politics were often as changeable as their jacket or shawl.*

TAM clung to the lip of the chimney and surveyed the scene. To the south he could make out the towers of Crookston and Haggs Castle, on the other side of the Cessnock Woods. Beyond that the braes of Cathkin and Gleniffer were blue in the haze that hung over the smoky town. Westwards the river wound away past the poplars that led to the mill at Partick and down river to Dumbarton Castle. Nearer at hand the Saltmarket, High Street, and Bell o' the Brae climbed the hill towards him, the Doctor's Orchards behind the College Quadrangle a patch of silver-green in the stiffening breeze. The smoke of 1,000 chimneys drifted below him, but lifting up his eyes, he could just make out away on the edge of sight Ben Lomond and to the left, mountainous as the clouds, the sleeping warrior of Arran. Tam coughed as the wind shifted, filling his nostrils with the acrid smell of burning peat and coal. His eyes watered as he peered down the lum he was holding on to, but chimneys were his business. "Halooo . . ." he shouted into the velvet darkness below. "Hulaw . . . rerrr?"

"The daft boy's stuck in the lum, more'n likely," Andy clambered deftly up the steep camber of the roof and joined his mate beside the silent chimney head.

"I'll flay him," said Tam crossly, peering inside. "He's a nae-user, so he is."

"He's wee enough," replied Andy with an air of professional nicety. "We need them thin tae get a right sweep at it, daint we?"

Tam stuck his head into the black opening and shouted again. "Bandy, Halooo. Are ye doon therr?"

A reedy voice floated up from the depths in reply. "Aye, right ye are Master Tam. Here it's comin' nooooo . . ." The last was a long drawn out "Nooo", like butter that has been scraped over too much bread.

Tam looked about him wildly. "Where the devil . . . ?"

A harsh scraping sound grew suddenly louder and without warning, a fist of black bristles accompanied by a generous cloud of soot and a rather bewildered mouse, emerged from the chimney next to them in a flurry.

"I WILL skin him," protested Tam, coughing and spitting. "The daft loon's pushed it up the wrong lum!"

Andy waved his arms about and gagged. "What a stour. I can hardly . . ." his voice trailed away as he slid from sight.

Keeping a tight grip on his chimney, Tam squinted in the direction of the forlorn cry. "Andy!" he shouted, his eyes red and stinging. "Andy! Where are ye? Gies yer haun!"

Andy's voice floated up from below. "It's all right. I've fetched up against the

gutter, but it'll no' hold long by the look of it.'' There was an ominous creaking sound from the edge of the roof.

Tam turned, crouched, and slid gingerly down the tiles on his backside. ''Haud oan,'' he said in a quavering voice. ''I . . . I'll get ye.'' He stopped short of the drop with his heels dug into the guttering. His fingers were white where he was clutching the edge of the slates.

''I'm fine though,'' Andy sounded relaxed. ''I'm better off than thaim doon therr.''

''Wh . . . who?'' Tam asked nervously.

''Those down therr, I said,'' Andy leaned out over the street and pointed below.

Tam opened one eye. ''Oh. I canna look down. It makes my stomach churn, Andy. I'm seek.''

''Some sweep you are,'' replied his mate scornfully. ''It's only 100 feet to the Bell o' the Brae. Look. There's a hale army coming up the street.''

Tam risked a quick glance down and looked away hastily. ''That's no' an army,'' he said through clenched teeth. ''That's the Jacobite prisoners gettin' marched up to the Castle.''

''How do you know?'' grinned Andy. ''You've got your eyes shut.''

''I just know,'' Tam countered defensively. ''After the battle at Sheriffmuir there was a . . .'' he paused and sniffed. ''Can . . . can you smell smoke?''

Andy let go of the guttering and began to scramble up the steep roof as if he was two feet of the ground. ''Oh my Jesus!'' he shouted. ''Do they not know not to light a fire under us while we are sweeping their lum?''

''That's the boy tellin' them the wrang one,'' Tam followed him slowly and painfully. ''He should be going to Glasgow Castle along with the prisoners.'' The Clyde Valley vanished completely as clouds of smoke mixed with the smell of chips and fried onions drifted towards them.

The fields of Yoker dropped behind jerkily as the oarsmen strained to put as great a distance as possible between themselves and Glasgow Bridge. Two women sat in the prow, watching the spires of Glasgow disappear round the bend in the river.

Isla leaned across, and in spite of her protests, wrapped a thick woollen shawl about her mistress's shoulders. ''You are not used to this life, mistress,'' she chided, ''and there's the rain on now.''

The brown mirror of the river was broken into countless little circles as a heavy shower pattered its way across the country from the direction of Paisley.

''I think we will all have to get used to this life,'' replied Lady Isla Glenbuchat

sadly, holding the shawl closed at her throat, hiding the red marks left where the jailor had torn her necklace from her.

"You'll soon be warm now, mistress," Jenny patted her hand reassuringly. "The man your good husband paid to let us go said the ship for France would be in the roads downriver waiting oor signal, so he did."

"Master Gordon is hunted himself, like an animal," Lady Isla drew the shawl across her face and peered at the weeping world through shadowed eyes.

One of the oarsmen raised his head. "The Laird of Glenbuchat is a Prince, Madam," he said proudly. "When he cried out, 'Oh for an hour of Dundee!' when Mar dithered against the British, there was not a Jacobite in Scotland that would not have laid down his life for him."

"Thank you for that, Angus," nodded Lady Glenbuchat, peering out from beneath her shawl. "But still, we lost the battle."

"Aye, but by the barest whisker of a cat," continued the oarsman, straining as he spoke. "We pushed Bloody Argyll back to the left, and he had our forces down on the right flank."

"If only that MacGregor had intervened!" exclaimed the Lady, tilting her head back to let the fine rain cool her forehead.

Angus nodded gravely. "Rob Roy is a canny fox," he replied. "He saw the way of it and lives to fight on, as we do, Madam." He grunted and resumed his battle with the river.

Lady Isla looked down at her shawl. "Jenny? Where did you get this?" she asked, holding the fringe out towards her servant.

"Why from the man that helped us escape, mistress."

"Have you noted that it is in the colours of our enemies, the Campbells," Lady Isla asked coldly.

Jenny coloured. "I'm awfu' sorry, mistress. It . . . It'll be a help to our disguise, like as not."

"I'll turn it round," Lady Glenbuchat took the shawl off. "I hate these lines."

The oarsman looked up again. "Begging your pardon, mistress. Be ready to turn it back again if need be."

"No Angus," she said firmly. "I'll never turn my coat, nor my shawl. No one can make me."

"Yes, my Lady," he replied bleakly, pulling manfully against the tide.

*Everybody has heard of the Jacobite Rebellions of 1715 and 1745, but there were others, and the waves they made swept up the Clyde and into every other neuk and corner of Auld Scotia. George Keith, Earl Marishall of the Rebellion in 1715 was "passed over" by King James VIII in the 1719 attempt. Glasgow's ruling powers remained loyal to the Government although large numbers of the citizenry were none too happy. There were riots and incidents that led to the shooting of a number of citizens, some more innocent than others, and the ARREST of the Provost of Glasgow. Wars and rebellions seemed to be the norm and then, as now, there was always someone in the pub only too willing to hold forth about their "experiences".*

THE grey waters of Loch Alsh were a fitting background for the rough-looking highlanders huddled round their fires beside Lord Tullibardine's tent. There was another Jacobite army a mere three miles away, also huddling in the recommended manner when the sleet is at your back and a plaid is all that is available to wrap a cold, hungry body in. The second army was under the command of the Earl Marishall, but he and Tullibardine hated each other so much that they had decided to keep a reasonable distance between what was, on paper at least, a single force.

Tullibardine unrolled the waxed map, holding it down with an inkwell and a powder-horn. "The Government forces must come north," he said, peering at the outline in the yellow light of the tent. "They must come by Glenshiel, and we could take them here, or here. But then again . . ." He paused and stroked a chin the worse for the almost complete absence of barbers in the highlands.

His aide, Gavin Kennedy, looked over his shoulder. "Our intelligence indicates that General Wightman has 12 pieces of artillery and 6,000 of foot." He walked round the camp table and stared at the map upside-down.

"I've read the report, Kennedy," replied Tullibardine without looking up.

"Yes my Lord." Kennedy was a man who knew his place in the order of things.

"As I was saying," continued Tullibardine, "our meagre troops are best coming from the heights and . . ." he broke off in mid-sentence as the tent-flap opened admitting a gust of icy wind and a rather dishevelled clansman.

Kennedy strode across and barred his entry. "What is it?" he demanded. "His Lordship is in conference!"

Slightly at a loss, the messenger looked at Kennedy, then at the frowning Tullibardine and back to Kennedy. He hesitated.

"What the devil d'ye want!" demanded his Lordship angrily, still peering at his map.

"Er . . . the Earl Marishall sends a message," the unfortunate highlander replied doubtfully.

"That much is obvious." Tullibardine flecked a speck of dust off his velvet sleeve. "Since you are patently . . . a messenger. Take it Kennedy and tell him to get out."

Kennedy snatched the paper. "Give it to me," he said unnecessarily. "His Lordship says to get out."

"And tell him to close the tent-flap," his Lordship relayed his further instructions.

Kennedy turned to the messenger. "Lord Tullibardine says to . . ." but the man was gone.

"He has, my Lord," said Kennedy.

"Well give me the damned paper then."

Kennedy strode across and held out the note.

Tullibardine glanced at the letter, crumpled it up and threw it across the tent angrily. "He speaks to me as if he were the General, not I. I am, after all, Commander by order of His majesty King James VIII. Keith may have sailed from France with a few toadies, but over 1,000 highlanders have come to Loch Alsh at my call, not his."

"Yes my Lord," Kennedy nodded dutifully.

"So why has he camped himself three miles away?" raved Lord Tullibardine. "Are we not one army?"

"Yes Lord."

"Yes Lord what?" Tullibardine strode across to his aide and poked him in the chest with a carefully manicured finger. "We are NOT one army or we ARE one army?"

"Er . . . I . . ." Kennedy took a step back.

"You must be more decisive," the Commander poked him in the ribs. "If the Jacobite cause is to succeed we cannot afford to disagree among ourselves . . ."

For the high-spirited or those intending to become as full of spirits as time and purse would allow, the Iron Ravel Cross was the place to be.

Tug, the local oracle, was the centre of a small but rapt circle of admirers. ". . . and they near shot ma heid aff, I'm tellin' ye," he concluded triumphantly.

"Mair drink, Tug?" Sandy pushed a full tankard towards his idol.

"I hope it's a full wan this time," said Tug haughtily, accepting the offering with ill grace.

Binky leaned closer. The strong smell of onions pushed the others back like an invisible wave. "You were tellin' us yer expeeriences with the Jacobite ermy at Glenshiel," he insisted. "Goat yer napper shot aff."

Tug looked round at the rapt circle and waved his hand in mock denial. "Naw, naw, I've telt ye that. That's HISTRY. Jist wan o' my campaigns," he drank noisily. "I wis tellin' ye about Brigton, though . . ."

Sandy looked disappointed. "Who wisny," he said. "I mind I wis . . ."

Binky reached across and pulled Sandy's hat down over his ears. "Wrap it youse!" he ordered. "This is interestin'. On ye go, Tug boy . . . gies the Brigton wan . . ."

"Well with the riots aboot the Malt-tax they sent for two companies of that Lord Delorain's Foot . . ."

"That was Captain Bushel," added Sandy.

Binky threw him a withering look.

"Catain Bushel," continued Tug, ". . . and Provost Miller persuaded him to leave the toon and even when they were oan their way out of Glasgow they kep' firin' up the side-streets. Shot a wumman right out of a windy, they did."

"I 'member," Binky shook his head. "It was hellish altogether. Tell us aboot your bit again, Tug."

"Aye, well. It was Thomson that dressed up as a wumman and started the raid on the magazine for arms, the same Thomson that used to bring us ale and buns when we were workin' tae fortify the Kirkintilloch Bridge, back when they thought the Jacobites were still comin'. I saw HIM, Thomson, killed, killed deid if ye can believe it. That's when the musket shot went clean through . . . here!" He pointed to the middle of his chest.

"Awayyy . . ." said Binky, awestruck.

Tug nodded slowly and gravely. ". . . and oot the other side. I heard it brak a windy, it bounced off a front step, and wounded the sodger that fired it in the first place."

Binky sat back and grinned toothlessly. "You're the man, Tug. Think they'll let Provost Miller oot the jile in Edinburgh?"

Tug shook his head sagely. "Aye, weel, ye see . . . That wis General Wade, the hale Royal Scotch Dragoons, Duncan Cambell of Lochiel, Duncan Fraser the Lord Advocate. The hale jing bang cam' tae Glasgow and took the Provost prisoner . . . Miller, Stirling, James Johnson, John Stark, Dean o' Guild, John Armour Deacon Convenor . . . all prisoners."

"You're the man, Tug. Whit a memory! Think they'll let them oot though?"

"Hard to say," Tug looked thoughtful. "There's banishings and whippings and all that things. No' fair it's no'. It's no' as if Glasgow supported the Jacobites. This is a peaceful town . . ."

*Three great Glasgow dynasties controlled the vast profits from the 18th-century Clydeside tobacco trade – the Ingrams, the Cunninghams, and the Spiers. There were other "barons", and together they made a tight-knit cabal related by marriage, mutual interest, and the unbelievable profits that flowed from an annual tally of seven-and-a-half million tons of tobacco. There was another "commodity", almost equally rewarding, dark as the black Paducah weed, cured and seasoned in vats of misery. As well as being masters of the Tobacco Boom, the Glasgow Traders were also Barons of the Slave Trade.*

THE air beneath the trees was warm and moist, heavy with the threat of rain. Like a net of diamonds the countless stars spread from horizon to horizon in an immense arc, untroubled by the world and its struggles. A twig cracked, and a monkey, startled and afraid, stared down wide-eyed into the gloom and chattered in defiance.

Abrim was restless. There was little he could do about the water situation, but until another well was sunk, it was his role in life as village headman to worry on behalf of other people. His wife Asita stirred, sensing her husband's wakefulness, and the new baby whimpered, deep in the dreams of a one-year-old. It wasn't just the well . . . an indefinable sense of unease lay like a cold stone in the pit of his stomach. In any case, the rains would come soon and there would be too much water. This year the ditches would be ready in time and take the excess water down towards the mighty Benue, father of all rivers. He would go up to Elmina when the dry returned and buy the yellow cloth he had promised Asita.

"Are you not tired, my love?" His wife had been lying awake, staring at him.

"No." He stroked her fine hair where it lay unbraided against the embroidered cushion, a black mist in the darkness. "You sleep. The baby will wake soon enough."

She smiled at him, her eyes wide. "Try not to worry." Her arm was cool against his back.

"How did you . . .?" he began.

"Am I not your wife?" She kissed his shoulder and put her arm around him. "I can't sleep either," she confessed. "I feel . . ."

"Troubled?" he said, completing her sentence. "I have felt it since early evening. As if, well, something was coming . . ."

Asita laughed quietly. "The rains are coming. The air is full of heaviness and thunder. You would not be headman if you didn't see a little of tomorrow." She sighed and turned over, but her eyes remained open.

Abrim lay back. The air was like a damp sheet across his chest and sweat gathered at the corners of his eyes. Allah willing, the dark efreet that sat on his heart would be gone by morning. Resting his head on his hand, he lay down to sleep. The house ghekko scuttled across the rafters and vanished into a crack in the wall.

Without warning the bamboo screen that half-covered the window opening was split by a long straight sword. A thick hairy arm thrust itself into the room, a WHITE arm. Abrim sat bolt upright in bed, his wife cried out, and the baby started to scream.

The arm was withdrawn and a harsh voice outside the hut shouted, "There's mair in here, Bill!" Screams were coming from other parts of the village. Through the half-open door red tongues of flame were leaping from the huts on the other side of the meeting-place. The flimsy door was ripped off its leather hinges and two men, both carrying swords and one with a torch in his other hand, burst in on the couple. Abrim was dragged out of bed and struck on the side of his head by the butt of the torch. As he lost consciousness he seemed to hear his wife screaming somewhere very far off. He knew they were slavers. He knew he might die before ever they threw him in the stinking hold of their ship, but his last thought was not of his wife, or even of death. He wondered if the new well would ever be finished, then darkness took him.

"Well, John?" William Cunningham looked pleased with himself, but then, he generally did. "Not at business?"

"I might say the same to your good self!" John Ingram lifted the corner of his scarlet cape clear of the mud with his gold-topped cane.

"Aye weel, I am actually, on my way to business," Cunningham nodded ahead. His negro boy was staggering round the corner of the Trongate with the kist that held the day's papers. "Thought I'd take the air first." He sniffed at a little muslin bag of cloves.

"I heard you made a good venture this month," said Ingram with a conspiratorial wink. "Virginia's the place, John, eh?"

"THIS is not the place," Cunningham took his fellow-baron to one side, "but have you given any more thought to the er . . . matter we discussed at the Club yestere'en?"

Ingram raised his cane to a passing washerwoman who had dared to step on the Plainstanes. She ran off, throwing him a curse as she went. "They don't have to like us, so long as they fear us," he sniffed. "Aye, I think that your scheme is well and good. We have the hire of 60 ships between us, and a bank's the thing."

"Quite right. Good." Cunningham beamed expansively. "We mun finance these colonists . . ."

"I believe they are calling themselves 'Americans'," sneered Ingram.

"I don't give a fig if they call themselves blackamoors, so long as they plant cotton on my credit and interest. The Glasgow Store System is building the Carolinas up, and that is good for us. That's why we need a bank."

Ingram threw his hands up in mock horror. "Blackamoors!" he exclaimed. "Are they to receive your line of credit also, Cunningham?"

"Ever the jester," Cunningham replied

dryly. "There are slaves aplenty though, and the tobacco fumigates the ships after they are taken off. It's a golden triangle, man. Glasgow . . . Africa . . . the Americas . . . Glasgow . . . Africa . . . the . . ."

Ingram laughed. "You are making my head spin. About the bank . . .?"

"Aye, weel, the Ship Bank, or Thistle Bank, or somesuch, that's what we could call it. It will give us room to grow."

"There's plenty of that."

"Indeed. Virginia, the Carolinas, I have six new men off to Annapolis to set up posts to the west this month coming."

"I thought we might go into something together," said Ingram. "I hear that there is a rich picking out of Fort Chisnall."

Cunningham looked doubtful.

"A risk shared is a risk halved," cajoled Ingram.

"Good day to you gentlemen!" A third scarlet-caped figure, dapper in a tricorn hat set at a jaunty angle, walked beneath the arches of the Tron Church and stood looking at them quizically. "May I take by your sudden silence that you have been discussing business?" he laughed.

"No. No, not at all," Ingram lied. "Weather, you know . . . matters."

"Ah . . . matters," said Bogle with a knowing nod. He doffed his hat and bowed as the daughter of a friend flounced past with her maid. "Well, I've a matter that I've been meaning to put to you both."

"Oh, really," John Cunningham stole a glance at Ingram.

"Indeed," grinned Bogle. "I have something for sale."

"So have we all, Bogle," said Ingram, looking down his nose at him. "And what, pray, do you wish to put in the market place? Some new commodities? Is it a good margin?"

"Well," Bogle polished the head of his cane with his glove. "I've come by one of these coloured boys. No need for one myself. Wife can't stand them, y'know. I would be prepared to let either of you take him off my hands for a very reasonable sum . . ."

Ingram shook his head firmly. "Tobacco, I might be interested in, good strong bodies for the Virginians . . . we may be able to discuss terms, but another black servant? No thank'ye, Bogle. I've got one, and they are a glut on the market . . ."

*Prince Charles Edward Stuart, "Bonnie Prince Charlie", came and went with a song, 10,000 starving Highlanders, and 12,000 Glasgow shirts. The great review on Glasgow Green had only managed to squeeze 60 recruits from the reluctant ranks of the Clydesiders, but neither the shirts, the 6,000 coats and pairs of shoes, the printing press, printers to go with it, guns and ammunition, hostaged town councillors, or his alcoholic mistress, Clementina Walkinshaw, could keep out the chill on Culloden moor.*

*The Jacobite cause fell and the indecisive Prince with it, but there were those who fought not for the Stuarts, but for their country. The bravery and nobility of men like the Cameron of Lochiel who saved Glasgow from the Prince's wrath, and the Highlanders who died then and in the years to come, are a permanent monument to the spirit of Scotland. Those who lived had a stark choice, submit, or . . . flee into exile. Many did flee, taking their skills of war with them to Germany, France, Russia, and just about everywhere else.*

*Where the River Lovat flows out of Lake Ilmen and north to Lake Ladoga, there stood a great city with wooden walls. Those were the days when every Russian city had its Kremlin, a high fortress bristling with watch-towers. To the east lay Moscow, to the west, Courland and Lithuania, and northwards the new city of St Petersburg, and league upon endless league, the frozen forests of the territory of Novgorod. For this was Novgorod, ancient, wooden, like the bole of an immense tree that has been carved into the likeness of a city, Novgorod the Great, a gilded fortress of the Romanov Empire.*

JAMIE Stuart hoisted his pack and leaned into the bitter wind blowing off the Polish plains. He had lost the feeling in his fingers and a rime of frost clung to his moustache and beard. The world about him was white as death. It swirled and howled, driving the sleet and snow towards him alone. He trudged forward doggedly, blinking the ice from his eyelashes. He was alone at the centre of driving lines of grey and wet, and only a will that had already taken him across wide seas and a wider continent drove him forward. He stopped and the snow began to drift over the toes of his boots. Somewhere, he could not tell whether it was near or far, somewhere outside his present universe of ice, a bell was tolling.

Suddenly a wall loomed up before him, its top hidden by the swirling snow. Set into the wall, which was made of wood, was an enormous iron-studded door. Reaching inside his tartan plaid he tried to make his fingers take hold of the pommel of his sword. Drawing it with difficulty he pounded on the gates shouting wildly. The wind whipped the words away and they were lost in the gale but someone must have heard the banging. With agonising slowness the great gates swung inwards and Jamie found himself confronting . . . a bear. He took a step back and shook his head in disbelief. The bear stirred himself and laughed. He realised that he was, in fact, looking at a man, so heavily clothed, hatted and booted in furs that he could have made a fortune doing tricks at the Glasgow Fair. Too hungry and cold to care what awaited him inside Jamie staggered forward and into the man's arms. He knew the most trusted adviser of the late Tsar Peter had been a Scotsman, but there had been four Tsars since then, and there was a Tsarina, Elizabeth, on the throne, or so he had been told in Vilna. The man was speaking to him, but Jamie's Russian was rudimentary and he was half-dead with cold. The gates shut behind him with a dull thud and the sound of the wind died away. His rescuer was smiling, pulling and pointing at the tartan plaid that had protected the young Highlander in his wanderings across eastern Europe. Jamie knew that wherever he was in the wild world, far from his home, he was not the first Scotsman to hammer at the gate.

"So," said Andra, picking at the pool of wax on the table with a broken fingernail. "That's quite a story. Why did ye come back?"

People always ask, "Why did you come back?" when someone has been living abroad. The answer could be, "Mind your own business." In fact, it's probably the safest answer, because there is always a reason.

Jamie was not a man for "safe answers".

"Like I said," he explained, "after those last months in Sweden, the Ruskis made me up to Captain. Then SHE came along."

"Aha! Now we're gettin' it," said Andra. "There's a she in it is there? I thought ye just couldn't stick it!"

"I was at Culloden," said Jamie.

"It's still no' safe to say that," Andra looked about him nervously. The only other customers in the "Ravel" that afternoon were a musician with a small Irish fiddle and his companion, a tall skeletal man with the remains of what had once been an extremely fine hat, crammed down over his greasy locks. Both were very drunk and attempting to sing a song that was remarkable for the complete absence of any words.

"I ken you were all right when the Prince was here," he continued, "and there are plenty in Glasgow that will keep you safe, but things have changed for the worse since you went away. There's money and trade aplenty for some, but Jacobites are still hunted."

"I don't care," said Jamie. There were streaks of white in his beard, like new-fallen snow. "Anyway I'll lay a wager that they've all forgotten. It was more than 20 year ago."

"You were tellin' me about this 'she'," urged Andra with relish. "Wan o' thae eastern women, wis she? I've heard aboot them." He licked his lips.

"No," replied Jamie, looking at a fly on the table as if it was a long-lost brother. "She was a German, and she was mad."

"Oh they are all mad," said Andra knowingly. "Don't have tae go to Russia to find that oot."

"I'm talking about the Empress," Jamie growled. Andra moved his chair back from the table a little. "The Tsarina Catherine . . . some call her the Great, like Peter."

"Who?"

"Never mind, anyway, she was a German actress, if that's what you want to call it, and she was hard as iron. Not particularly good-looking but by God she was more of a man than any of them. Know what she did?"

*90*

"No?" said Andra, eyes wide. He leaned forward again.

"She had a great big elephant . . . that's one of those muckle beasts with two tails from Africa!"

Andra nodded, his mouth open.

"See this elephant?" Jamie continued . . . "She had one made out of ice . . . with ROOMS in it to keep prisoners in. And she did. Right in the middle of the square in St Petersburg, kept them there 'till they died of cold. She was mad."

"I see what ye mean," said Andra, awestruck.

"Well," continued Jamie, staring into the past, "she had a well-known habit of taking a fancy to tall sodgers."

"Oh aye," Andra winked at him, but Jamie continued, oblivious.

"Catherine was reviewing the elite Scots Guards and their captain this day. That was me. There we were on parade, six hale companies, not all Scots mind, mostly just the officers. We were all lined up on the field at Peobresanskoe . . . the Winter Palace. Here she stopped at me. The big Kulak that goes everywhere with her looked at her, then at me, then gives me a bit o' paper."

"Whit was oan it?" gasped Andra.

"Nothin'. Nothin' at aw'."

"Whit was it fur then?"

"I had to write ma name oan it ye fule. She's mad. Only takes men that can write."

"And . . .?"

"And whit?" Jamie wrote his name in the beer on the table-top with the knuckle of a finger long since lost in battle.

"Aboot the paper . . . and this . . ."

"Catherine."

"Aye, Catherine. Tell us!" squeeked Andra in desperation.

"Well I'm here, anyway." Jamie grinned at him mirthlessly. "She did give me something though."

"What was that?"

"Yer drink, man. Ye havna' touched it."

"Oh aye . . ." Andra looked down at the concoction in the dusty glass in front of him. "What was it called again?" he asked doubtfully.

"It's called a 'Cathy' after herself. It's gin and these . . ." he spread out a handful of shrivelled objects on the table in front of him. Andra suspected they were somebody's ears.

"Very good," he said nervously. "Aye, right."

"They're mushrooms, ya fule," said Jamie with feeling. "I pit the right amount of juice in yer drink. Try it. SHE invented it."

"Who? The . . . the wumman that was mad . . .?"

Jamie frowned once, then sat back and watched in satisfaction as Andra drank his first "Cathy".

91

*Burke and Hare were amateurs compared with the activities of the Glasgow Resurrectionists. In the closing years of the 18th century the old town suffered a virtual invasion of body-snatchers. Great advances in surgery, culminating in the work of the Hunter brothers, were fuelled by a plague of grave-robbing. "Job-lots" of bodies were bought in Ireland and imported to Glasgow labelled "Tea". The Necropolis, Ramshorn, Gorbals, and Cathcart burial grounds became known as "Doctor's Larders", and the citizens of Glasgow went in terror of students and paid "corpse-baggers" disturbing their eternal rest.*

*Feelings ran high. The mistaken identification of some red dye, accidentally spilled on a window sill, as blood, led to a riot that was only broken up when the mob was charged by soldiers led by a cutlass-wielding town councillor on horseback. "Bob Dragon," or Dreghorn, the ugliest man in Scotland, was also thought to be associated with the Resurrectionists. Anything out of the ordinary aroused suspicion, and a hysteria akin to the days of witch trials led to the construction of sentry boxes and iron "mort-safes" bolted across tombs. In 1813 a gang of student body-snatchers known as the Patent Leather Club or Brotherhood of the Knife were found to be stockpiling spare limbs in tubs of salt water in secret rooms off the High Street. They were led by a suave and brilliant student called Granville Sharpe-Pattison. When he was tried by a University Court which still had the theoretical right to condemn its students to death, he was "allowed" to escape to America where he became one of the United States' greatest surgeons. He was buried at his own request, in Glasgow.*

*With an equal number of doctors and town watchmen in the city, about 50, no gas and only a few oil lamps illuminating the winding streets and alleys, the dark work of the Resurrectionists went ahead almost unhindered.*

**M**RS McAllister was among friends. They had all died at roughly the same time, victims of one of those brief epidemics of cholera that continued to attack the city until the great Loch Katrine water scheme was opened in Victorian times. She lay beside her uncle, her brother, and several near neighbours, the fresh earth of the recent internment scattered and scuffed about the leaf-strewn path of the Necropolis, city of the dead.

From the cemetery hill, the panorama of the ill-lit city, a dark mosaic of shadow against the darker night, flowed down the hill towards the river, pale in the westering moon. Candles and oil-lamps gleamed weakly in distant windows and a torch shone briefly down by the ancient Cross as a link-boy led a gentleman home after a night's revelry, by the shortest and hopefully, safest route.

The three figures crept up the hill softly. One had a lantern, but it was shrouded by a cloth, a deep, hidden glow like subterranean fires far beneath the earth. They stopped beside Mrs McAllister's resting-place and looked at the ground in silence.

"Are ye sure this is it?" A stocky figure with a heavy serge coat and a "lum" hat set at a jaunty angle, turned to his two companions.

"Aye," replied another, slim and small as a child but with a face centuries old. "See!" He held out a grubby scrap of paper.

"I canna see it in this light ya fule," the top-hat swayed angrily as its owner knocked the hand away. "This'll dae. Wherr's the spade?"

The third member of the expedition, laden with shovels, picks and other nameless implements, handed a curved spade to the little man. "Here ye are, Heg," he said slowly. "Is this the right one that ye want? Is it, eh?"

Heg scowled in the darkness. "Ya daftie, Stim, it's no' me that's askin'. They are aw' aw' right, so they are."

Stim offered the spade to the leader of the company with a flourish. "Yer spade, Biff," he said with a nasal whine. "It's the right wan. Heg says it's the right wan."

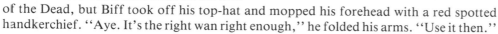

There was a chill wind on the Hill of the Dead, but Biff took off his top-hat and mopped his forehead with a red spotted handkerchief. "Aye. It's the right wan right enough," he folded his arms. "Use it then."

"What? Me?" The daftie struggled to keep hold of his armful of implements.

"Aye. You. Dig."

Heg and Biff sat on the edge of the open grave sucking their unlit pipes. About six feet below them they could hear thumps and scrapes as the luckless Stim dug his way down into the darkness.

"Are . . . are ye still up therr . . .?" The nervous voice floated up from the damp gloom below.

"Naw," replied Biff, taking his pipe from his mouth and spitting.

"Ye are, aren't ye . . . ?" A note of hysteria crept into the voice from the grave.

"Keep diggin', ya fule." Bill cast a knowing glance at his companion. "Tell us when ye . . ."

There was the sound of wood splitting and tearing, followed by a choking gasp from the open grave.

"That it?" Biff asked coldly, standing up and peering down into the darkness.

"Christ! Aye . . ." coughed Stim. "What a reek. It's awfy . . ."

"That'll be gas," Heg nodded knowledgeably. "Builds up fast."

"I think I'll risk a wee bit of the lantern," Biff held the light over the yawning opening, lifting the corner of the cloth. A pale yellow beam struggled down beneath the lip of the grave, illuminating the panting Stim, ankle deep in loose earth, the lid of the coffin propped to one side in two parts. The corpse lay white and pale as ice on a silk pillow. Jagged slivers of wood pointed outwards from the heavy brass plate at the top like a crown of thorns. "Aw for pity's sake," complained Biff. "It's a cholera. They gie ye half-price for a cholera. Too far gone."

He jumped as Heg tapped him on the shoulder. "Watchies!" he whispered urgently. "I think it's watchies comin'."

Biff turned. Below and to the left a light twinkled briefly, then was hidden. "Right enough," he stuck his pipe in his pocket. "Looks like they are just comin' over the Cathedral wall. We've time to get off up the Garngad." He ran into the night, followed by Heg, and they vanished among the tombstones.

"Biff . . . Heg . . . ?" a voice floated up from the open pit. "Are ye still therr . . . gies a haun'. I'm stuck. I canna get oot o' the grave . . ."

*Following the Puritan days of the Reformation, music, dancing and theatre were all regarded as inspirations of the devil. That was back in the early 1600s and things had been improving gradually ever since. Anyway, Glasgow people have always had a natural ability to entertain others, if not themselves, and as early as 11 November 1699, a certain John Smith, not related to the John Smith who is a regular guest at a major hotel in the city, received permission from the Town Council to teach dancing. He was only allowed to work provided he did so during reasonable daylight hours. Furthermore, there was to be no "promiscuous dancing", which meant men and women . . . together! On no account was the aforesaid Mr Smith "to have any balls at all". The Town Council was then, as now, very strict in the matter of public morality.*

*The city was used to the incursions of travelling tumblers, magicians, quack doctors, actors, and other undesirable elements, especially during the Fairs. It was 1750 before actual theatrical entertainments began to be held, something between musical comedy and tragical farcical comedy, a potage of as many as 20 "plays" in the same programme based on mythical and romantic themes.*

*The very first of these may have been held in Burrell's Hall off the High Street, but two years later, Glasgow's first Concert Hall was cobbled together. The backers rather misjudged the mood of the populace at the time, and far from attracting crowds of culture-hungry theatre-goers, the actor-managers of the day had to be protected from the mob by the soldiery. This may have had something to do with the fact that the theatre, a lean-to affair of wood and canvas, was built against the ruined wall of the Bishop's Palace next to Glasgow Cathedral. Eventually, stirred up by a fire-breathing minister called Reverend George Whitefield, the mob, that is to say, congregation, censored the proceedings by the simple expedient of pulling the theatre to bits. There is still a legend in the Theatrical world that once you have played Glasgow on a Saturday night, you are a true professional. Although the legend refers mainly to the late-lamented Glasgow Empire, actors have long and highly trained memories, and having the theatre demolished in the middle of Act Three is not an experience that the Brotherhood of Thespians is liable to forget in a hurry.*

THE Duke of Florentino pulled up his trousers and shouted at his reflection. "'Thou art forever damn . . . ed darkling knavish poltroon of a . . . of a . . .'"

"'Count', darling . . ." a mass of red-gold curls and a turned-up nose intruded into the glass over his shoulder.

"Thanks, Georgie," His Grace the Duke, otherwise known as Everard Bean, pouted and drew himself erect. "I can never get the 'Count' part. Why could he not be a Duke as well, or even something common, like a Captain of Arms or a hostler's lackey?"

"Dukes are common enough," grinned Georgie, setting his wig straight. "Bound to overlap you know, with ten parts each and the twiddly bit with the songs."

"Seen the crowd?" asked the Duke, buckling on a wooden sword and striding up and down the narrow space, waving his arms about and muttering to himself. The Green Room, a flap of canvas pegged to the ruinous wall of the Bishop's Palace, was heavy with the smell of powder and sweat.

"All three of them," Georgie leaned against the cool stone wall and folded his arms. "Two old men and a dog. Glasgow is not a theatre place, I think. No culture."

"No money, more like," the Duke bowed and his shadow, after a moment's hesitation, did likewise. "Otherwise they would be flocking in. They flocked for the *Calumny of Apelles* and *Gerda, Princess of Tyre* in Newcastle. Not enough handbills, that's what I say."

"The Scots don't look very . . . amusable," drawled Georgie, picking a bit of 1,000-year-old stone off the wall behind him and aiming it at a tent-peg. "I hear the Churches don't think very well of us."

"Mmmm . . ." nodded the Duke, licking his fingers and smoothing down his eyebrows, ". . . not ready for it. Too far north. Cut off."

"What is?"

"They are."

"Mmmm . . ."said Georgie archly. "No feeling for the boards."

"Really!" protested the Duke, looking shocked. "We don't want that kind of custom."

"What on earth are you talking about darling?" Georgie tossed his curls crossly." The boards are our life."

"Oh . . ." the Duke looked apologetic. "Sor . . . ee. I thought you said 'bawds'."

Georgie giggled. "You are dreadful, you know."

"I'm a Duke," said the Duke with an air of gravity. "And I don't care who knows it."

"More like a Count," muttered Georgie. "Shall we . . . ?" He held up the tent-flap that led to the theatre.

The Duke marched out on to the stage which, as everyone knows, represents the world, closely followed by the Duchess, still holding a piece of the Bishop's Palace.

The Reverend George Whitefield was not a man for jokes. The nearest he had ever approached to any hint of levity was when he had stopped frowning for an instant the day that news had reached him of the death of Prince Charles Edward Stuart in Rome. "So perish all the ungodly," he had said, and the frown had closed in again. Today it had doubled, crossed from one side of his forehead to the other, and reinforced a series of furrows rather than wrinkles, that made his broad white forehead look like a new-ploughed field covered in snow. "'They shall perish,'" he thundered with feeling,

*95*

rehearsing his favourite passage. "'They shall not desecrate the precincts of ancient tombs and the Great Reformed Kirk of Glasgow with a temple to their vanities and profanities, their antics and mummery . . .'" He licked his thumb and turned the paper, "'. . . and flummery'," he added, the last bit being written on the next page. He enjoyed re-reading sermons almost as much as writing them. He felt sure that the current piece, delivered that very morning to a rapt audience, would have the desired effect.

"Reverend! Reverend Whitefield . . .!" the door burst open. It was John Fleg, one of the Elders of the congregation who had stood, wrapt as the great man in the High Churchyard had delivered his thunderous sermon against the Theatre, for all to hear.

"Indeed, John," Reverend Whitefield looked up from his reading. "You seem somewhat discommoded, I would say."

John Fleg's chest heaved as he fought for breath. "It's the congregation, Meenister, oor congregation."

"What is?" enquired the curate quietly, putting his papers inside the heavy bible on the desk and closing it with a sigh of satisfaction. "What's to do? Calm yourself man."

"The congregation, Reverend," gasped the red-faced carpenter. "They and others of the citizens are pulling the theatre down, and the soldiers from the Gallowgate Barracks are awa'!"

"Are they indeed?" The frown looked almost benign.

"And the actors have fled."

"Have they indeed?" It seemed for the barest fraction of an instant that a smile might be knocking at the underside of that granite jaw.

"Aye, Reverend," continued the Elder, getting his wind. "The hale contraption, painted trees, stage, tents, all down and trampled underfoot."

The Reverend Whitefield sat back and made a steeple of his fingers, secure in his knowledge of the power and the professionalism of his performance.

*"In the land of the hatless, the man with a bunnet is a toff," or words to that effect, and the same relationship existed between Glaswegians who were stuck with Shanks's Pony, and the gentry who heaved their bulk into a sedan-chair after a heavy Saturday night. In 1753, 237 years before the days when 50 taxis lined Ingram Street at two o'clock on a Tuesday morning, back in the days when Ingram Street was a muddy avenue leading to a country house, sedan-chairs were being pushed aside by state-of-the-art horse cabs.*

*Glasgow was very pretty in the 18th century, pretty impassable at the least sign of rain. It was well endowed with "footpads", which is what muggers and thieves were called at the time. Anyone with a few coins in their purse, or gold pieces, was well advised to take a "chair" or a "cab" home after dark.*

*Those were the years of the Clubs, the gatherings of merchants, gentlemen, and others, which included The Lucky Black Tavern, My Lord Ross's Club, The Chop Society, the Tinkler's Pot, the Face Club, the Hodge Podge, and the Old King Coul Club. Many clubs employed "cravat-looseners" whose sole job was to make sure that those who had slid beneath the table through no fault of their own, were not about to be choked by their clothing. There were hunting parties, and celebrations that occasionally resulted in fires, riots, and other expressions of middle-aged high-spirits.*

*The 1750s were the years of the Glasgow Academy of Fine Arts, jointly supported by the University and Glasgow businessmen, a brave adventure ten years ahead of the Academy in London. The Foulis brothers, Andrew and Robert, were publishers and printers as well as founders of the Glasgow Academy of Arts. Their price of £4,000 to anyone who could find a typographical error in their works remains unclaimed to this day.*

*Glasgow had become a "city of culture". It was a place of innovation and modernity. There were carry-ons and carry-outs, a Florentine potage of high-jinks and art, in which the outmoded sedan-chair was soon to join lepers, witches, battling Provosts, Jacobites and clubgoers alike, in the bottomless lobby-press of the vanished centuries.*

CRUICKSHANK'S Tavern was awash with laughter. The Royalish and Not-So-Ancient Chop Society was in session.

The Chairmaster, grave, imposing, and bald as a bisquit, apart from the red wig, adhering by a miracle to his left ear, was attempting to give some kind of order to the proceedings.

"The Honourable and Ancient . . ." he hammered the table with his plate, having misplaced the gavel in his pocket. "Order!" he cried to general applause. "We of the Chop Society are gathered tae consider chops of great merit, drink rum and watter, and look into the arts, verse, singing, fiddle and the like."

Bogle the Locksmith was sick on a waiter's sleeve, taking advantage of the temporary lull.

"Greetings . . . ahem . . . Brethern . . ." the Chairmaster continued. "It has already been hinted at by oor worthy comrade up the back before he passed oot, we are but six months old as a body . . ."

"My body's older than that," the locksmith offered, staggering past.

"If you PLEASE sir," the plate banged in desperation.

"I will if you will," called out a voice from the fug at the end of the table.

"To continue," the Master of Ceremonies shouted resolutely. "It is my greatest of pleasures, or almost so, to bring afore your attentions a very distinguished applicant for joining this here famous company of scholars and gentlemen." He tapped the shoulder of the hunched figure seated at his left. "Gentlemen and fellow Choppers, I give you, I recommend to you, that notability in the world of the Weed, Master Ingram of that ilk. How say you? Say you 'Yay or Nay', or perhaps, 'Nay or Yay'?" He sat down with a crash and Ingram got shakily to his feet.

A chorus of fists, plates, and in one case, teeth, greeted his rise.

"Thank you," Ingram stammered over the uproar. "I know that ye number among your good selves mair humble merchants like myself, professors, surgeons, so I hope to . . ."

"Mair sherbet in that man's rum," cried the locksmith, quite recovered and sucking the end of an over-done chop. "He's had nae sherbet."

"That's an allegation I deny," retorted Ingram, swaying unsteadily. "Let the alligators stand forth."

"The question!" The assembly began to chant. "Put the question! Gie him the QUESTION!"

"S'right," nodded the Chairmaster, struggling to his feet and leaning heavily on the candidate. "Must give ye the question!" he grinned sheepishly and staggered back a step.

"Do your worst sir," Ingram frowned in concentration and joined the querent by tripping back daintily over his own boots and grabbing his partner's sleeve. "Ask away then."

"And the penalty if ye fail," the Master of Ceremonies warned in a brief moment of lucidity. "Tae continue. Weel sir . . . here it is. Is the inside of the outside, the outside of the outside's inside . . . yes or no?"

Ingram stared at the table spinning round in front of him.

"Er . . . could you let me have that again?" he asked quietly.

The assembly dissolved in uproar. "Failed!" They shouted. "Give him the forfeit. Failed."

"'Fraid that's right . . ." The Chairmaster shrugged his shoulders and shook his head at the same time, finally dislodging the reluctant wig. "On the table with you."

Ingram looked at him in disbelief. "What . . .?"

"You mun stand on the table and sing for us or the Choppers will black-ball you sir, damned if they wilna' . . ." he pointed at the board.

Ingram looked doubtfully at the long table, rocking up and down like a lugger in a gale. To the waiters standing about it seemed to be perfectly stationary, but they were not members of the Chop Society and it was not their table.

"On ye get," the Chairperson waved his hand imperiously. "The preferred ditties are rhymes of the nursery time . . ."

The sign outside the grocer's shop in Queen Street informed passers-by that "Henry Lawson's One-Horse Coach Office" was in the back shop, and that a loud knock on the window was required. Ingram was in no condition to knock on anything, although his head didn't know that as he leaned forward against the thick bottle glass. The coolness of the window was soothing to his over-heated nose.

"Chair, sir?" a distant voice asked from beside his elbow.

"Eh? Wassat?"

"Chair, sir? Drury Street Sedan Chairs at your service, master. Take you to your home, your honour?"

"Home? Yes . . . Take me . . ." replied Ingram distantly, searching for a vertical surface. His eyes seemed to be trying to imitate a lizard and swivel in opposite directions.

The door of the grocer's shop was flung open with a "crash" and a small rotund figure, angry as a bee that has sat on its own sting, buzzed past the rubber merchant and accosted the sedan-chair operator.

"Get oot o' my bit," Henry Lawson growled. "This here is horse-cab land, so it is. This is my customer. Aren't ye, master?" He pulled the unresisting Ingram towards him.

"He's askin' for a chair," the carrier motioned his partner, the back half of the sedan chair pair, to help him corner the hapless Ingram's custom.

"Naw he's no," Lawson's three assistants emerged from hiding behind the turnips and leeks. "Here's a horse waiting for ye sir." Ingram was propelled towards an open phaeton and a patient old nag.

"Sedan chairs are just good for keeping oats in. Their days is over, so they are," Lawson called over his shoulder. "Horses is the things of the future. Horses is the boys."

"Future?" asked Ingram blankly to the back of someone's head.

"Aye sir," replied Lawson breezily, bundling the merchant into the little carriage. "Horses is progress, so they are."

"Progress?" replied Ingram with a great effort. "Does that mean . . . will I get where I'm going to . . . to . . ."

"Oh aye, sir, 'Progress' is my motto. If you can remember where you want to go, my horses will guarantee to get you there."

*Scotland's greatest natural resource is not coal, oil, nor even the industry of its people, it is ideas. A vast inshore field of Scottish genius was struck in the latter part of the 18th century. It was called the "Scottish Enlightenment", and it was fuelled by great minds and hearts. Men like Adam Smith, Professor of Moral Philosophy in Glasgow who gave up his post to become tutor to the son of a Duke, met Voltaire in Paris, and discussed with him, by proxy, the political theories of Benjamin Franklin, father of the American Constitution. David Hume the philosopher, James Watt the Engineer, Syme, Symington, Professor Black . . . Deep well-springs of ideas were tapped and a new Renaissance set in motion by men who were unafraid to let their spirits roam in the new universe of science and invention.*

*The Scots have always numbered the multi-talented among their congregation, the "lad's o' pairts". A man o'pairts is essentially a practical dreamer, his feet on the earth and his head in the clouds. He is someone who feeds off flashes of insight, like bolts of lightning from a clear blue sky. In the late 18th century, the intellectual air of Glasgow and Scotland was alive with the electricity of imagination. For a time a few gifted minds became a collective powerhouse, charged with a brilliance that still shines like a lighthouse from the badlands of ignorance. Those were the days of the Scottish Enlightenment.*

ALL day long the midnight sky built its bastions of cloud over Fenwick and the south. Slowly, almost imperceptibly the towers and battlements grew, reaching upwards, the darkness of a bad dream devouring the last of the day. Watchers on the Springburn Hill saw the shadows creep across the valley until the city lay at the bottom of a deep pit of shadow, dwarfed by a gargantuan wall of night that marched across the southern hills from Cathkin to the Gleniffer Braes.

Benjamin Franklin was delighted. Having received an honorary degree from St Andrews University, and through his friendship with Principal Robertson of Edinburgh University, had managed the business of a Divinity Degree for his friend Sam Cooper. Franklin had also been invited to advise Glasgow University in the matter of a lightning conductor.

Since his famous experiment in 1752 when he flew a kite during a thunderstorm, and via a key and a wet thread safely discharged the power of a thunderstorm into the earth, his lightning rods were much sought after. He had first installed conductors on the roofs and spires of tall buildings in his home town of Philadelphia. He was toying with the idea of bifocal spectacles on the eve of his appointment as Ambassador to France, and the future held a key role for him in the drafting of the American Constitution. Ben Franklin was a "lad o' pairts".

No one knows how Franklin survived his experiment with lightning. Discharges can often involve 20,000 amperes at temperatures of 30,000 degrees centigrade.

As the storm broke over the High Street and a great fork of raw energy stabbed downwards, it struck the very tip of the copper spire of the Old College. The incredible power was chanelled harmlessly down to earth. Glasgow's first lightning conductor drank the power of creation and waited for more.

As for the vast energy of the lightning itself . . .? It was an unknown; electricity, uncontrollable and dangerous. When asked what use it was, Franklin gave the same reply as when he saw the first balloon ascent in 1783 . . . "What use is a new-born baby?" he said.

Like the lightning conductor, the University waited to channel the energy of a coming storm, the new-born power and majesty of original ideas and invention that would spread from Glasgow and across the world.

101

*No newspaper in history has ever had such a lead story for its first ever first edition as the* Glasgow Advertiser and Glasgow Herald, *207 years ago. I remember the long faces in the Tontine Coffee House at Glasgow Cross on the morning of 27 January 1783 when the news broke. Peace had been made between the British, French, Spanish and Colonial Governments. The United States of America was born.*

*During the War of Independence Glasgow merchants had found it hard to believe that anything could ever threaten their old, safe monopoly in sugar, cotton, and the "golden weed". The city had raised troops to fight for the Government, and the British army, a great continental power, could hardly be bested by a ragged colonial army and a handful of farmers and fur-trappers! But the American War of Independence was not about territories and Powers, it was about freedom and liberties, and the victory was forged as much by the quill pen as the sword, by the men who wrote and signed a document not unlike the Declaration of Arbroath in content, the Declaration of Independence.*

*Glasgow and west of Scotland sons were as much a part of the company of the "Founding Fathers" as they were involved with the vested interests of the Tobacco Barons. The Scots spirit of liberty, frustrated at home, had been exported to magnify the noble principles that helped create a new world across the wide Atlantic. Of the 56 signatories of the Declaration of Independance, nine were first or second generation Scots; nine of General Washington's 22 brigadier generals were Scots; nine of the 13 governors of the newly created United States were Scots or of Scots descent, and the Reverend John Witherspoon, formerly Minister of the Laigh Kirk in Paisley, was the only cleric to sign the Declaration of Independence. He was also the first man to use the word "Americanism" in 1781.*

THE Reverend John Witherspoon looked at his turnip watch as the bells of Princeton University chimed the hour, and exclaimed, "Indeed, sir, we have played our part".

His companion nodded and smiled. The two strolled across the neat lawn before the Professor's Hall. "All of us," he agreed, glancing up at the circle of 13 stars on the flag fluttering above Princeton in the April breeze. William Livingstone, first Governor of the State of New Jersey, was the grandson of a Scot, but looked every inch an American. Tall, thoughtful, a brightness in his eye that hinted at both humour and stubbornness, William Livingstone was an American, but he looked every inch a Scot.

"It was Scots generosity that founded Nassau Hall and Princeton itself," continued Witherspoon expansively. "This has moved from its beginning as a Presbyterian College to a major seat of learning. I pray that the Faculty will continue to be given its part in New Jersey."

"Parts are not given, they are written and played by men of moment sir," said the Governor quietly. "Men like your good self, sir. You, John, signed the Document."

The Reverend Witherspoon shook his head and grinned at his tall friend. "Paisley, Trenton, Washington . . . it's self-evident. Some few may write a Declaration, others may sign it, but they are stating what has been God's law from the beginning, 'That all men are created equal . . . that . . .'" he paused and consulted his watch again,

opening and closing the engraved case with a brisk snap. ". . . That . . ." he continued, "is the *true* power of the people."

*When Bonnie Prince Charlie's ragged army marched into Glasgow there were already steam engines pounding away in the mines, but those early beam engines were as crude as the Young Pretender's understanding of popular democracy.*

*It was not until James Watt, instrument maker at Glasgow University, was given the job of repairing a model Newcomen steam engine, that a major breakthrough was made in the business of powering up the early beginnings of the industrial world. Watt, out for a sabbath stroll past the Golf-House on Glasgow Green when he should have been in church, had a flash of inspiration that was to change the lives of every man, woman, and bairn on planet earth. James Watt realised that steam engines as they then existed could not create enough power to be truly economical. His revolutionary "separate condenser" led to the generations of steam engines that drove countless trains and ships into an ever-expanding world of trade and industry, a future that Watt's insight had created out of the slave and horse-power eras of the preceding 2,000 years.*

*Watt was not alone as an engineer and canal-builder, and his work laid the foundations of the industrial north of England, together with Thomas Telford of Dumfriesshire, greatest of the early civil engineers, William Symington, who designed and built the first steamship in the world as well as giving poet Robert Burns a rough ride during its promotional voyage on Dalswinton Loch, Henry Bell and his* Comet, *Nasmyth, there is nae doot that the Scots have a very special genius.*

*The Scots engineer became as much a part of the legends of the land as Bruce's spider and the story of Sawney Bean. Every ship, from tramps and puffers to mighty Clyde-built liners racing for the Blue Riband of the Atlantic had its Scots engineer. Covered in oil, coarse and wholesome as an unwashed tattie, practical, loyal, he loved his engines "like a very brither", cosseting the gleaming machinery, as smooth and sparkling as he was rough and grubby. Even starships* en route *through the galaxy to yet another unlikely planetfall, seem to have Scots engineers on their establishment. But whether the engine in question is a model Newcomen in Glasgow University, or a warp-drive in geostationary orbit over Barnard's Star Six, the hand on the spanner could hardly be anything but home-grown and very likely, Clyde-built.*

T HE tower of the Danish Church at Well Close stood sharp and clear against the clouds, and a line of rooftops and gables marked the long line of Cable Street and Rosemary Lane leading to Little Tower Hill. Rooks dipped and wheeled above Tower Wharf, little specks of black above the glittering mud-flats.

St Catherine's Dock was busy as a Hogarth etching and smelt as if something should have been quietly buried a long time ago. East Smithfield, Nightingale Lane, Burr Street, St Catherine's Way; like London's wall they hemmed in the huge dock area that had seen 11,000 people moved from the crowded houses and thieve's kitchens, and vast amounts of earth shifted to create new hills and rises in Chelsea and Pimlico. The Irish colony of Knokvergence at Cable Street stood out against the newer buildings of Pennington. Something was burning in the gardens behind Virginia Street, and a yellow smoke spiralled upwards before being caught by the wind and spread across the eastern sky in flat sheets of opalescent grey. It was low tide at St Catherine's Dock, and the Thames was about to meet its match.

Two shire horses and 12 cursing, sweating men coaxed the six-ton pump forward towards the quay.

The foreman paused to wipe his forehead with the back of a hairy arm. "Heave away there me boys!" he gasped. "PULL, Jacko. Pull boys . . . HEAVE!"

"Watch it there cap'n," warned one of the lead team, straining to keep the main body of the device on an even keel. "Yon rope's goin' to jump the groove, so it is."

"Keep your boot on it then, Jacko," urged the ganger. "Pull, damn you . . . PULL! Hold your bloomin' place, you bucket of Hell's slops, you Chinese runner's nark, I'll . . ."

"For the love of God, take care, you men!" Thomas Telford ran the last few yards to the pump site.

With a brief sound of tearing wood and a squeal of tortured metal, the enormous pump slipped, sank slightly, and stood upright beside the river.

"That's yer pump in position now, Mr Telford," said the foreman with a satisfied nod.

"What's left of it, Mr Bragg. Look at the state of the casing flanges, will you? Look at the drop the mechanism has taken from the rollers!"

The foreman cast a professional eye over the indicated damage. "A few marks there," he said with another nod. "Definitely a few, but it's not made of feathers, that, sir, I can tell you."

"Nor are my Principals made of gold, sir!" Thomas Telford waved his hands in the air excitedly. "If my design has been broken by its fall, I shall have to . . ."

"Here's your other colleeg coming, surr!" Mr Bragg nodded towards a lean figure picking his way towards them among the splintered remains of the wooden rollers.

"Would you look at this James?" Telford gestured towards the pump. The newcomer smiled.

"It's solid man," said James Watt. "Looks all right." He took Telford by the elbow and drew him aside. "I'm surprised you spoke to the foreman like that, Thomas, what with the labour shortage in London. There were plenty of hands for your Caledonian Canal, but it has taken us three months to assemble a workforce here at St Catherine's Dock. How can we site our machines without muscle?"

"Perhaps we should build machines to site the machines," said Telford wryly.

"There's power enough," agreed Watt, taking him at his word. "I have found that a horse can raise 150 pounds with ease. Now if each of these engines for the dock can lift 1,200 pounds, and they can, Thomas, I've checked with my assistant Murdoch five times . . . then they are not machines at all."

"What are they then, pray?" Telford watched nervously as the team of workmen drifted towards the second pump at the top of the rise.

"Why man," said James Watt, slapping him on the back. "They are horses, or as good as. They can muster the power of 80 horses. So long as we have heat, water, and reciprocal motion, then we shall also have 'horse power'."

*The "Auld Alliance" and the French Connection should more properly be called the Scots Connection. It dates from the days of Charlemagne, Charles the Great, who signed a treaty of mutual assistance with the legendary Scots King Achaius against the Saxons about 800 A.D. In historical times the links between Scotland and France have been close at every level from the monarchy, to trade and language. Many Scots words are of French origin, which is bonnie, and an élite guard of the French Monarchy was formed from Scots who journeyed to France as mercenaries.*

*In 1789 on the eve of the French Revolution ties were still strong between the two nations, but the emphasis of union with England had made Scotland part of a broader European picture. When the Bastille fell, largely by accident, and the National Assembly declared the French Republic, there were many enthusiastic supporters of the new libertarian principles in Scotland, including Robert Burns. Before long, however, the euphoria and hope turned to terror and tyranny, and first under the Committee of Public Safety and the Triumvirate, and then led by the Corsican dictator Napoleon, France became for a time, a threat to every nation in Europe. The great war that ensued and lasted until 1815 was, in many respects, the "First World War", and its conflicts raged across Europe and the Americas.*

WAR news arrived by the London Mail Coach at the Tontine Hotel. When a special event or a victory like the Nile, Trafalgar or Waterloo was to be announced, the Mail Coach and horses were decorated with laurels and a red flag floated from the roof of the coach. As the coach thundered into Glasgow, the post-horn would be sounded and a blunderbuss fired into the air.

William Wordsworth and his sister Dorothy were staying in Glasgow at the Saracen's Head Inn, and Dorothy records in her diary that the accommodation was "tolerable and cheap". While in Scotland they called on Sir Walter Scott, but he was out. They also remarked on the frequent riotous assemblies that seemed to take place in or about the city of Glasgow.

Revolutionary fervour produced discontent at home, and there were frequent uprisings and riots. These were swiftly put down and the Glasgow Volunteers, as fine a body of men as ever struggled from one ditch to another, were always ready to spring into action at the drop of a rifle.

When news came that discontented workers were marching on the mansion of Lord President Campbell at Garscube, the Glasgow Volunteers were hastily assembled in George Square. The recommended muster-signal was a wooden rattle operated by some deserving unemployed person with nothing better to do than run around the town making an incredible racket, as opposed to marching on mansions with a view to burning them down.

The bold 300 were ordered "up the line", which is here applied as a military term as this was well in advance of the creation of the Glasgow Underground . . . they marched "up the line" to the old bridge at Kelvinbridge. There were no rioters in sight. In spite of the heat, parties in full dress uniform were sent to scour the countryside. A bayonet was snapped in pursuit of a threatening dog, but no other contact was made with the "hostiles". It seems that the Volunteer Cavalry, and Cavalry exist to give tone to what would otherwise be a mere vulgar brawl, had already dispersed the rioters, after they had rioted along through Garscube and burned the Parish Records in Old Kilpatrick.

The Glasgow Volunteers, disbanded after the Peace of Amiens in 1802 and then called back to the colours again, included the Fifth or Grocer's Batallion, the Canal Volunteers, and the Royal Glasgow Volunteer Horse of 60 men and, presumably, 60 horses. There were over 5,000 in the Volunteers when they were at their greatest strength and although future years were to see Glasgow regiments of men who fought and died in many lands, the old Volunteers who fought a dog and lost, were soldiers too. Unless, of course, they had actually "volunteered", in which case they weren't *real* soldiers.

*In the year 1820, 170 years of uprisings and reforms ago, usually law-abiding folk were driven by poverty, unemployment, and hunger, to take the dangerous road to conspiracy and rebellion in an attempt to right their wrongs. The Industrial Revolution was gathering pace, and the new machines were throwing skilled men out of work. The prolonged wars with France had geared everything towards the production of material for the army and navy, and that was no longer required. The ranks of the discontented were also swelled by returning soldiers who found things less rosy than they had hoped. Unrest was aggravated by an outdated and corrupt parliamentary system.*

*This was post-Napoleonic Scotland, the age of Count von Metternich, and the re-birth of the "old order". Repression, Government spies and agents provocateur were the order of the day. Remembering the bloody tide of revolution in France, paid informers and Government agents lured leading revolutionaries into a trap at Bonnymuir that was to end in transportation for life to the antipodes . . . Australia. It also led directly to the headsman's axe for Andrew Hardie of Glasgow and John Baird of Condoratt in the Parish of Cumbernauld. Poverty and starvation were no excuse. Rats in their thousands fed on the grain in the Government stores while the people went hungry. Those who could survived. Unlike the rats they had the right to trial and execution if found guilty, but then . . . rats have no rights.*

THE "Mason's Arms" in Cumbernauld Village was unusually crowded. "Can I serve ye mister? Come in if ye will, or half that wet will come in alang wi' ye?"

The stranger closed the door and elbowed his way past the landlord.

"I'll have some salt beef and a bottle of brandy. Over there!"

He nodded towards the far corner, an island of space miraculously untouched by the tide of bodies crammed into the main room of the inn.

"Aye weel," the landlord struggled after him, scrubbing his hands up and down on his apron. "Don't mind the crowd, sir, thank'ee. It's all this talk of er . . . troubles . . ."

"I can do without that," replied the stranger brusquely, squeezing his bulk into the corner. "Just the brandy and beef will do for now. Here." A silver coin rang tunefully on the scored wood of the little table.

"Right away sir," replied the landlord with alacrity. He had seen the colour of the money and was already halfway across the room, parting the throng like the Spanish Armada.

When he returned the stranger was rocking back and forwards on his chair, his heels on the edge of the table. He regarded the approaching host darkly from beneath bushy eyebrows. "About time," he grumbled. "I've walked from Glasgow since noon."

"Oh aye?" replied the landlord, avoiding his gaze.

"Ken most of the folk hereabouts?" demanded the customer, uncorking the bottle with his teeth and filling the grubby glass that had been set in front of him.

"I might," replied the innkeeper suspiciously. "Or I might not. Cumbernauld's no' as big as Glasgow."

The stranger seemed to nod. Tearing a piece of beef off the cut with his fingers he popped it in his mouth and swallowed greedily. "Thought you might have seen some friends of mine," he continued with his mouth full. "One's a Condorrat lad. John

Baird. Said I'd meet him here." He stopped in mid-chew and stared the landlord in the eye.

"Never heard of him," The innkeeper made a show of wiping the table. "Naw . . ." he edged back into the crowd, turned, and before the stranger could call after him, a voice spoke, close to his ear.

"Just keep yer heid, son, and this'll no' go aff. . ." it rasped.

The stranger half-turned, but a warning pain in his ribs held him still.

"Looking for Baird, ur ye?" sneered the voice. It had an unpleasant, oily quality to it. "Weel. If he kens you too, then it will be a re-union, if not . . ." he made a clicking sound with his tongue.

"What do you mean . . .?"

"I mean stand up slowly and make yer way to the back shop and we can all have a wee chat. No trouble now. Thaa . . . at's it . . . We're off to join the Provisional Government . . . in Botany Bay, eh?" the voice behind him laughed dryly. "Is that no' right . . . MISTER HARDIE!"

*New Lanark is beautiful. When New Lanark was a unique industrial settlement, with over 2,000 workers, the weaving-mills of David Dale and his son-in-law Robert Owen, the community was revolutionary in character, with a school, a "company store", and a works' canteen, the first in the world. David Dale had been worried by the anarchistic stirrings in France and Europe and was anxious to provide a working environment that would satisfy and care for his work force, as well as increase production. According to the poet laureate Robert Southey, Owen called his workers "human machines" and delighted to demonstrate that he was able to make his workers happy at any time.*

*For all that, New Lanark was a semi-socialist and humanitarian experiment in the midst of universal industrial barbarism. Vast masses of people were subject to conditions that would barely have been tolerated in the Dark Ages. Entire families, forced off the land and driven to the cities, found themselves tied to a treadmill of existence that involved the entire family working, quite literally, night and day. There was no concept of industrial safety, no minimum wage, no law against child labour. It was slavery in all but name, and names meant little to those who had to endure it. New Lanark was the exception, but in the mines and mills of the west of Scotland, there was only one law and one policy. . . .*

**M**ARY and her brothers were asleep in their bed.

"Mammy!" Mary uttered as she stirred in her sleep, scraping the back of her elder brother's leg with an uncut toenail.

"Ya wee devil," cried her brother as he punched his brother in the small of the back, received a savage kick for the injustice, accompanied by cries of "It wisny me" from both ends of the bed. Before long the coffin-like space of the box bed was a threshing mass of children of all sizes pulling, biting, scratching.

After a few minutes the noise began to subside. Exhaustion triumphed over hurt pride and other parts of the anatomy. A further five minutes saw the entire family asleep again, the battle in the bed forgotten, a violent expression of servitude to the Cotton Masters. Their mother, pale as the highland moon that she had known as a child, slept like a ghost embroidered on smoke. Her husband was nowhere to be seen.

Without warning the air was split by a high pitched banshee wail, rising and falling on a sliding scale of pain that would have made the slates fall off the roof if there had been any. Another day of dreadful toil had come to the industrial ghettos of early Victorian Glasgow, a world often forgotten and ignored, a world echoed throughout Britain where families lived and died bounded by a few streets, walled from the world of green and life by an invisible fence, a dead hand that bound them in chains of language, and rags, and marked them for life more surely than any thief was ever branded at Glasgow Cross.

The street was black as night which was not suprising. The sun would not rise for five hours yet. It was November and the white rime of frost formed a dim halo at the feet of those fortunate enough to have clogs. The street was full of people. A dark mass trudged towards the entrance to the mill, lit by two lanterns. The grey folk were funnelled inside. The gates shut with a "clang" and the evil wailing ceased.

Mary stood on tip-toe and plucked dry cotton dreff from among the spinning wheels. On either side as far as the eye could see, long lines of children, dwarfed by the adults stooped over the restless machinery, reached or crawled, snatched or darted, in and out of the network of rattling belts and hissing pipes, playing a constant game with death. She felt her eyelids dropping and woke just in time to feel her hand being tugged towards the throbbing drums. Wheels spun, and spread, and crushed, and flattened, and the calico, bright with blue and pink flowers, rushed down the endless miles to dress the market place of the world . . .

Blue was popular that year.

*There were never any metal gods or iron horses in Glasgow. As soon as steam trains were invented, up and running, they became the tools of the industrialist and of the punter on holiday, noisy, smelly, usually late, and the last word in ways to go down the coast.*

*The canal system felt the pinch. It had been possible to board a steamer for Norway at Port Dundas. The overnight sleeper to Edinburgh, popular with honeymoon couples, was a sedate and leisurely way to travel. Attempts to prove that canals were safer than railways, and, "a man could not live at speeds greater than 30 miles an hour", were doomed to failure. The new railway companies like the "Glasgow to Garnkirk" were already beginning to spread a web of track and sleepers from the city to the mines and forges, beaches and bathing huts of the West.*

OLDER than canals and trains, the stagecoaches still plied the virtually non-existent roads. One gentleman who braved the bumps and pitfalls of the post-coach from England in 1846 was Thomas de Quincey, the son of a Manchester merchant. He rattled into Glasgow one fine afternoon with his books and manuscripts, pipes, packages, and his precious hoard of opium.

What to the Russians is a "dacha" and to the Scots is a "but and ben" used to be found in fair numbers along the east end of Cathedral Street . . . "summer quarters" they were called. Like the legendary Atlantis, the street pattern of the 1840s has become completely submerged by a whole new ball game, several primary schools, and a generous sprinkling of inner-city whin and bashed saplings.

In the days of de Quincey, the Royal Infirmary end of Cathedral Street, near where the Blackies and the Collins bible empires thrived, was a warren of gardens and lanes . . . Love Loan, Angel Close, North Portland Street by the Common Gardens, Cherub's Wynd, and passing Balmano Street where Doctor David Livingstone and "Paraffin" Young shared digs, Dean Place, where de Quincey, the author and rambler, studied and ate the dreamflower up a close.

Thomas de Quincey rented a single room from a long-suffering lady called Mrs Isa Tosh. He lived in the top attic right, up against the east end gable of the building. He must have had as fine a view of the burgeoning industry of Glasgow, as he had of the stars when he peered up at the heavens from the University Observatory at Dowanhill.

Sitting in his gambrel shack on the skyline, brains fairly addled with hallucinogenic drugs, de Quincey was left very much to his own devices by the good Mistress Tosh. Among the dream visions that came to the strange visitor to the Clydeside were "The Spanish Military Nun", "The Revolt of the Tartars", and "On the knocking at the gate in *Macbeth*".

De Quincey was more or less in hiding from Edinburgh people to whom he owed large sums of money, so Glasgow, a thriving and blackening metropolis of 365,000 souls, was the ideal place in which to eat your opium and keep your head down.

# A FISH, A GIANT, A BLACKSMITH, AND TWO GODS  1856 A.D.

*There were Dram-Divans and Music Saloons, the Hairy Man of Java, kilted magicians and panoramic views of Volcanic Eruptions and Satan's Revolting Army. As well as the mixed delights of the Glasgow Fair and a wee burst of the cholera mixed in with bread riots, the 1850s saw giant strides in the techniques of battleship-building, and the amount of noise that could be generated in the interests of progress.*

WHEN Robert Napier bought four acres of Carntyne and added it to his Parkhead Forge, it was to create something that would become a cross between Hell and Armageddon for the thousands who worked there. Napier also employed about 15,000 men in the Vulcan Forge between Washington Street and McAlpine Street, and extensive construction yards at Govan, but Parkhead Forge was to be a tumult of fire and heat for 100 years. It lit up the night sky above the East End of Glasgow like a burning city that was never consumed, every night flaring up again and again with a distant tumult of mountains of slag and iron, drinking the cold air and casting their baleful glow on the clouds that spread over the Valley of Pandemonium.

Four mighty steam-hammers pounded iron at Parkhead – Chromis, Cyclops, Tubal, and Vulcan, served by a gigantic crane called Hercules. Tubal and Vulcan laboured to make the four-and-a-half inch thick steel plates for the Royal Navy's first all-iron warships, HMS *Terror* and HMS *Erebus*. Even after this, there was one wooden warship built, but with the metal *Warrior* of 1860, the days of the wooden walls of England, and Scotland, were numbered. The iron-clad *Monitor* and *Merrimack* hammered away at each other in the American Civil War. There were also the "Popoffkas", two circular Russian battleships that weighed 2,490 tons and went precisely nowhere. It was impossible to know which direction they were going in. The age of modern naval warfare was at hand.

At the heart of the universe there was fire. The universe had been enclosed with wood, but there hadn't been enough to go round, and through the gaps nothingness waited, strips of bottomless black stuck on the rosy sky.

"Gonny wipe ma' eyes, Jim?" Alec stood his ground and hauled on the heavy chain. Forty tons of Hell bubbled overhead as the dark crucible dipped slowly towards the pit.

Jim reached across and wiped his mate's forehead with an oily rag. Immediately Alec's eyes filled with sweat again and he strained to hold the delicate balance of the bucket of fire as it moved lower and closer to the shape carved out of the ground.

Jim took up the slack on his own chain and four others, like the Casting-Master almost naked except for a blackened leather apron and tight-fitting skull cap, pulled and cursed the liquid iron on its descent to the earth.

"Easy now," Alec shouted. "Left draggers tight up! Loosen a bit left draggers . . . JUST A BIT! CHRIST!" They all held their breath in the stifling heat. Tons of liquid yellow-white metal tilted slightly, directly above their heads. A solitary star plummeted downward to bury itself in the sand beside Alec's foot. He bit his lip but stood his ground.

"Easy . . . Easy . . ." Creaking and swaying ominously, the crucible moved

away fron them inch by painful inch. "Ready for yer tilt now!" he called out, his voice echoing round the vast wooden space. "Tilt her down . . . SLOW . . ."

A tremor ran through the earth beneath their feet. Balancing 40 tons of liquid metal above your head would be enough for anyone. Add a small local earthquake and most men would have given up the ghost. But this was work. Alec MacLean was an earner, and a good one. Dancing on the edge of a volcano was an everyday challenge for the men of Parkhead Forge.

"That's Tubal," someone called out, gritting his teeth.

The earth shook again.

"Therr's Vulcan noo!" Jim leaned back in a tug-of-war with the long iron chain. His palms were red with sweat and friction.

"I don't care if Satan's got his teeth in your bum!" Alec shouted. "TILT WIR IRON . . .!"

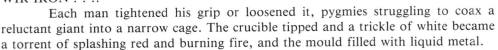

Each man tightened his grip or loosened it, pygmies struggling to coax a reluctant giant into a narrow cage. The crucible tipped and a trickle of white became a torrent of splashing red and burning fire, and the mould filled with liquid metal.

"Easy now," Alec was more relaxed as the last of the metal dropped into the sand. The earth shook again as two mighty hammers pounded cooling plates of iron. The pit in the sand, now filled with burning liquid, was forming a scum of slag. Several men reached forward with long-handled rakes to clear the surface. "That's that." Alec scratched the singed hairs on his forearm. "I hope there's something good for my tea."

"Are ye not for a wee something after?" queried Jim, taking his apron off. "We'll be away any minute now."

"Naw, naw," Alec steadied himself as the ground shook again. "You know what herself is like. If I'm late I'll get a right hammering."

*America was the place. It still is, but back in 1861, 129 years of black-eye peas and porridge ago, the United States was faced with a terrible conflict. The American Civil War, the first "modern" war with ultimately more than a million men under arms, divided families and friends as much as it split a great nation in two.*

*The war cast long shadows across the Atlantic. Glasgow had close ties of blood and interest with the Southern States of the Confederacy. Reconditioned Royal Navy ships were turned into Confederate blockade runners by Clydeside arms dealers. Raiders like the* Savannah, *most feared of the Southern privateers, were secretly handed over to the Confederates in the Azores, by a merchant class who had helped finance and develop the southern plantations and economy. Of 8,855 miles of five-foot gauge railroad laid across the Southern States, most had been engineered by Scots.*

ABRAHAM Lincoln, advised by a Pastor who used to take care of St Enoch's Church in Glasgow, sent out a call for volunteers two days after Confederate guns fired on Fort Sumter, the Union Garrison in the harbour of Charleston, South Carolina. Among the first to respond to the new President's call for 75,000 men was John MacArthur, born in Elderslie in Renfrewshire, and Commander of the Highland Guard of Chicago. Chicago had been founded by John MacKenzie, a Canadian who lived from 1763–1823. By 1850 there were nearly 5,000 Scots in Illinois. MacArthur's guard was a formidable force.

General "Little Mac" McLellan sat back on his horse and looked up at the sky. It was a golden autumn in the hills about Antietam Creek. President Lincoln had had his victory and 11,500 Northern soldiers and over 9,000 Southerners lay dead. General Robert E. Lee had almost won the day but had retreated to Virginia in spite of a final attack by the last of his reserves under General Hill. A few days later, on 22 September, President Lincoln would announce the Preliminary Emancipation of Slaves. It had all hinged on one of MacArthur's Guard finding three cigars.

The air was full of falling leaves – red, gold, some reduced to a filigree of veins like a sketch of a leaf drawn in the misty air. The river was carpeted with them, turning and dipping in the fast-flowing waters as they swept towards the Chickamaw Weir and Sharpsburg Corners.

General Lee had entered Maryland with 50,000 men, but the Brigade that was skirmishing its way towards Harper's Ferry had left nothing behind but blackened camp-fires and crushed grasses, while the advance line of MacArthur's Guard moved warily upstream in the late evening in persuit.

"That's a day old." Trooper Kean kicked at the ashes of the camp-site and hunkered down beside the bushes.

"If that," replied Tom Wilson, sniffing the air. "Where's the Naragansett?" He looked about him nervously.

"Tracker's gone up the line. Orders." Jim Kean stood up stiffly. "This damp gets ye. Wonder where the Rebs are?"

"Wee Mac knows, but he's no' tellin'. MacArthur's waiting for word and then we'll be on our way, don't you fret yourself, Jim, son."

"Here. What's this? . . . A smoke!" Jim Kean stooped and picked up something

from beside the ash-cold camp fire. "Ceegar! Smoke these later when we can mak' a light." He took the paper wrapped round the three precious cigars and threw it away. "Reb's gettin' careless or in a hurry. Could be a good sign, that."

"Wait a minute, will ye?" Tom Kean strode across the clearing and picked up the discarded paper.

"We can't light anything the now," urged Jim. "MacArthur'll flay us. Field punishment No 1 the very least."

Rifle in one hand, Tom flattened the crumpled paper against his knee and frowned. "Don't be daft," he said. "I'm not going to set fire to it. I'm . . ." his frown deepened as he read the crabbed hand scrawled across the paper. "Here!" he exclaimed with growing excitement. "Do you know what this is . . .?"

"If I had a magnifying glass screwed intae ma heid I might," his friend replied scornfully. "You tell me, or is this a guessing game?"

"This . . ." said Tom Kean carefully, reading the paper again to convince his brain as well as his eyes, "– is General Robert E. Lee's orders to his Commanders for the battle . . . we've found their plan of action wrapped round three cigars."

"We'd better take it back to Brigade," said Jim, turning. "You keep the paper, I'll haud on to the cigars."

*In the opening decades of the 19th century Glasgow woke up and found that it was no longer an ancient market place reached by tree-lined avenues. Foundries and mines, factories and tenements were spreading outwards from the old heart of the town, and an ever-present pall of smoke and soot hung in the air over the river. By the mid-19th century the Machine Age had arrived with a vengeance, which was only fitting, since that Age had itself begun in the west of Scotland.*

STARK horror inhabited the closes and wynds of the overcrowded metropolis. An investigator of the time, identified only as "Shadow", reports, "I visited a low shebeen, not 200 yards from Central Station. Inside there were a dozen poor people. But for one or two better clad of the group, the place might truthfully be designated a shopful of rags. One young man is leaning back upon a seat, dead drunk. In less than two minutes a wreck of a woman staggers, rather than walks towards the counter. She presents a broken tea-cup to the landlord, who charges four pence for whisky. Two other women lay upon the counter a pickle-bottle and a glass vessel of a kind which altogether defies description. Both are partially filled with whisky and the victims leave." Crime and passion were not the prerogatives of the poor. As well as dens and thieves' kitchens like the Bush and Tontine Closes, polite society had its problems also.

Sandyford place was fairly polite. Constable Campbell, lately arrived from Keppoch near Oban, and youngest of the "B" Division force, was already running over the evening's instructions in his mind when he left the temporary barracks, a Methodist Chapel, and set out to patrol his beat. He had been asked specifically to look out for prostitutes in the back lanes near Sandyford Place. Complaints had been received from local residents that their wash-houses were being abused, and he expected that by the end of his beat at 6 a.m. he would be busy enough.

He patted his side pocket. The letter to his father, a ploughman, was still there. He would try and remember to post it in the Sandyford Toll Receiving House on the way back, if nothing else intervened. He plodded up the street. All was quiet. It was July and still light, but most of the better-off inhabitants of this end of Sauchiehall Street were away for the summer. They would have houses or lodgings down the coast, and the families would decamp to Largs or Argyll until the weather broke. Occasionally, the head of the house would commute up and down the river by paddle steamer during the week, visiting the Stock Exchange and attending to business, but apart from those few and the servants, the street was deserted.

Colin Campbell strode through the lengthening shadows, pausing now and then to try a door handle before moving on. A caricature of a dog was sitting on the lawn in front of one of the town houses as he passed, and it laid its head on its paws and looked at him with dark eyes.

"All away, laddie?" Constable Campbell asked.

The dog watched the retreating policeman's back philosophically and closed one eye.

Constable Campbell rounded the corner into Sandyford Place about quarter to nine. It was Saturday, and the long street was still, empty as only Glasgow can be during the summer, a stage set patrolled by a solitary policeman. Something very like a shriek,

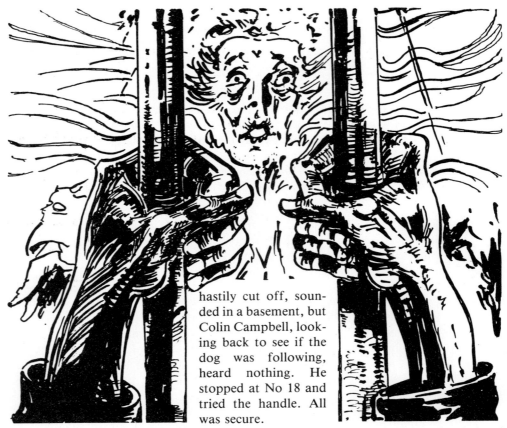

hastily cut off, sounded in a basement, but Colin Campbell, looking back to see if the dog was following, heard nothing. He stopped at No 18 and tried the handle. All was secure.

The door of No 17 opened and he half-turned. Two women came out, obviously servants. They took no notice of him and stood on the front step, talking in low voices. One was a stout, red-faced woman with a straw bonnet and blue ribbons. The other, a maid or tweeny in No 17, had thin, wispy dark hair, and a white apron.

That was the night that Jessie McPherson was chopped into little pieces by a meat-cleaver.

The Flemings were all on holiday except, that is, for old Mr Fleming. When his son came back on Monday he found his old father resting in bed. Everything in the house was neat and tidy, and the kitchen was spotless, but there was no reply from Jessie McPherson. When they broke down the door the remains of her body were found scattered over the floor.

This was the first case investigated by the Glasgow Police as opposed to the Procurator Fiscal acting together with Sherriff's officers, and they were determined to get a conviction. The Constable could identify neither of the two women he saw in the doorway of No 17. The lack of evidence and the circumstantial nature of the testimony caused a public outcry. Jessie McLachlan, a friend of the murdered woman, was almost certainly innocent. She claimed she and the murdered girl had been drinking with the old man, and that he had killed her friend, but the old man was acquitted and McLachlan was sentenced to hang. She was reprieved, and served 20 years in Perth Prison.

Even in areas with more than 500 people to the acre, murder remained an uncommon crime in Glasgow, as it does today. The celebrated cases make the point that in spite of its ill-deserved reputation, Glasgow is actually more peaceful than a lot of other places I could think of . . . unless, of course, you were an innocent wee serving lassie in 1862.

*The telephone has been ringing in Glasgow for over 100 years. It's about time somebody answered it! It was Scotsman Alexander Graham Bell who first gave meaning to the expression "If ye want me thungummy, ring me." Bell had been a teacher of the deaf, but one day, while he and his assistant Thomas Watson were trying to adjust a fault in Bell's new "musical telegraph", he heard a "twang" coming from the receiver. Bell began to experiment, and within a year, on 10 March 1876, Watson heard the first words ever spoken on the newly invented telephone, "Come here Watson, I want you." It is said that Watson replied, "Is that you Mr Bell?" but since there was only one telephone in the whole of God's creation at the time, Bell's reply to HIM is not hard to guess at. In 1878 Bell travelled to Scotland and London on his honeymoon, taking the opportunity to present a pair of ivory telephones to Queen Victoria.*

*1879 saw Glasgow's first telephone exchange, the Douglas, named after Douglas Street. Within living memory, like mine for instance, it was possible to dial numbers beginning D.O.U. . . . The "Douglas" was installed for the use of doctors, and was closely followed by subscriber exchanges for other businesses like the Iron Consortium, otherwise known as the "Iron Ring". Within a few years over 800 exchange lines and 300 private lines were in use operating from the new headquarters of the amalgamated telephone companies, the National Telephone Company Headquarters at 13 Royal Exchange Square. Bells were rung at either end of a conversation to signal the beginning and end of the call. Exchanges were even open on a Sunday! There was a lot of bell-ringing at the time, but then, 1883 was the year of the Dynamitards and the* Daphne *disaster.*

**T**HERE was a blue-red-chrome yellow-pink light in the long hallway, outlined with a sharp glare, where the sun caught the bevelled glass surrounding the stained-glass panel in the doorway. Severe oak, polished to within an inch of its late-lamented life, lined the walls to the door of the morning room. An umbrella stand conversation piece, largely fashioned from the remains of some unfortunate denizen of the rainforest in imperial Ilorin, but lately conquered somewhere north of Lagos, was dappled in a garish replica of its native twilight. A picture of Mrs MacKenzie's brother George in the uniform of an Assistant District Commissioner, hung square and true above the aspidistra in the copper pot. Further down the hall where the colours of a middle-class afternoon could not reach, a strange box of wood with cloth-covered wires, clung to the wall like an intruder from tomorrow's mail-order catalogue, stark, mechanical, and not at all decorative.

The peace of the terrace and the quiet of the afternoon, shaded by the elm trees opposite the Western Cathedral, was shattered by a tinny ringing sound. It continued intermittently, shattering the peace of the hallway as the dust motes drifted past in the beams of coloured light. For a long minute nothing happened. Suddenly the sound of running feet could be heard approaching from the depths. The door at the end of the hallway was wrenched open with a "crash" and Delphinia MacKenzie, her hands white with flour, pounded down the carpet with as much grace and haste as her station in life and her stays would allow.

"Oh bother!" she allowed herself a wee expletive and reached for the telephone daintily with whitened fingers. Cook had the afternoon off and she had been coming to grips with her occasional soufflé, when the "monster" had started its cacophony.

"Hello?" she asked, holding the wooden earpiece as close as she could without upsetting her hair. "Hello?"

"Hello subscriber?" said a disembodied male voice. "I have a Mr Dougal for you."

"Oh, er . . . yes," said Delphinia, glancing at her reflection in the mirror. She was in no fit state to receive a call from a gentleman. "Very well," she added nervously. "Hello?"

She looked at the earpiece and blew some flour off the metal diaphragm. "Yes?" she asked. "Who is it?"

"Delphinia? This is George. George Dougal. Is John in at this hour? It is most urgent that I speak to him."

"No . . . er George, Mr Dougal. Is he not at business?"

"Why no . . . is he not at home?"

"Er no, should he be? Perhaps he is at his club."

A dry laugh echoed down the wire from Buchanan Street. "No gentleman is ever at his club to answer a telephone call." The voice became grave. "I must contact him. Must speak with him. There has been a terrible disaster."

"Not another one?" said Delphinia.

"I am afraid I don't understand," George Dougal sounded puzzled.

"Mr Dougal," continued Delphinia patiently. "This telephone has rung four times in this house since it was installed in January, and the first call brought us news of the Glasgow Ribbon Society, the Fenian Dynamitards destroying the Tradeston gasworks in which my poor husband has substantial interests. The other two calls were from my mother. Pray, what is the 'disaster' that you speak of?"

"Our new steamer at Linthouse . . . the launching your husband sent me to . . . the *Daphne*!"

"Well?"

"It has capsized. I fear 200 working men are drowned in the Clyde."

The earpiece fell from Delphinia's hands and she stared into space.

"Hello . . . hello. Please ring your bell if you have finished your conversation . . ." the operator's voice cut in.

She picked up the earpiece. "Mr Dougal. Are you still there?"

"Yes."

"I'll tell my husband the moment he arrives home from . . . the moment he arrives home. Where shall I tell him to contact you?"

"I'll wait by the telephone," came the crackling reply. "There may be more news. I'll ring immediately there is."

"More news . . .?" Delphinia stared at the mirror blankly. "Perhaps you should write."

*The dark nights of Glasgow became a "blaze of gas-lit glory" after the Glasgow Gas Company was formed in 1817. On 5 September 1818, James Hamilton, grocer extraordinaire and showman by nature gave the first public commercial showing of the new "light-brackets" by installing "sex jetties", or six of the "wee lights", as we might say today. This led to an invasion of courting couples in his doorway, looking at the wonderments of the bright peep, and the Trongate being described as "among the best-lit streets in Europe". The old Theatre Royal in Dunlop Street soon followed, and it seemed that a new age had been ushered in as the gas light glinted on the crystal chandeliers and the illuminati of Glasgow clustered like moths about a bundle of bunsen-burners.*

*The old Corporation bought out the two private gas companies in 1869, and by 1877 vast strides in the world of Glasgow by gas-light resulted in the universal installation of Siemen's regenerative lamps and Sugg's argand lamps. Electric street lamps were still eight years away in the future, in 1894, and 1,000 years away from the old pre-Suggs rat-tail burners and the "Rat-Tail" men who lit them.*

A DROP of ink drifting downwards in a glass of clear water, night darkened the cup of the valley.

Old Betsy blew on the crinkled taper and it burst into flame. Sheltering it with a hand the colour of yellow smoke, she shuffled across to the table by the far wall and lit the candle. Shadows fled into every corner of the poky little room as the flame flickered, shrank, a knife of burning air in the damp room.

"That's yer tea out John!" She turned towards the dim glow of the fire in the grate. "John! Ye'll need to get out to your work!"

The figure curled up in the chair by the fire, stirred and yawned toothlessly. "Is it that . . . time already." His jaw cracked as he gave another cavernous yawn. "I jist dropped aff!"

"You've been snorin' in that chair all efternoon, John Williamson," his wife said, lifting the old coat off his knees.

"Me snore?" he said incredulously, standing up and stretching. The cold pipe fell off his knee. "I'll be needin' mair shag and all," he bent and picked up the clay stump and peered into the empty bowl sadly. "And the shoppie'll be shut now."

"You'll get a fill off Grantie when ye meet him on yer rounds," his wife pulled the chair back from the bare table. "Now come and get yer food. You've a night's walkin' ahead of ye and there's a fair bite in the air."

"All right, all right," John Williamson grumbled as he made his way to the table and sat down. "That's a good bit of herrin'," he said appreciatively, looking closely at his plate.

"Better than your eyesight," said the old woman, standing next to him and looking at the grey in his hair. "It's as well seein' it's your last night at the leery work."

John said nothing. He broke off a piece of bread, took a sip of beer, and attacked the herring with a knife and spoon. "Bit salty," he mumbled, chewing with difficulty. "It'll dae, though. Seem to have lost my appetite."

"You'll have plenty of time to get your appetite back after the night," said his

wife. "Come on now, ye've never been late in 30 year at the lightin'. C'mon now, John."

He pushed the plate back and squinted up at her. "You are in a fair hurry to get rid of me? The bidey-in waiting in the close, eh?" he grinned.

"Get on with ye John Williamson. I'll 'bidey-in' ye. There's the Tolbooth clock at eight. I'll keep the fire at a glow for ye comin' in."

"Well, last night then," he stood up. "That's me, last of the Rat-Tail men."

"Well, ye said yourself that thae new Suggs Lamps don't need a mannie with a tinder pole."

"Aye, there'll be new leeries, younger wans with gas sticks to licht the elements. Just as well it's not me. I don't trust these modern lichts. I'm glad I'm the last wan . . ."

"I'll be glad when you're back. You'll be late . . ."

She heard him picking his way carefully down the spiral staircase at the back of the tenement and stood by the window, looking down into the street.

Faint starlight glimmered on the steep sloping rooftops, the milky way a net of luminosity beyond the black silhouetted chimneytops of the Bell o' the Brae.

Bobbing lanterns wove in and out of the goods trains in the College Rail Yard. As a young man he had walked past the University to light his lamps, but the Old College had gone, removed to the rural splendour of Gilmorehill in the 1860s. The High Street had been left to the pimps and the down-and-outs, and in the ancient College grounds were once the Black Friars had taught and studied in a universe made of crystal spheres, there was only the clang and clatter of brake couplings and buffers. The Collegium had surrendered to the night-shift.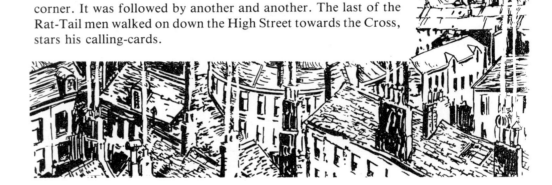

After a few minutes a little flame blossomed at the far corner. It was followed by another and another. The last of the Rat-Tail men walked on down the High Street towards the Cross, stars his calling-cards.

*In the 1880s Glasgow's Victorian prosperity was approaching its peak, and the noon-tide of Empire was to witness the arrival of electricity, the cable subway and the electric trams, photography, St Andrew's halls, the Great Exhibition of 1888, 1901, and on into the new century, hospitals, bridges, effort and endeavour. These were the days of the Second City. A scant 100 years before there had been none of these things, and the world was powered by horses and lit by candles.*

*Glasgow was for long suspicious of "the electricity", and St Enoch's Station and the General Post Office remained the sole public buildings lit by the new method until the 1890s. At last, the Corporation bought the Mavor and Coulson works, and a new power station was built in Waterloo Street. The day of the great switch-on was 25 February 1893.*

*There were 18 miles of electric cables and 13 dynamos at the 1888 exhibition, but the star use of the "new force of the new age" was the Fairy Fountain, lit by "Electric Rays" from 18 arc lights shining through cells of coloured glass, and using a quarter of a million candlepower.*

SADIE watched the two workmen hammering at the brass plates. "Are you glad we came, Agnes?" she asked her friend who was standing back a little from the craftsmen as they worked.

"Oh . . . yes," Agnes gripped the brim of her straw hat nervously. "It's marvellous, so it is."

"This is a real Indian Street," grinned Sadie expansively. "There's jewellery, sweetmeats, native pottery."

"Why is it in the dynamo shed?" asked Agnes, nodding towards the humped giants glistening and spinning in the distance. The air was full of the smell of ozone. An occasional spark crackled along the cable strung from the iron beams.

"Oh, is it?" replied Sadie distractedly. She held up a pair of earrings, a composite of Benares Brass and delicate enamel. "Is that not lovely?" she asked.

"Beautiful," Agnes snorted. "And just where would you wear them, Sadie Dale, eh? Mr Crum would dismiss ye on the spot if you presented yourself at the warehouse wearing those . . . those . . . dancing girls' things . . . probably send me packing as well if I was along with you."

"Oh but they are beautiful," Sadie replaced them on the tray with a look of longing. The earring-maker paused at his work and smiled at them.

"Oh come away," Agnes said, shocked. "Sa . . . dee . . ." She tugged at Sadie's sleeve and they walked on down the long aisle of the hall. "There's surely other things to see except these decorations?"

"Oh yes," said Sadie, opening her pamphlet. "There's a section for Women's Art and Industries, or we could see Royle's Self-Pouring Teapot. The Engineering Place is a bit smelly," she giggled, "but there's galas on the Kelvin . . . with gondolas." Sadie was a good reader.

"What's 'Gondolas'?" asked Agnes.

"'Member . . . there was that row in the Council. One of the high-heid yins wanted to have 20 gondolas, but another councillor said they should only get a male and a female and breed them."

"Och . . . I don't know anything about politics," Agnes pouted. "Lets get on and have a wee something to eat. Not by the river though."

"Why ever not? It's lovely. The Groveries . . ."

"They are calling it the 'Seweries'."

Sadie stopped, her hands on her hips. "Agnes Dooly, we have a whole day to enjoy ourselves. We can see the whole world here, the Empire, that's the same thing as the whole world, and you'll profit by it. Help ye in conversation with nice young clerks, and that."

"I'm hungry."

"Well we'll go to Lyon's Bishop's Palace Temperance Restaurant. That's bonnie. It says here the waitresses are all dressed as Mary Queen of Scots."

"She got her head chopped off," Agnes snorted.

"Agnes Dooly . . . I've a good mind to go to the Bodega Bar with ye . . . they sell alcoholic beverages."

Agnes gripped her hat with both hands. "Sadie . . . you wouldn't! Unaccompanied ladies don't . . ."

"Well just you behave yourself then," said Sadie firmly. "We'll go on the switchback railway then. That'll give you a reason to hold on to your hat."

*There was never anything like the trams. By 1894 Glasgow Town Council, the same august body that had fought at Flodden and given its trousers to the Bonnie Prince, changed its name and became "The Corporation of Glasgow". This was the name, together with that of James Dalrymple, emblazoned on the "caurs" from 1902. Dalrymple presided over the halcyon days of "c'moan or get aff" until his retiral in 1926, and Dalrymple's days saw the expansion of the system to 100 miles of track and an annual profit, together with a yearly 300 MILLION passengers, not all on the one tram of course.*

*It all began on 13 April 1898 with 37 miles of the Corporation's very own tramway track, and an extra four miles kindly leased by Govan. The first service ran between Springburn and Mitchell Street, then Glasgow Cross on 23 January 1899, and Ovrenewton via Eglinton Street, Jamaica Street, Union Street, Renfield Street, and Sauchiehall Street, for the incredible electrifying cost of £32,610.*

*By 1903 there were 385 electrics in operations, 103 conversions, and 42 salt trailers. A few years earlier it had been calculated that if the populations of modern cities continued to increase in the 20th century, so would the horse-traffic, and that by 1960 cities like New York, London, and Glasgow, would be 100 feet deep in horse manure. By 1903 the spectre of that environmental disaster had vanished.*

DIGGING her fingers into Agnes's padded shoulders and squirming a little, Sadie moaned, "My whalebones are killing me!"

Agnes looked up and down the street anxiously. "I'm black afronted, so I am. What if somebody was tae come by?"

"Huh! Let them!" Sadie was defiant. "Look at that!" She lifted the hem of her skirt a little, which didn't take much doing since it was practically touching the ground. A neat pointed toe and a tight row of buttons climbing her calf revealed themselves. "Scuffed! I knew it!"

"Sa . . . dee! See you and yer whalebones and yer ankles! Ankles can drive men mad ye know."

Sadie looked at her scornfully. "Aye. Maybe. If I knew any. Do you know any?"

"Any what?"

"Men!" Sadie gave her friend a hearty "dunt" with her linen handbag.

"I don't know what ye mean," Agnes sniffed and stared up the street defiantly, ". . . and I don't want to know."

"What about Kenneth, then?"

Agnes looked at Sadie out of the corner of her eye without turning round. "Oh . . . him? He's a nae-user. He telt me he was to get promoted to Under-Presser in Gentlemen's Separates, but I canna see that happening. He's nae sense of responsibility. Now thon Davie Gregor . . . HE'S got 'Boyd's Separates' written all over him, so he has." She nodded, agreeing with herself.

"Ach, so has the *Evening Times*," said Sadie dryly. "Here's oor caur."

The motor tram rattled down the road at a steady 15 miles an hour.

"Oh God! A Motor-School Car. It's full of drivers learning no' tae stop."

"Oh, yer language!" Agnes's plucked eyebrows shot up at an odd angle.

The tramcar thundered past. Twenty trainee drivers, moustaches bristling, risked a backward glance at the two lovelies at the fare stage, before rivetting their attention once more on the words of wisdom being spouted by the clean-shaven official in command of the steering handle.

". . . and a cyclist must be allowed time to free himself from . . ."

The tram dwindled into the distance, scattering sparks on the pavement, and the street was quiet once more.

"If I was a toff I'd have a watch," said Sadie glancing at a wrist that needed no additions. "We'll be late for the Tivoli, so we will!"

"I hope it's good. It's fourpence, and I've got to give my mammy my wages yet." Agnes peered inside the shapeless felt bag covered in black jet that styled itself a purse.

"It's the best pit in Glasgow." Sadie extracted a well-thumbed programme. "Betty gave me this. It's got aw'thing on it. See!" She began to read aloud. Sadie was a good reader. "Monday 22 January 1900. The Cast includes a Comedienne, Burles . . . Burl . . . Actress and Dancer, Miss Lottie Lunn, Madam . . . waselle . . . Ra . . . fine and her Female Troupe of Performing . . ." She paused. "Oh. Sorry, that's just Performing Monkeys, no 'female' at all. It's Arthur Farren that's the Female Impersonator . . . and there's . . ."

"Here's the caur noo!" said Agnes, interrupting her. "About time, and all."

The open-topped Standard Tram, brass rails glistening and wooden blade-guard jutting out at the front, ready to usher the unready and the steamboats aside, clattered to a stop. The girls prepared to clamber aboard.

"Oh, wait!" said Agnes, agitated.

"Come on," Sadie pulled at her sleeve. "The conductor's waitin'."

Agnes looked up at the young man and simpered. "That's the rain oan. Will I get an electrical shoak of I put my fit oan the rail?" she asked.

"Not unless you put the other one on the overhead wire," said the conductor. "C'moan or get aff? If it's no oan then it's aff!" he added sagely, ringing the bell. The girls went inside and the tram for Anderston thundered down the road into the 20th century.

*Scotland v England, the REAL "old" firm and the oldest international fixture in the world, was first played in 1872. The People's Palace opened its doors and its Winter Gardens to a stupendous half a million visitors within the first five months. Well-known painters of the day showed off scenes of Glasgow, and John Knox's "Trongate" drew admiring crowds. All that was a drop in the Clyde compared with the crowd at Celtic Park in April 1898, when 50,000 turned up to see THE game . . . and the rest!*

THE road to Celtic Park was paved with punters. Every Street in the Gallowgate and the Calton had become a parking place for horses, hansom cabs, buses that could well have been the "taxis of Waterloo" if Napoleon had been on our side, broughams with the seats held together by faith and carpet tacks, open coaches decorated with scraps of cloth and coloured paper, growling, fuming motor-cars . . . the invasion of the East End of Glasgow was total. Trams like tins full of pilchards with brown bowler hats on, crept along Great Hamilton Street, or the Gallowgate behind the Victoria Biscuit Works. Hordes on foot thronged the streets leading to the "Great Gemme"; Rowchester Street by the Tramways Depot, Henrietta Street at the Cattle Sheds opposite the cemetery yonder, Campbellfield Street by the Rag and Boot Factories. The football crowd was at fever pitch. An army of Glasgow's Finest, together with soldiers, manned barricades, specially erected iron fences, and wooden railings, funnelling the massive crowds towards the field of the Thistle and Rose.

There was to be no repetition of the disaster two years previously in 1896, when a crowd in excess of 60,000 had spilled on to the pitch. It was the punters who remained in the stand that "persuaded" the invaders to get off the field, by the simple expedient of throwing bottles and pies at them, beer-cans not yet having been invented.

The Roman Emperor Antonine, while he would have looked in vain for the wall he built across Scotland 2,000 years before, would have been quite at home in the vast amphitheatre of Celtic Park. Red-coated, kilted soldiers ringed the pitch. Trumpets sounded, press-men hoisted their notebooks and their Kodaks, and cinema newshounds began to crank the handles of their cameras.

The players ran on to the field and the roar was heard five miles away at Kelvin Park, where preparations were already in hand for another Great Exhibition to be held in 1901.

From the beginning, the match was a struggle for Scotland. English wingers Bloomer, Spikesley, Wheldon and Smith drove a wedge in the Scots defence and England scored early. By the second half Scotland was fighting for her life, and a missed tackle gave the opening that led to the home team's great goal. Still fighting back, with Doyle tackling Athersmith, striking, and almost giving Scotland her second goal of the match, the final whistle went. The score was Scotland 1 England 3.

The crowd went home quietly via the 300 pubs that were to be found in the East End of Glasgow in the good old days. The general concensus was that the Scottish Selectors were at fault in putting up a team that couldn't beat half-decent third-raters. At 3-1, 50,000 disgruntled punters melted away like snaw aff a dyke. Those were the days.

*Once under the Kelvin and twice under the Clyde, the making of the Glasgow Under-
ground began in 1891 and involved two enormous explosions under the Clyde to open
up twin 20-foot holes for the tunnels. The grand opening was in the Christmas season
of 1896 on 14 December. Glasgow took to the subway with a will, but an unexpected
flood of passengers and an accident that injured 19 people, closed the circles until
January the following year, when the Glasgow Subway Railway Company began
operations in earnest.*

*Almost 1,000 years after its beginnings, Glasgow approached the new century in a
mood of careful optimism and vast industry. Wealth, culture, and international adventure had turned a tiny collection of huts into a huge sandstone metropolis. Like the sand
under Argyle Street where the new subway ran down to the river, the fortunes of the
future were already shifting. No one knew it then, but the first shadows of a terrible
war were gathering, hidden by the glory of an Empire that coloured one-fifth of the map
of the planet Imperial Red.*

**D**AVIE Gregor was a "masher". His thin, aristocratic face, fixed in a
much-practised expression of confident disdain, crowned his gleaming white
celluloid collar like a fresh pie on a paper doily. Striped blazer with brass
buttons, tennis "whites", blue shoes with white spats, a pair of kid gloves
held casually in his left hand, here was young, working-class Glasgow out on a spree.
It was *la belle age*, and elegant ironwork enclosed almost everything, even the stained-
glass compartment dividers on the underground train bound for Cessnock and the
mysterious "south side".

He slipped his arm protectively round Agnes Dooley's shoulder as the carriage
dipped and the leading compartment turned through almost a complete right angle. The
radius of the curve in the track was almost as narrow as his trousers.

"Have ye had a nice day, darlin'?" he asked.

"Oh the best!" Agnes snuggled up to his manly breast-pocket. "The yellow ice-
cream fudge, the fountains . . . everything. It was like a dream, so it wis."

He cleared his throat. "Are we going to be courtin' regular?" His face donned
a mask of decisive coolness and he twiddled the end of his moustache without letting
go of his gloves. "Are we . . . dearest?"

Agnes blushed. "We've only known each other a year."

"One year and two months, to the very day," he said firmly. "I feel like . . ."
he paused, watching the tunnel walls racing by outside the window. "I feel like this is
OOR subway, Agnes. You're special."

"Oh Davie! You're just saying that!"

"We're under the Clyde now," he cast an intellectual eye at the roof of the carriage. "Just think of all those tons and tons of water over oor heads. That's engineering,
you know. We can do anything these days."

"Oh . . . Davie . . ." Agnes's eyes shone.

Someone had left a copy of the evening paper beside him, and he picked it up
and glanced at the headline. "Cape Colony and Natal . . ." he muttered.

"What was that darlin'?" asked Agnes, showing an interest in his every word.
"Cape where?"

129

"This is great news!" He looked at her, pointing excitedly at the paper. "See here, darlin'. There's going to be a war with the Boers. They must be daft to take on the British Empire. Don't they know we canna lose?"

Agnes looked doubtful. "There's soldiers for that kind of thing, aren't there?" she asked.

"I heard about this today from auld Timmins, him that's the under-manager to Brackenridge in Soft Bric-a-brac and Genteel Furnishings. He knows aboot current affairs. There's men from the town wanting to join up all over, and there's enough for two serving companies frae Glasgow already. What do you think of that Agnes? Wouldn't it be fine?"

"Where is it?" Agnes was definitely worried.

"Oh. Africa. It'll not affect the shops or the trams or nothin', so don't you worry my pet lamb . . . but wouldn't it be exciting?"

"Davie. You're not thinking of . . . of JOINING the army, are ye?"

"I want you to be proud of me, Agnes. Start oor life an' the new century with me in uniform. Grand, eh? Start the way we mean to go on . . ."

*The first ferries across the Clyde in the early 19th century were large rowing boats, but after a tragic sinking, the first steam ferries were introduced by the Clyde Trust in 1865. Within five years they were carrying over seven million passengers a year. At Clyde Street alone paying punters pushed out the boat to the tune of 5,680 passengers every day.*

*The North Rotunda, now a first-class restaurant, and its sister dome on the south bank, were the termini of the Glasgow Harbour Tunnel. This was operated by a series of huge lifts at either end, and horses, carts, and thousands of Glaswegians made the daily descent into the Stygian depths beneath the cold waters of the Clyde. Elevating deck ferries, introduced in 1890, finally vanished from the river-crossing scene in 1966.*

*The Clutha River-Buses operated their 12-strong fleet on the run between Stockwell Street Bridge and Whiteinch, all for the standard charge of one penny. The Cluthas could carry 360 passengers, and in the 60 years from the turn of the century the entire population of Glasgow must have moved back and forwards across the Clyde annually without ever getting its collective feet wet.*

A FINE rain was falling, filling the air with insubstantial droplets of water that seemed to hang suspended in limbo above the cobbles. The billposter attempting to paste the second of his "Cooper and Co's Teas" posters on the hoarding watched the paper slowly curl back from the wall and drop on to the ground. He lifted his collar philosophically, leaned against the hardier Theatre bills that he had stuck there the day before, and lit his pipe.

It was four o'clock and already getting dark. A leerie walked past, lifted his long pole, and opened the glass panel at the front of the nearest gas lamp-post. There was a soft "plop" and the blue light welled out of the mantle as he closed the door, deftly trapping the light inside. Shadows wavered backwards through the green railings and down on to the sunken slipway leading to the chain-ferry.

On the other side of the river opposite the outflow of the Kelvin, lamps were also being lit in the Pointhouse Inn, and the choppy river waters reflected the lights, struggling to shine in the damp, smoky air. There was a subdued "clanging" from Henderson's Shipyard at Meadowside to the left, and the passengers waiting for the ferry on the Govan side at Water Row, could see the glow of fires where the boilermakers were busy putting the finishing touches to the Anchor Line's new flagship, the *Columbia*.

A crowd of Glaswegians waited patiently for the ferry. A scant quarter-mile away, but almost invisible from the Govan bank, the ferry was moving slowly out into midstream. The chains took up the slack and emerged from the river, long dripping lines of rusty tension, bound to the circular ship with its two little funnels. Gripping the chain with determination the ferry hauled itself bravely through the grey twilight.

At this hour on a winter's afternoon, before the works came out, the crowd was mixed. Later it would be a solid mass of grey serge and flat caps, blue pipe-smoke mingling with the breath of 1,000 workers in the chill air. Two women with shawls wrapped tightly about their ears and heads were deep in conversation, their low voices barely audible to themselves, let alone the other 30 or so damp travellers awaiting the arrival of the ghostly ferry. Some mill-workers on a mid-shift and a group of men

crossing the river to look for work made up the rest of the throng, with the exception of a portly little man with a bowler hat, waistcoat and watch-chain, a foreman from one of the Govan yards on an errand for the Head Office.

The ferry drew close to the bank and the crowd surged forward. The bill poster had moved on to dryer pastures and all the gas-lamps were now lit.

For 300 years part of the Minister's stipend in Govan was the first salmon drawn from the river each year, but this was 1902. There would be no salmon, not this year.

*Every "Toshie" watcher, and there are many devotees of the great Charles Rennie Mackintosh from Hill Street to Hiroshima, knows that Glasgow was once thought of as the very acme of a Tokyo for tea-rooms. Those were the days when what are now old-time good manners and fashions were the newest of the new, and Kate Cranston's wasp-waisted Mackintosh Tea-room, the Willow, was but a sapling in the street it was named after – Sauchiehall Street means the Street of the Willows. Together with Buchanan Street and Argyle Street, they were as well, if not better, known as Regent and Bond Streets in the heyday of brown derbys and the Dheli Durbah.*

*The expression, "Up Sauchie, doon Buchie, and alang Argyle", which referred to nocturnal activities that ran parallel to the day-time ambience of these great Clydeside boulevards, might also have included Blythswood Square, once home of the infamous poisoner Madeleine Smith, and latterly, numerous other ladies with hearts of loose change and the instincts of a blushing tarantula.*

SAUCHIEHALL Street was the place to be seen of a Friday or Saturday evening, and not only men but unaccompanied young ladies would stroll up and down in their finery, smoking in public. There were plenty of eating places about the heart of the city. There were chop-houses with fine cooked sirloins of beef, and lobsters, black as coal and swivelling their eyes on sinuous stalks, or still as Sunday and red all over. Tubs of oysters from the sea-lochs vied with clams and other sea-food brought to what was, after all, one of the greatest ports of the Empire.

There was an American bar and a Bodega, resurrected from the Great Exhibitions. Patrons could drink "American Style", with an entire bottle of Bourbon to mark for themselves while nibbling on cinnamon bark, stuffed olives, pickled herring, cloves, or dry salt crackers. Downstairs smoke-rooms sent the odour of fine Havana leaf up into the street to mingle with the scent of fresh-roasted coffee or the exhaust of an occasional motorcar. Primarily, between the marble staircases of the Grosvenor and Waterloo Rooms of this world, there was life – rich, content, brash, and above all, utterly and completely confident that tomorrow would hold the same as today, if not a few ounces, inches, or a pickle-jar more for all concerned.

There had been an attempt at a revolution in Russia, but then nobody concerned themselves much with the eccentricities of the world south of Cathcart or east of Camlachie, unless it might touch on trade. The Royal Navy stood between the sanctity of Saturday nights and the rest of the world.

"It's Sadie, Sadie Blaine . . . with an 'E'," she smiled shyly. The band struck up another pastiche of Strauss and the tide of skaters waltzed round and round in a hypnotic swirl of hats and feathers.

"Pleased to meet you," Bobby Coul held tightly on to her gloved hands, as much to stop himself from falling as anything else. "Good band, eh? Hope you don't mind me asking you up."

Sadie looked up at the tall boy coyly. "No. No. Not at all. I like the skating."

"Come here a lot, do you?"

"Oh, not very. Once in a blue moon, in ectual fect." A few bools crept into her mooth. "Nice cless of people come doon here."

She was lying. She came to the Skating Palace in Sauchiehall Street nearly every Friday night, and certainly every Saturday. Ever since her friend Agnes had married Kenneth Milligan from Drapery their paths had separated. Agnes was expecting her second now and Kenneth, back from the wars was re-installed in the upper levels of the department store in Buchanan Street. The pressures of wedded bliss excluded Sadie as effectively from the life of her former friend as if they had been on different continents. Sadie was about to become 22. She felt "on the shelf" and a burden to her parents. She had a good career behind the counter in Ladies' Separates, but no desire to become a spinster. Her mother had said nothing to her, of course, but every glance, every cup of tea was full of unspoken reproach. Sadie gripped her partner's hand tighter although there was no danger of her falling, not yet at any rate.

"Where do ye work?" she asked casually, making the question sound as disinterested as a comment about the weather or the conductor's handkerchief. "Work in Glasgow?"

"Oh . . . I'm a student," the young man laughed. "Materia Medica."

Sadie's heart sank. Why could she never meet anyone of her own class? Her father was a good man, and always paid his way, but he was an upholsterer. A student! "Oh . . . that's nice," she forced a grin and loosened her grip.

He wobbled suddenly and slipped sideways. "Oh . . . not very good at this yet!" He steadied himself, holding on to her shoulder. "I hope . . . you don't mind a man . . . leaning on you," he asked with an innocent smile. His straw boater was new and his plus-fours neat, but there was something of the air of a little boy about him. He needed looking after.

Sadie looked boldly into his brown eyes. "No . . . not at all . . ." The pheasant on her hat was long dead, but the bird of hope in her breast took wing. "I'll show you how. Watch my feet. You'll be good at learning, being a student, and that. . . ."

They skated off together as the band began a new German waltz.

134

*On the eve of the Great War the entertainment world in Glasgow was going great guns. The Admirable Crichton was on at the Royalty, the Three Ragtime Boys at the Alhambra, and at A. E. Pickard Unlimited's Panopticon (Doors open at six during the Spring holiday), there was "Fancy Fair and the Laughter Mirrors". The Panopticon and Pickard's Waxworks, formerly MacLeod's Waxworks, in the Trongate near Glasgow Cross, had a reputation as eccentric as its owner.*

*Albert Ernest Pickard, once the "millionaire" candidate for Parliament in the Maryhill Division, was the* eminence grise *behind the "Hall of Laughing Mirrors" and "The World's Thinnest Man". Chaplin and Stan Laurel appeared on stage at the Panopticon, but even these pulsars in the milky way of mirth had the feet ca'ed from under them by Fergus the Legless Leprechaun.*

FERGUS sat in a glass case resplendent in Limerick Green. Every hour on the hour the glass case was opened with some ceremony, and the wee man would sign copies of his autobiography. That was the main, but not the only cause of the subsequent riot, when the bonnie lieges, not a few "in drink" as they used to say at the magistrate's court, toppled the case over with the luckless, as well as legless leprechaun still inside. The main complaint was that the whole thing was a fraud, which could be proved because, as everyone knew . . . leprechauns canna write!

When it came to Glasgow fun Fergus stood alone, but Lord Roberts, that same whose statue and cuddy stand in splendid isolation looking down on Kelvin Park from Park Circus, told the graduation audience in Glasgow University in 1913 that, "Britain stands alone still". He begged that a citizen army should be formed, declaring, "an untrained man with a rifle would be useless in modern warfare". As the armed alliances of Europe, intertwined in a deadly dance and wrapped around with train-timetables, struggled into the nightmare to come, nobody realised what modern war was going to mean, least of all Lord Roberts.

Halley's Comet, back for a re-run of the Norman invasion of England and King Harold's unfortunate compulsion to look up, plummeted past the outwardly serene blue-green island of earth. On 4 August 1914, Great Britain, together with her Dominions and Colonies, declared war on the German Empire. The Austrian Empire, the Russian Empire, the French Republic, "poor little Belgium", everybody fought for the privilege of committing social and collective suicide on a spectacular scale, and for no particular reason. People THOUGHT there were reasons. National pride, unbridled aggression, living-space, colonial ambitions, sea-power, honour . . . the world of the Laughing Mirrors was forgotton. No one wanted proof or reasons, which was just as well . . . there were NO reasons.

The bells in the Tolbooth Tower rang out and Cameron of Lochiel was not in town. If he had been he would not have been alone. Almost 3,000 people filled the space in front of the ancient tower, and spilled into the railway station and down the steps. They hung from railings and lamp-posts like baskets of old clothes. The square was a sea of flat caps, all tilted upwards towards the notices plastered on the medieval stonework.

"I canna help it," shouted Tam by way of apology. "It's thaim at the back shovin'."

135

"S'awricht, Tam," Wull was endeavouring to stand on tip-toe, but so was everyone else. "Still up though," he added, peering over the shoulders of the man in front. "Same mobilisation order."

"Och, that's been up for days," replied Tam scornfully. "General Mobilisation of all regular and special reservists. Naval boys are away and all."

A subdued murmur became a roar as a number of soldiers pushed their way through the crowd towards the tower.

"Hull-aw . . . what's up?" said Tam, taking off his cap and scratching the back of his head. "New bulletins. Ye can see through the back. It's . . . it's printed in RED!"

"Aye, look," yelled Wull in excitement. He threw his cap in the air and whooped for joy. "Look! They're pastin' them up all over the Cross. Hooray! BRITAIN AT WAR!"

Someone started singing "God Save the King" and soon everybody was joining in, thousands of strong hearts and lungs, shipyard workers, foundry men, train drivers, some still on strike, were swept away by the tide of emotion.

"Is this no' great?" Wull shouted, tears streaming down his cheeks. "War! War! It's like hogmanay . . .!"

"Yer no' wrang," Tam replied, slapping him on the back. "We've goat the best Navy, the best aw'thin'. We'll knock them oan their knees by Christmas . . . the hale jing bang o' thae Proosians."

"It would be grand to see the cavalry chargin' and the cannons and that like thon play at the Royal we seen. Bugles blowin'! Here . . ." he paused and looked at his friend. "Tam. Do you fancy it, eh?"

Tam looked slightly taken aback. "What do you . . ." his eyebrows shot up. "Are you talkin' about what I think ye are talkin' about?"

"Aye!" the bunnetless Wull nodded vigorously. "Let's jine up."

"If I went tae fight the Germans ma wife'd kill me," said Tam with awe.

"Oh here," replied Wull. "That's right. We might get killed deid."

"Don't be daft. That disny happen these days. This is a modern war. C'mon. Let's be the first."

"It wis my idea. I'm gane." Wull pushed his way towards the soldiers. "Are ye comin' Tam Slater? –" He paused and half-turned. "Yer no . . . feart?"

"I half-killed a man for sayin' that once tae me," replied Tam, abashed. "Here . . . mister," he yelled out and struggled to the front. "Here. We want tae jine . . . afore it's all over . . ."

*The first Christmas of the War was the Christmas when everybody thought it would be over. After the deluge that decided the first battle of Ypres, King-Emperor George V arrived at the St Omer Headquarters of the British Expeditionary Force in Northern France, and went away again. The days of death rolled on inexorably towards the ending of the year.*

*Then it was Christmas Eve 1914, and from ''Wypers'' to the Masurian Lakes a strange event occurred. The troops of both sides stopped fighting in many places. They exchanged addresses, bits of old sausage, gave each other presents of socks that their wives and sweethearts had knitted, and hoped and pretended, that it was all over.*

CHRISTMAS was over but the war was not. Following months of preparation the mood of the Allies in Greek Lemnos was one of excitement. British action, thought to be carefully camouflaged, had been obvious to the Turks for weeks. Greece was full to the brim with German agents, and the Greek King, Constantine, married to the Kaiser's sister Sophia, held the rank of Field Marshal in the Imperial German Army. Lemnos was not a very clever place to choose as a base for British operations.

The troops landed at Gallipoli, 3 Australian Brigades at Ari Burnu from HMS *Ribble*, *Usk*, *Chelm* and others, and a host of ships and battalions, signals corps, fusileers, ambulance and Anson battalions. On HMS *River Clyde* and attendant ships were the Royal Munster Fusileers, 2nd Hants. (less two companies), a field corps of the Royal Engineers, a GHQ Signals Section, and three subdivisions of the 52nd, the Glasgow and Lowland counterpart of the 51st Highland Division. The wee men were there in force. All across the little bay west of Seddulbahir, the very southernmost tip of the Gallipoli peninsular, there was ''standing room only'' for the Allied Army. None of the 70,000 English, Scots, Irish, and Anzac troops expected the reception that awaited them, and the rain of death that would greet them from the machine-guns of the Turkish 9th Division, hidden in the hills above.

Between the Western Front and Gallipoli, men were in short supply. Kitchener's ''Your Country Needs You'' poster was plastered up all over Glasgow. Recruiting was taken in hand by Lord Provost Sir Thomas Dunlop and the former Lord Provost Sir Archibad McInnes. Altogether, Glasgow provided 26 battalions, like the 15th, 16th, and 17th battalions of the HLI, the latter including many members of the Tramways department, becoming known as the ''Tramways Battalion''. The 16th had close ties with the Boys' Brigade, with flags presented by the Trades' House of Glasgow. The 17th had four Companies to begin with, recruited from the Royal Technical College, F.P.s of city schools, and from the businesses and trades of the city. The Chamber of Commerce Battalion – known as the ''featherbed'' because of its comfortable initial billet in Troon – and the others went south. They were in the trenches by Christmas 1915 and eventually, from July 1916, in the carnage of the Somme.

The Somme dragged on through July, a futile and terrible battle of attrition that cost hundreds of thousands of lives, through Aubers Ridge, Delville Wood, where the Cameronians had a section of trench they called Buchanan Street, and into a dreadful September, when Haig decided to try and break through on the Somme with a secret

weapon, the tank. It was four weeks since Z-day and the opening of the battle. Nothing was gained either way. Much was lost.

When Lloyd George talked about the Empires and Kingdoms, kings and crowns of Europe falling like withered leaves, he should have been talking about the millions of ordinary people, the music and laughter and minutiae of countless lives, washed away like a child's map drawn on a slate left out in the rain. In over four years of "The Great War for Civilization", something that could never be assessed had been crushed by the imbecile violence of the Great Powers.

When Peace came on the 11th hour of the 11th day of the 11th month, the citizens of Glasgow at home and abroad were elated, relieved, delighted, and very, very tired . . .

# THE CLOUD-WALKERS

*It might have been Icarus and Pilcher, instead of the Wright brothers . . .! Glasgow had taken wings at the end of the 19th century. Percy Pilcher, a naval architect at Glasgow University was experimenting with a powered glider and, but for the tragic accident that ended his life, would have entered the history books as the first man to fly an engine-driven aircraft.*

*The First World War saw enormous advances in flight technology, and Glasgow was a major centre for aircraft production. On 13 July 1919 the first two-way crossing of the Atlantic was completed by the Beardmore-built R34, which made the flight to Minneola in the USA in spite of carrying the world's first airborne stowaway.*

*It was Glasgow-born American Lieutenant Arthur Whitten Brown and Captain John Alcock who had first flown an aircraft across the Atlantic one month earlier in June, and their terrible journey in a giant biplane bomber powered by Rolls-Royce engines was very different from today's high-cruising world of in-flight movies.*

THE land lay in the quiet light of a golden afternoon. Gentle valleys climbed gradually to rolling uplands, which were in turn pierced by towering crags and cliffs. On some of the cliffs there were castles, clinging impossibly to sheer faces and ragged outcroppings. A few were connected with neighbouring towers by spidery bridges, 1,000 feet above ravines of deepest blue. Shadows ran down like rivers from the airy uplands, filling the depths with a gathering chill. Towering over all, their inaccessible faces as high and massive as peaks on the moon, a gigantic range of mountains tipped with red ringed the quiet valleys.

There was a growing sound of thunder, low at first, then gathering force, the deep-throated rumbling filled the afternoon with vibration and threat. Steadily it rolled, the onrushing wave of sound leading the storm, like a tidal wave echoes some distant catastrophe. Deep and steady, seeming to fill the land with its sound, an earthquake in the air, the rumbling grew steadily closer.

Without warning, a huge biplane burst from the side of a cloud-mountain, scattering castles and crags in puffs and wisps of smoke, its shadow gliding ahead, rising and falling as it sped across the wide landscape of cloud. A valley broke, its sides drifting apart to reveal a sparkling sea, 3,000 feet below.

"That's the last of the chocolate," Arthur Whitten Brown tapped the altimeter.

"What was that, Arthur?" John Alcock turned towards his navigator.

Whitten Brown held up the empty wrapper and shook his head.

"There's the sandwiches and beer!" Captain Alcock shouted. "What's our position?"

Whitten Brown leaned forward and smoothed the transparent cover on the chart open across his knees. "Our total path is 1,900 miles," he muttered to himself. ". . . Journey should take all of 16 hours, mean speed 120 miles per hour." He looked up. "Here," he said firmly, pointing with his indelible pencil at a point mid-way between Newfoundland and Ireland. "We can expect to sight land here, about Bantry, or maybe Cliffden, allowing for the wind speed."

Captain Alcock watched the needle on one of his gauges warily. "The extra fuel is holding up . . . better than 18 112-pound bombs." He laughed. "Smith and his brother are going to attempt the 11,000 miles from the UK to Australia in another Vickers."

Whitten Brown folded his map carefully and wiped the rain off the leather cover with his flying-glove. "I suppose we'll see passenger flights after this," he looked thoughtfully at a bottle of beer. "Still, they'll be protected from sleet and hail, enclosed like the *H12*."

"The *Large America*? She's a flying-boat."

One of the Rolls-Royce VIII engines gave a throaty cough and resumed its serene drone. "So will we be, if anything comes unstuck." He looked beyond the scudding clouds to the sea far beneath. "You know, the future is with flying-boats. Cheaper than building runways."

"Let's just make our own landfall," the Captain buttoned his collar as the rain began in earnest. "It will likely either be an Irish bog or the drink for us."

"Don't they go together?" Whitten Brown gave in to his instincts, and since they were cruising at 20,000 feet they were definitely higher ones. He opened the bottle of beer. "I'll take the drink," he said.

*Civvy street was full. That was because there were over four million men being demobbed at the rate of 10,000 a day. The War was over, Rutherford split the atom on 3 January 1919, and the workers' war had just begun.*

*With the sea-routes open again trade picked up for a while. Prices had been driven up 125 per cent since 1914 and the wave of nation-wide strikes and industrial unrest that had been coming to a head on the eve of the great conflict, burst into flame. Trade Union membership had risen from four million in 1914 to eight million in 1918. Campbell Steven, John Muir, the ILP "philosopher", Jimmy Maxton, Neil MacLean the publicist, Manny Shinwell, men thought of as "the new Covenanters" took up the banner. It was the same banner that flew over the columns of marching men converging on the Women's Battalion guarding the Provisional Government in St Petersburg . . . the same banner that was raised in front of the crowds surging into George Square in Glasgow. It was red.*

**H**ARRY McShane was a fighter, but then, so was his friend Johnny Milligan. They had plenty to fight for. Out of a population of 1,081,600, over 40,591 families lived in single rooms, and 112,424 in "room-and-kitchens".

The Anderston Unemployed Committee had decided to use their meeting to mount a boycott of the Argyle Picture House. The manager was refusing to allow the Committee to use the hall for nothing. It began to look as if a wee riot might be in order. Then there was the police baton charge. In Hydepark Street, Harry McShane broke through a police cordon by running at it backwards. Another meeting was held, a second cordon formed, and Harry pulled Milligan against the wall as the policemen rushed by, waving their batons. McShane, one of the driving forces behind the Hunger Marches of the 1930s, and Milligan, a founder member of the British Communist Party, hid in a pub and downed a few pints until a party of workers arrived from the Gorbals to rescue them. With difficulty McShane restrained his saviours from starting an all-out street war with the police. It seemed as if Glasgow was on the brink of revolution.

The frosty pavement in front of the Royal Technical College in George Street was crowded and the ice in the gutters cracked by countless tackity boots marching into George Square. Hands that did not hold banners and placards were thrust deep into pockets, and every street was thronged with lines of men pouring into the heart of the city past the "Chambers". They skidded and slid down Montrose Street past the Maternity Hospital, they shoved and jostled through the Candleriggs, blocking traffic in front of the Sheriff Court; they poured past the great arches of St Enoch's, Central, and Queen Street Stations, filling the Square to overflowing. Trams stood marooned as they were engulfed by a rising tide of workers demanding a hearing. The air was heavy with the threat of revolution and reprisal.

All the way from Springburn the cobbles were cracked and broken. A gas lamp on the corner of Glebe Street near St Mungo's Academy was askew. The pavement beside Alen Glen's was smashed and a Corporation junction box that had stood outside Jackson's Dog House in Dundas Street lay up a close. The tanks were coming.

Silently, ranks of police edged their steaming mounts closer to the crowds, hemming them in. In the city where James Watt had harnessed the pressure of steam to create the Industrial Revolution, thousands of men and women were being driven into

the Square by the piston of Government, fearful that another revolution was in the making. Manny Shinwell stood in the back of a lorry, speaking bravely and loudly. A great roar swept from every throat as the vast mass of grey parted and a single flag was raised above the heads of the throng. Simple, uncompromising, the cloth hung limply in the frosty air. Like the poppies in Flanders it was red as blood. Police whistles blew, the shouting turned to screaming. The revolution-that-might-have-been was over for the day. The Strike continued.

*It was boom time and depression time. There was rationing at home and war in Ireland. Hemlines were up and tunes like the "Black Bottom" and the "Charleston" were part of a new sense of freedom that could be seen every night in Glasgow at over 50 "Palais de Danse". The delights of the "Pally" of your choice could be sampled for the princely sum of sixpence, and girls in page-boy cuts and boys with paraffin on their hair, shuffled around the polished wooden "flerr" to the strains of "Broadway Baby"; the twinkling glass stars of the mirrors hanging from the ceiling spun them round and round, moths that nested in a box-bed in a single end, and danced at the Butterfly Ball.*

*The twenties had not quite started roaring for the Clydesiders. There was a sugar shortage as well as a miner's strike. The domestic sweet-ration was to be increased by a quarter ounce to help the thousands of war-widows the Government thought "were gainfully employed" in running the myriad sweetie-shops of the Second City of a battered Empire.*

SADIE cuffed the wee boy who was playing with the leather strap that opened the front window and settled down to watch the world rush past and eat her batter. Gino's chipper in Duke Street, near where she normally boarded her tram after work, charged one penny for a bag of crispy batter, and if you were lucky, there might be a nice piece of fish, or a stray lump of white pudding hiding among the golden, greasy flakes. She crunched appreciatively and watched the urchin out of the corner of her eye. She was sure the conductor would put him off. There was enough dirt on his knees to grow potatoes, and his short trousers obviously belonged to someone at least three years younger, but he gave her a toothless grin, slid back in his seat and picked his nose. She turned away and looked out of the window.

The tram was careering towards Dennistoun and was just passing the Eastern District Hospital. A Tennent's steam lorry, belching oily wood smoke because of the coal shortage, clanked past in the opposite direction, a rag-and-bone cart overtaking on the inside. It was tea-time and the streeets were busy as people walked home from the many small factories and warehouses in the East End. Bigger employers, like the vast Beardmore's factory at Parkhead, as well as many of the shipyards, employed people who lived within a mile's radius, but there was large-scale unemployment, and many now had to travel miles to work. She remembered the tea-time throng before the war, when she was ten and working illegally in the Biscuit Factory near Bridgeton. The crowds were thinner now. So many men had been killed or wounded in the war, that it would be ten years before another generation would fill the gaps. The wounded and disabled, of course, would not be returning from work or anywhere. Sadie's Dad had died at Gallipoli, and her mother had to make do with a tiny pension and the income of the shop.

The "shop" was the front room of their ground floor flat. In Glasgow, a flat was a room and kitchen, and during the day, jars of "Bull's Eyes", penny sookers, sherbet packets, chocolates, "Grannies", and the other sweets slowly re-appearing on the market, filled the spaces where Sadie and her mother spent their evenings after their tea. "Tea", in the lands of the tenement canyons was not a mid-morning "tiffin", but the evening meal. Between the sweetie shop and Sadie's earnings in the hosier's they barely managed.

The door of the front compartment opened and Sadie held her money out.

"I've nae tickets, but I'll gie ye a chip," Dierdrie sat down noisly beside her friend.

"Naw," Sadie refused with a polite shake of her head. "Fullup, so ahm ur."

Dierdrie accepted this formal rebuff and stuffed the remainder of her chips and peas into a small but sensuous mouth. "Good, that." She wiped her lips on the paper and crumpling it up, tucked it demurely between the seat and the wall. "Goin' oot the night?" The tram whined and sparked as it pulled up at the fare stage near the Dennistoun Palais and Whitehill Street.

"Nae money."

"Want a sub?" Dierdrie, a sorter in the "Offal and Lights" section of the abbatoir at Bellgrove, was relatively "flush".

"I couldna'," Sadie looked away with just the barest hint of a micro-second's hesitation.

"I'll get it when ye've goat it. We've been pally for years Sadie. Here, ma Da'll only get it if you don't." She held out a shilling.

"Thanks then," Sadie took the coin quickly and stuffed it in the pocket of her coat.

"We're on for the night then?" Dierdrie leaned forward, peering up cheekily at her friend's averted face.

"Aye," Sadie turned, smiling reluctantly. "Aye. Mammy willny mind."

"That's settled then," said Dierdrie cheerily, absently cuffing the small boy, who was still picking his nose.

The music stopped with a roll on the drums and an accidental "toot" from the saxophonist, who was a painter and plasterer to trade. There was very little painting work about at present so music and plastering were currently his major occupations.

Sadie let go of the young man's lapels, smiled grimly, and limped across the floor to Dierdrie, waiting by the fan-shaped mirror.

"How did you get on, Sadie?" Dierdrie asked, trying the feather in her hair at another angle.

"Och . . . terrible. Mine was all feet . . . and hands! Whit about you?"

"Ye widny credit it!" Dierdrie stuck the feather in the band at the front and squinted at herself. "Mine was an undertaker's apprentice with a gammy knee."

"Did he have black hair and yella teeth?"

"Aye. How did you . . . ?"

Sadie's reflection grinned at her. A third figure swam into the blue-green fan of the mirror. "Hullaw . . . rerr," he said. "Back again fur mair. Ur ye dancin'?"

"Aw' I've left ma eyelashes in the ladies," Dierdrie squeezed past. "There ye are, Sadie . . . Therr's a man askin' ye tae dance."

144

*Winston's Water-Lions and Diving Nymphs were appearing at the Glasgow Empire, busily proving themselves as "the aquatic marvels of the 20th century". At the Metropole, the eager theatre-goer could revel in* That Fantastic Fantasy . . . It'll Ticklem or Rips Raps, *presented by a powerful cast of gifted comic thespians including Cullen and Carthy, a double act, the Wee Mon, and the popular Will E. Wont E. Beanland.*

*In spite of this galaxy of stars and performing dugs and the like, the Theatre with a capital "T" was up against it, which doesn't mean the wall of the Theatre next door. The cinema was moving in. This was particularly appropriate because the "Flickers" did just that; they moved, ran, fell off bridges, drove trains through parlours, rode wild horses, attacked poor wee Indians, flew aeroplanes, and rammed just about every aspect of everything that normal people never did, on to a square screen in the local box of delights known as "The Picters", "The Flicks", or if you came from Clarkston, High Burnside, Shawlands or Jordanhill, "The Cineemaaa" . . .*

IN the early twenties the genre of the moving pictures went through the cultural life of the lieges of the auld toon of Glasgow, like a dose of the Epsom. Glasgow began building picture houses like there was no tomorrow, and by the early thirties there were more cinemas in Glasgow than in any other city in Europe. There was also a boom in organ-building and piano-playing because music was not only "the food of life" as it always has been, but also the mood background to films. Pictures were completely and utterly silent except for the whirr of the projector, or the mutterings of the projectionist when he changed reels and dropped one.

Round about this time the Salon in Sauchiehall Street was showing *Rob Roy, Scotland's Wonderful Adventure*, filmed at Aberfoyle and Stirling. It was advertised as, "The loves, romance, and adventures of Rob Roy, well-known outlaw and Highland Chief". Rob Roy was played by David Holburn, the Duke of Montrose by Sir Simeon Steuart, the "Dougal Cratur" by Alec Hunter, Sandy (The Biter) by Tom Morris, and Rab, Rob's eldest son and apple of his sporran, by the athletic heart-throb Bob Celino, who couldn't talk anyway. The whole silent performance was accompanied by specially arranged bagpipe music and "orchestral diversions". The stalls cost one shilling and three pence and the stately elegance of the circle a whole two bob. The climax of the evening was perhaps on the premature side, as the star of the saga, David Holburn alias Rob himself, appeared complete with fake beard on stage before every performance, "Just tae greet ye." It is possible that the greeting was not all that one-sided.

And then . . . as if people had not been hearing things since Noah hit his thumb with a hammer, SOUND arrived. On 7 January 1929 the Coliseum in Eglinton Street opened its doors to miles of queues, and the original *Jazz Singer* starring the original Al Jolson. There is currently another "Al Jolson" in Glasgow who would be better off singing in a silent movie, so it is important to remember that there was only ever one real "Al", and he regaled Glasgow with "Mammy" and the rest in real sound for a six-week run.

Pringle's Picture Palace in Sauchiehall Street was the first picture-house in Glasgow when it opened in 1907, and the Electric Theatre, also in Sauchiehall Street,

the first purpose-built movie-house in 1910. By the thirties there were picture-halls galore, over 130, and with more cinemas than any other city in the world outside the United States, Glasgow was no mean Cinema-City.

*The Glasgow Gangs grew out of the First World War, when those too young to fight or know any better began to hang around street corners. Before long youngsters fell under the influence of older men, forming into "gangs" like the Redskins, the Black Hand, the South Side Stickers, the San Toi, the Parlour Boys, or the Beehive Gang. These were not the "professional" gangsters of Chicago and New York, hoodlums and racketeers. Glasgow gangster Frank Murphy changed his name to Frank Earn and went on to win the Scottish Welterweight Boxing Championship, but he was the exception. Most of the corner boys were experts in their preferred weapons, the bottle, the half-brick, or the sharpened pick-axe handle. All through the twenties the gangs became increasingly violent and there were constant running battles between the South Side Stickers and the San Toi. Each of these master gangs had "satellites", smaller groups that supported them at need and stayed in the general area.*

*Gang battles became open street-warfare until the appointment of Yorkshireman Commander Percy Sillitoe to the "plum" £1,500-a-year job as head of Glasgow's Constabulary. He smashed the gangs partly by using charges by mounted police, known as "Sillitoe's Cossacks". He also introduced police call boxes to Glasgow, invented the check pattern on police hats, and by reducing police manpower from 11 to seven divisions, saved enough money to buy modern police cars. Following a visit to Edgar J. Hoover and involvement in a machine-gun shoot-out in Chicago, Sillitoe returned to introduce the UK's first radio cars to Glasgow. Sillitoe broke the power of the gangs forever, but there were still "terrortories" where invisible borders drawn by fear and ignorance crossed otherwise ordinary streets.*

IT was Friday night in the Gorbals. Bull Hughes was making his way down the stairs from the hoose, a single end top right off Cumberland Street. He paused beneath the gas jet on the second landing, licked his fingers and tucked the ends of his fine dark hair behind his ears. He looked at himself in his mind's eye, squared his shoulders and carried on down the stairs. His shadow swaggered after him. He paused again at the next landing and peered out of the open window into the back-court.

The grey tenements walled in the space completely. A thousand windows, some reflecting the dying light of the day, stared down with him at the trampled earth, the lines of washing-poles, the puddles. Middens and wash-houses, already deep in shadow, echoed with the shouts of half-glimpsed children at play. Two small boys ran from the damp gloom of a back close, closely pursued by a third, who raced after them, swinging something over his head, then hurling it high in the air. It arced across the well of the court, striking the smaller of the two in the back. He ran on laughing, used to having rats thrown at him.

Bull leaned out of the window, gripping the edge of the crumbling sill with spotlessly clean hands. His bitten fingernails scraped the grey sandstone. "Hey . . . Danny! Get up thae bliddy sterrs. Yer Mammy's wantin' ye!"

The rat-thrower paused, looked up, and grinned. Blue eyes twinkled in a face the colour of burned chalk.

". . . You hear me?" A flock of birds passed overhead, sensing the barreness of the space beneath them.

"Aye," replied a wee voice below, recognising the threat. "Here ahm ur . . . "

*147*

Bull turned and leaned against the wall, waiting as feet scampered up towards him. "In ye get, ya wee bastard," he said affectionately, ruffling the urchin's brown locks as he ran on past. "I'm awa' oot." As the elder brother, it was his priviledge and his right to "go oot" whenever the fancy took him, especially as he was a toiler. His brother vanished upstairs and a door, seldom locked, opened and closed noisily. " I'm awa' oot," Bull challenged the damp walls of the close like a cockerel on a midden. He hunched his shoulders and stamped his way defiantly down the rest of the stairs and out into the cobbled street.

Birds and beasts have senses we do not have. They can see and smell lines and shapes that lead them through the darkest night, point out lines of demarcation, isolate territories. Bull sniffed the rain on the evening air and hurried down the street towards the corner pub. An invisible line ran past the corner, left at the second gas-lamp, straight as truth across the grass beside the upright sleepers that lined the railway track, and on towards the enemy territory of the Baltic Fleet.

Heat and smoke buffeted him with welcoming arms as he entered the bar. It was crowded with heavy drinkers. At the bar stood several men, well-dressed, hair slicked back, sharing the knowing sympathy of lions waiting until something passed that struck them as worth killing. But lions kill to eat, and these were creatures of another breed. Next to them stood the second rank of drinkers, "troops" of the gangs, not yet vicious enough to challenge the leaders or even each other, unless they were mob-handed. Other locals, not directly involved with the gangs, but basking in the glory and the protection bought rounds of drinks or waited for a chance to join in the conversation. There were one or two figures in the corner who were hopelessly drunk. As Bull watched, an elderly man with his glasses hanging from one ear bent backwards at a strange angle, as if he was made of rubber, and slid off his seat. No one took any notice of him. There were no women. This was a men-only bar.

"How's the man?" enquired one of the toughs as Bull strode up and joined them. "Aw' right, well?" He smiled and the long scar that ran from his forehead to his chin became a livid white.

"Aye," Bull replied laconically, accepting a glass of whisky and a pint of pale beer that appeared in front of him. "Nae rumbles?"

"Na," replied the other, draining his glass and sweeping the company with a slightly glazed aye. "Aw' feart efter the last go." He turned and stood with his back to the bar, relaxed, like a cat. "Nae wunner." He spat into the sawdust on the floor.

"There's still an account tae be settled. I'll have that bastard Kyle that runs wi' them. He wisny there."

"Gonny call him oot?" Scarface turned towards the gantry and waved. A whisky appeared in front of him.

"I'm gonny stick him for thon Saturday." Bull searched in his pockets for a cigarette.

"Here ye are, Bull," a man in his twenties, thick-set but already balding, held out a crushed packet of ten Woodbines.

"Tryin' tae be funny Harry?" Bull asked. "Where the hell did ye drag thaim up frae? I want a fag that's no' been given a doin'."

Harry had tensed at the criticism, but Scarface laughed and the whole bar started roaring at Bull's subtlety and wit. He took a fresh cigarette offered by somebody else, lit it and then blew the smoke in Harry's face. Nothing was said, but his Lieutenant knew he had been reprieved at the last minute.

"Well," Bull continued. "I'm gonny cut thon Kyle and dae the rest o' thaim and aw', and I says nixt Saturday at Adelphi, thon wey at the back to the auld bridge at the green." He opened his jacket and tilted back on his heels. Two mother-of-pearl handles jutted out of the top of his waistcoat pocket. "I've been saving these weapons up for him," he continued. "Nothin' but the best."

"Aye," replied Harry. "That's the wey, Bull. Nothin' but the best."

*Ports, especially great ports, are never quite where they seem to be – a corner, a quay, the light filtering past funnels and masts on either side, there is always something that belongs to other places and other times.*

*From the times of the original Glasgow Harbour at the Broomielaw in the 1660s, the atmosphere of the Clydeside had been acquiring something of the West Indies, the South China Sea, the coasts of Africa and India, and all the magic, terror and richness of the seven seas of the world. The Broomielaw Quay was enlarged as years went by and after the arrival of steamships, created and born on this very river, the quays on the north bank were completed past Finnieston and down to Mavisbank by the 1850s. The vast shipyards that stretched back from either bank of the Clyde led to deep cargo-handling docks, graving docks and the opening of the first, the Queen's, by Lord Provost James Bain on 18 September 1877.*

*Ultimately there were five, and the last and fifth of the great docks, which included the Rothesay, the Merkland's Lairage, the Yorkhill, the Queen's, the Prince's and the Kingston Dock, was the King George V Dock. Spanning three centuries, the wooden quays and piers of early dockside beginnings expanded until there were more than 12 miles of berthing for ships of every size and purpose. In a very real sense there were two Glasgows and the second city was the one that clustered along either bank of the River Clyde and all the way to Clydebank.*

*Ships filled the river, ships were built by the river . . . ships like 534. Although the early "fire" of the Red Clydesiders lost much of its impetus in Westminster as the years went by, it was Maxton's fellow social crusader David Kirkwood who was responsible for the announcement by Neville Chamberlain, then dealing with bits of paper as Chancellor of the Exchequer, that work was to be resumed on hull 534 in Clydebank. These were the words that Kirkwood hoped would, "sentence Clydebank to life".*

*On the morning of Tuesday, 3 April 1934, at 7.40 a.m., the workers marched into the yard to the skirl of the pipes and began to clean away the rust and the nests of rooks that had appeared in the giant skeleton of the hull as it lay neglected during years of depression. Nobody knew then what the great ship, 1,018 feet long and with a gross tonnage of 80,000 tons, would be called. She would employ 250,000 men and women in over 80 British towns and cities, and drag 1,006 tons of chains after her into the Clyde at her launch, but she was still 534 until the day a city went to sea and the farmer's field was flooded across from the Glasgow Road.*

WILLIAM Milligan Robb was made in Clydebank. Clean-shaven and with a full head of greying hair, he was known as a gentle man, but nobody crossed him. He could "clear a bar" without interrupting his conversation. Officially titled "Fireman" he was the stoker in the boiler house of the enormous Singer Sewing Machine factory off Kilbowie Road. His wife, blind for many years, was a pianist for the Glasgow Orpheus Choir and William Robb had built her a complete organ which occupied one wall of a room in their home in Singer's Buildings. The stoking, the music and the difficulty with which he could be knocked over, earned him something that even Mr Singer himself couldn't buy – respect. Respect was grudgingly given in Clydebank, a ship-building and factory town.

Everything was hard to come by at the moment. Apart from the rusting cathedral of steel and rivets towering above Brown's, the abandoned *534*, there were no ships being built.

"Pint, Tam." Fireman Robb shouldered his way through the bat-wing doors of the "Seven Seas" on the corner of Kilbowie Road. He tapped his pipe out on the edge of the gleaming spitoon and looked up and down the bar.

A man sitting in the alcove beneath the etched glass window depicting "The Pacific", stood up and walked across. "Bill . . ?" he asked .

Fireman Robb half-turned in the act of paying sevenpence to the barman. "Who. . . ?" His bushy eyebrows shot up in recognition. "Danny!" He clapped the newcomer gently on the shoulder and the bar shuddered. "How have ye been? Where have ye been keepin' yourself?"

Danny Crombie recovered slightly and smiled. "Haven't seen YOU either, Bill . . . been down south, looking for work."

Bill Robb took a sip of his pint. "Any luck?" He wiped the froth off his upper lip with a finger and drank deeply.

"Nothin'. Nothin' doin' at all. I've been everywhere. Sunderland, Newcastle, Liverpool."

They both looked up. The "Seven Seas" was full of the strains of the big hit of 1934. The bartender was whistling as he polished the glasses. "T'was on the isle of Capri that I met her . . ."

Bill Robb winced. "D'you have to?" He looked over the top of his glass at Erch the barkeeper, who paused in mid-shine.

"Everybody likes that." Erch gestured with a soapy hand at the vibrating cloth speaker of the wireless.

"Not everybody," Fireman Robb put down his glass and stared at him in silence.

Erch switched the radio off and resumed his washing and polishing. He was no longer whistling.

The doors burst open and a small man wearing an enormous cap rushed in, accompanied by a blast of cold air from the Glasgow Road.

"Have ye heard the radio!" he shouted, rushing up to the bar.

"It's not THAT good," replied Bill Robb with a grin and Danny nodded.

"Aye it is, aye it is," gasped the little man. "It's . . . the . . ." he choked. "The shipyard," he continued with difficulty.

Erch turned the bakelite switch and twiddled the dial all the way from Hilversum to Daventry and back.

## 151

"Naw, it's . . ." began the wee man agitatedly, then the calm voice of Queen Margaret Drive flooded the "Seven Seas".

"It has been announced by the Chancellor Neville Chamberlain that work will recommence on the hull designated *534* in Clydebank. Now cricket. England were all out for five at the . . ." The last words were drowned out as four or five people produced as much sound as several shifts of riveters on a super-liner.

"Who would have thought it?" asked Fireman Robb, puffing as he lit his pipe. "Funny though . . ."

"What is?" asked Danny and the wee man together.

"Hearing about Clydebank on the radio," replied Fireman Bill, blowing out a cloud of smoke that would have done credit to the *Queen Mary*.

*At 3 a.m. on the night of 31 October 1933 a piece of heaven fell on Ruchill.*

SADIE and John Hemphill were finishing their evening meal. John pushed the plate away from him and stuck his thumbs in his braces. "Well darlin'?" he smiled across the table at his wife. She lifted the tea-cosy off the pot and pointed the spout meaningfully at him. He shook his head. "Not for me. I'd better get on my way."

"Your piece box is on the table at the door." She picked up a small piece of paper lying beside her and began turning it over and over in her fingers.

"What IS that?" he asked, holding his hand out. "You've been playin' with that for hours."

She handed it to him without comment.

"Oh aye!" his face lit up with a smile. "I mind that! Where was that?"

"That was us when we all worked in the shop, afore the War."

"Oh aye . . . ?" he frowned. "Who . . . ?"

She took the photograph back from him and reached inside her apron pocket for her spectacles. "There's me, and Millie Dooley, thon big bossy boots Aggie . . ." she smiled to herself, remembering some imagined riposte 30 years ago. "There's wee Bobby, him that got lost at sea."

"Aye, Jutland, I mind now." He reached for the tea-pot.

"And there . . ." she stood up and walked round the table, placing the browning photograph firmly in front of him on the bright red and white of the American-cloth table cover, "there's . . ." she pointed to a figure dimly glimpsed beside a pillar in the background.

"Naw it's no' . . ." he leaned forward.

"That's you right enough. Same ears. See." She pointed again for emphasis. "Next to the overhead wires for the money-carrier. THERE!" She pointed again in exasperation.

"I see. I see." John sat back and looked up at his wife. "'Member we all went to the Great Exhibition thon time at Kelvingrove?"

". . . and Millie was sick on that man's hat when we were oan the roller-coaster."

John sighed. "Aye . . ."

Sadie sat down again and nibbled her bread and dripping.

John was still looking at the photograph. "Think I've changed much?" he asked.

Sadie looked across at the open, honest face of her husband. She had seen it every night and morning for at least 15 of their 18 years of marriage. "No' very much darlin'," she smiled at him. "Same ears."

Across the canal beyond Cadder, the sky above the Western Necropolis and St Kentigern's Cemetry was black as the Earl o' Hell's waistcoat. The silver shield of the moon was rising in a cloudless frosty sky, and the November stars wheeled low. The great nebula of Andromeda, was a misty smudge in the belt of Orion lying on the jagged edge of High Possil.

John blew on his clenched fists and drew his knees closer to the brazier. He had finished his piece over an hour ago and the night was wearing away towards dawn. A distant clock in Maryhill to his left began to chime and was answered by another, far off in Springburn away beyond the football ground and the timber basin. It was 3 a.m. on the edge of Ruchill, and the watchman was doing his job.

He reached across into the back of the hut for his piece-box. He nearly fell off his bench, groping behind him in the darkness, and heard the metal box clatter as it slipped past his fingers. Peering down at the ground between his feet, John saw the box, its lid stamped "J.M." in sharp Roman capitals by a pal in the dye-works across the road. He could see it . . . ? Light flooded the earth in a cool many-coloured glow.

He sat up and stared at the sky in wonder. John had travelled half the world in the merchant navy and seen many strange and wonderful things, both sober and not-so sober. He had never seen anything like the night rainbow.

For almost ten minutes an arch of subtle colour, like the wings of a vast angel, spread out across the sky on either side of the moon. From the Maryhill Paper Works to Possil Loch the bridge of colour stretched over the city of Glasgow. Tenement roof-tops like giant steps climbed the hills about him, their tiles and chimneys, lit by the true colours of the night, pale silver and green, deep carmine and chrome yellow, a wavering purple-blue.

Sadie couldn't sleep. She had never got used to the hours since John had been made redundant when all the ships were laid up. She frequently sat up in the wee sma' hours staring out of the window. Not long up, her cambric dressing-gown was held tightly about her throat as the chill seeped through the air. Crossing to the window of the best room, she scraped the rime of frost off the inside of the pane with her fingernail and looked out into the darkness. It was full of colour! The spirals and stars of frost on the window were stained with pastel hues, as if droplets of glowing inks had been scattered across the icy glass. Away over towards the canal beyond the golf course, a bridge of coloured light arced to the silent earth just about where her husband would be just now, crouched in his little watchman's hut, at the foot of the night rainbow, where a piece of heaven had fallen to earth in Ruchill.

*154*

*The crowd scrambled away as the Clyde burst its banks and flooded the fields. When the people stopped and turned, their socks and shoes full of muddy water, they were rewarded with a sight none of them would ever forget. The biggest, safest, and most powerful ship in the world, the Cunard White-Star Line* Queen Mary *rode the middle stream in serene majesty. A cheer went up from 1,000 throats, greeting the floating city as it towered above Clydebank Town Hall. It wasn't the end. There were warships to be laid down.*

*Work was returning to the yards and down the river. Men who had formed associations to go hill-walking, cycling, even mountaineering, clutching pamphlets like* Initial Efforts on the Boulder Face, *or* Coping with Crevices, *and spent long days toiling up braes and free-wheeling down glens, now had a wage to earn. The inhabitants of the closes and the tenements had headed for the high ground, leaving the trams and turmoil behind for the mist, the heather, and a good brew-up in the but and ben. For a brief time the descendants of those Highlanders who had been forced down into the valley to find work a century before had returned to the land of their fathers. Now they were back in the Lowlands again, once more bound to the rivet-gun and the crane, the furnace and the foundry. They were needed. Europe was drifting towards another war.*

*The previous year, on 9 February 1933, the Oxford Union had voted, "That this house will in no way fight for King and Country". It was unthinkable, and yet everybody thought about it. There was revolt in Catalonia, with martial law declared throughout Spain and street-battles in Madrid. Many Glaswegians were to join the International Brigade within a few years, Scots like James Robertson Justice, pointing rifles upwards at the Heinkel 111 and Junkers 52 of Adolf Hitler's Luftwaffe. General Mao-Tse-Tung was leading an army of 100,000 peasants on a long march south through Sianfu. The new German Führer had exacted an oath of "unconditional obedience" from all the officers and men of the German armed forces.*

*Better than most, the men in the yards knew it. War was coming . . . again.*

FREDERICK White walked briskly along the Unter den Linden towards the Brandenberg Gate. He was concentrating on demolishing the last of the lime and liquorice sweets he had brought with him in his haversack from Partick, and he trod purposefully on the wet red leaves with his hiking-boots as he strode along. There were at least two miles to go. In the distance the pinnacle of the Monument, its golden figure of Winged Victory hovering impatiently over the autumn mists, pointed the way. A knot of men stood on the other side of the broad avenue as he walked through the gate. Beyond them, the rib-cage of a gigantic prehistoric leviathan poked upwards, black against the delicate hues of the sky – the remains of the burned-out *Reichstag*. The men watched him silently as he strode on, their brown shirts at one with the autumn in the *Tiergarten*, as colour drained out of the world in preparation for winter. After a few minutes one of the men detached himself from the group and walked after Fred at a smart pace.

Fred reached the zoo end of the Ku'damm, the most fashionable street in Berlin, broad and busy with the traffic of a great capital in the middle of Europe. The cafés were full of well-dressed people, portly men reading the paper, ladies with cloche hats

smoking cigarettes in metal or ivory cigarette-holders, armless ex-soldiers begging for a pfennig. He decided against a tram and turned towards the underground station at the Wittenberg Platz, a neo-classical building complete with the purity of doric capitals and pediment. One or two of the shop windows nearby were lacking glass, while others had a white star painted on them. Not the *Ka de We* on the corner. Frau Goebbels shopped there. No stars were necessary. He entered the station and walked down towards the trains, kilt swinging, leaflets tucked beneath his jacket.

The long passageway towards the platform was spotless, gleaming like a hospital ward. Approaching rapidly with measured pace from the other end, a detachment of soldiers marched towards him. In full kit with helmets a dull grey, they stamped on three abreast. The officer was very tall. He was one of the old school, part of a military family since the days of the Grand Order of the Teutonic Knights. He probably thought of Adolph Hitler as an Austrian upstart, and the rest of the Nazis as gangsters and scum, but he obeyed orders, and Hitler was Chancellor. Expressionless, their ill-fitting jackboots thumping up and down as they marched, the soldiers approached the lone kilted figure. Without so much as an order, the line parted, one and two, and flowed on past Fred White without even breaking step. One soldier's glance flickered briefly towards his kilt, but there was no other sign of recognition as they marched on and up the stairs. Perfect discipline, perfect order, perfect cleanliness. He crunched the last of his sweets and gave a leaflet to a passer-by. The man was a Jew, but to Fred he was a German. They all looked the same to him. The man hurried on, throwing the leaflet in a waste-paper bin as soon as he was around the corner by the newspaper stand. A figure in brown detached itself from the shadows, reached into the bin with a look of disgust on his face, and pocketed the crumpled paper without reading it.

Fred stayed on the train all the way to the Grunewald, a huge area of forest and lake south of Berlin, large enough to harbour ferocious boar, as well as innumerable cafés and restaurants, beerhouses and secluded dells. In the days of the Weimar Republic, artists, writers, cabaret entertainers, and gypsies would meet in the woods and entertain each other and the day-trippers. The area was still packed at weekends, despite a frenetic quality to the enjoyment; and, it was the same sun and the same lake as it had always been, dotted with the yachts of the rich. Fred White and Sandy, the friend he had agreed to meet here, sat on the shore and watched people splashing about in the water.

"Any left?" asked Sandy, lying back on his elbow and chewing a blade of grass. The vast bulk of an airship droned overhead and slipped behind the trees on its way to Templehof Airodrome.

"A few," replied Fred, reaching inside his jacket and producing half-a-dozen crumpled leaflets. "You need to watch who you give them to," he added with the understatement of youth. "I hardly met anybody that looked 'right' all the way from Alexanderplatz to the Zoo."

Sandy stood up and dusted off the seat of his shorts. "The people look tired and afraid to me," he said, hands on hips. A yacht crewed by a man and three laughing women careered dangerously close to the shore. "Nobody will listen, except the converted, the communists and that's nae use."

"Aye well, I'm knackered." Fred stood up. "I've walked halfway across Berlin for the International Anti-War Youth Movement, and I'm for a swim."

An elderly lady who had once asked Franz Liszt for his autograph, felt quite faint as Fred took off his kilt and reached for the laces of his boots.

"Race ye!" shouted Sandy, already in his bathing-trunks.

Together, they splashed out into the cold clear waters of the lake.

A figure in a brown shirt stepped out from behind the bushes and stooping, picked up the leaflets that Fred had left lying on his jacket. He blew a whistle and a group of men marched down the path with precision, and stood silently on the shoreline.

"Oh Christ!" Fred shook the water out of his eyes. "Storm Troopers."

"Pretend ye don't understand," said Sandy urgently. "The worst they can do is send us back tae Glasgow."

157

*Glasgow grew ever outwards in the thirties, swallowing up the countryside in huge bites as poured-concrete bungalows sprouted out of the fields of Newlands, Merrylee, Cathcart, and all points south. In Merrylee Park, Newlands 130 bungalows went on sale for £25 down in cash with 21 shillings a week to pay. The offer included free removal and no legal fees. MacTaggart and Mickels's showpiece, Broom Estate in Newton Mearns, included bungalows with loggias, a word unfamiliar to Glaswegians in general, but obviously a bargain at the price. The entire estate was enclosed with glass walls that could be folded back, "should the weather prove sufficiently clement", and some of the bijou residences were also graced with towers and castle-like turrets. Most of these desirable "town cottages" were in the £450-£750 range. Something really up-market with walnut veneer in the kitchen and a hand-painted dado in the inside toilet and perhaps, the very latest in all-metal window frames, might break the £1,000 barrier.*

*Not many teachers bought bungalows. Students were on a grant of £40 a year and a primary teacher's salary was £18 a month. Schools went in for a lot of physical education, "drill", which involved jumping about in a drafty hall with your skirt tucked into your nickers if you where female. Sometimes the bicycle shed was pressed into service for "physical jerks" or a quick sortie with the bean-bags, usually in bare feet. In some schools the janitor was responsible for drill, although by the enlightened year of 1937 this was being phased out together with the use of wooden rifles. With income tax at three shillings in the pound, diptheria, bronchitis, tuberculosis, and scarlet fever combining with the efforts of the ubiquitous "nit", teachers in schools in the industrial districts led a very different life from the polite school environment of the West End or the South Side.*

*Sometimes bungalow-land and the world of the tenements met, however, and Scotland remained a body politic with democracy as its core and Glasgow its heart.*

EMILY MacPeake turned the corner from Merrycrest Avenue into Ashlea Drive and then left up Merrycroft Avenue. The juniper in No 26 next door was looking as tired as she felt as she opened the gate. David had been promising to paint the new metal design for two weeks now, ever since they had had it fitted. If they had realised when they answered the advertisement in the *Evening Citizen* that it was bare metal, they would have gone elsewhere. David was not very handy. "He can't knock a nail in a wall," his mother had said before they married. She was wrong. He could knock nails in walls. The drawback was that they fell out again. Painting gates, fences, and the like was not exactly in his line either. He was a young and hopeful solicitor, still very junior in the practice.

Most of the other people who lived in the street were professionals, a doctor, two more lawyers, a manager. There were one or two teachers, but they were, like herself, working wives, a rare phenomenon in largely working-class Glasgow. But this was the land of trimmed hedges and chuckies in the path. Window-cleaners called here, there was the occasional gardener, and bread, milk and newspapers were delivered. It was a quiet street, not two years old. Emily and her husband, and little Alexander were the first residents at No 28. The hedges were just beginning to take a firm hold, and the lawns still showed the geometric pattern of the turfs as they had been fitted together.

She walked up the path, her sensible shoes making a crunching sound on the

gravel, and searched in her handbag for the key to the front door. Before she could fit it in the lock the door opened. Alexander stood looking up at her.

"Hello, Mummy," he said, hugging her knees.

Mrs Dooley, the lady who "did" for them and was at home when Alexander arrived back from school, hovered in the background beside the hat stand. She looked worried.

"Is everything all right?" Emily closed the door behind her and took her hat off, shaking her hair loose.

"Oh yes, Mrs MacPeake. Fine. Aired the beds like you told me and cleaned the shoes. I hung the carpets out and gave them a good beating."

"It's just that I thought there might be something wrong . . ."

Alexander ran off down the hall and vanished into the sitting-room.

"Well, not . . . wrong, exactly," Mrs Dooley lowered her voice and adopted a conspiratorial air, not easy for someone as broad as she was tall, and given to smiles more often than frowns. "It's Alexander . . ."

Emily started forward but the redoubtable Mrs Dooley laid a reassuring hand on her arm. "It's all right," she whispered. "It's just . . . he's brought someone home for tea."

Alexander was sitting on the carpet. Next to him, his back to the gramophone, his friend Danny was looking at one of the *Meccano* magazines he had been given. Danny's freckled face and upturned nose was crowned by a shock of bright red hair. Short trousers, grubby knees, odd socks, and a pair of indescribable shoes that had belonged to his elder brother, completed the picture of a happy child, unlikely to be able

159

to spell simple words like "class" for a very long time. "Here's a great crane, Lexy," he leaned forward and shoved the magazine in front of Alexander who was busily driving a toy lorry into an invisible garage.

"Oh yes," replied Alexander. "You need a Number Nine set to make that. I've only got a Seven-and-a-half. Dad says he will get me more Meccano at Christmas, but I want to buy a pulley and those thick flange-plates in Wylie Hills on Saturday when I get my pocket money."

"That would be great," said Danny without rancour. "Could you make it then?"

Alexander thought better of lying. "No," he said. "But I could make the aeroplane. There's an Imperial Airways 'Heracles', the one that flies to India."

They both knelt on the carpet and peered at the large magazine, turning the pages. "I'll show you my Meccano Club Certificate after tea," said Alexander expansively to his new friend. "If Dad comes home early we might get my Hornby down off the top of the wardrobe."

"Is that '00' gauge?" asked the urchin knowledgeably.

"No, '0'. But I've got a station and porters, and some milk churns."

"What else have you got?" Danny asked, eyes wide.

"This!" Alexander held out a yellow box. The words "Dinky Toys" were printed on the outside in red. There was a picture of a long, terribly modern-looking car with fins sticking out the back. "Want to see?" Alexander opened the box and took the contents out without waiting for an answer. "It's Sir Malcolm Campbell's. He did 129 mph in Switzerland and captured the world land-speed record."

The door opened and his mother came in.

"Hullo Mum!" Alexander stood up. "I've brought a friend to tea. This is. . ."

"Hullo Miss MacPeake," said wee Danny, standing up and hanging his head. His palms were still red from the belting he had got for talking that afternoon.

"Oh you know Danny, Mum?" said Alexander cheerily. "I was just showing him my new Bluebird."

# TOWER OF THE LATE EMPIRE *1937–1938* A.D.

*It was the year of the 39/6 pence washing machine in Lewis's basement. A hundred warplanes were scouring the east coast of Scotland for a vanished prototype Vickers Wellesley bomber whose crew of three had "sandwiches and coffee sufficient for a 12-hour flight". Glasgow's great blackout experiment, affecting 400,000 people and covering the triangle from Glasgow Cross to Springburn and Shettleston, brought a deeper night to the city in those darkening days.*

*In England, a Scots Magistrate at Bow Street ordered that bagpipes were a noisy instrument and unsuitable to be played in Regent Street. Back in sunny Glasgow, under a placard bearing the words "Dinny Doot Him", Harry Hayward Dinney, ex-pugilist, wrestler, self-styled "Birdman of Argyle Street", was arrested for touting his "Genuine Nightingale Warblers" without a licence.*

*There was talk of building an air-raid shelter for 250,000 people under Hampden Park, and while plans were being made to dig down beneath the city, in another park, Bellahouston, work was far advanced on the tremendous Empire Exhibition and a tower that would rise 300 feet above Bellahouston Hill, 470 feet above sea-level. Tait's Tower was to be the symbol of the progress that peace and tomorrow must surely bring.*

ANDY pulled back the spring-loaded handle of the machine and released it with a thump. "Come on, ya wee toe-rag!" The silver ball sped up the slight incline lighting up the Bakelite mushrooms as it struck them, ricochetting back and forwards, up and down, before vanishing down the hole in the corner. It was the last one. He pushed the wooden frame of the machine violently with the heels of his hands. The coloured numbers that had flashed into life all across the face of tomorrow-land vanished again. "TILT!" said the sky accusingly.

"Toe-rag!" he muttered, picking up the drink that had been standing on the glass above the labyrinth of numbers and wires.

The street door behind him opened. A tram whined and groaned past and the door closed again.

"That the Exhibition?" joked Tam, pointing towards the futuristic city with his cigarette as he walked up.

"Aye. Ye wish," replied Andy laconically, draining his glass.

"It's comin' on though," Tam waved to the barman and held up two fingers. The barman laughed and began to pull a couple of pints. "I was lookin' for ye," continued Tam breezily. "If ye can bear to pull yourself away from thon American machine, there's more overtime goin'. Baxter wants workers for the Sunday."

"This is the first afternoon aff I've had in five weeks," Andy accepted the cigarette and lit it. "That's good." He took the cigarette out of his mouth and blew on the glowing tip.

"How dae ye mean 'good'?" Tam looked puzzled.

"No' the OT, ya steumer! The fag. We used to get them for one penny the pack in the navy. Naw. The overtime's no good, but I'll dae it. It's money isn't it?"

Tam paid for the drinks and they walked across to a table by the door. "He want's you up the flange-plates," said Tam as they sat down.

"How me?"

161

Tam waved the paper-boy across and bought the *Evening Times*. "Says he only wants the best men up the top of the tower." Tam opened the paper and began to turn the pages.

"Aye, well. Suppose so," said Andy, sipping his pint and accepting the flattery with good grace. "The Glasgow Steel Roofing Company's daein' well enough out of building Tait's Tower. I might as well and all."

"Look at that!" Tam folded back the paper and pointed to the banner headline. "The Italians and the Germans are still at it in Spain. Where's next?"

"Aye, weel, it'll no' be Govan anyway," replied Andy sagely. "They couldna' get their tanks over the holes in the road."

Thomas Tait in the lead, closely followed by Jack Coia, Basil Spence, T. Waller Marwick, A. D. Bryce, and other members of the team, the architects picked their way through the mud and piles of bricks that were to become the Empire Exhibition. As controlling designer for the exhibition, Tait, together with Coia and Spence, mounted the hoist and began to ascend the half-completed tower. As they rose upwards into the damp air the site spread out before them on either side.

South towards Cardonald, with the Cat and Dog Home in the distance, lay the facade of the Palace of Industry, from this height, a gentle curve with long glass galleries running backwards towards Bellahouston Drive. Directly in front of the main entrance, the central avenue was already flanked by the futuristic blue and white towers of the Scottish Avenue and the Pavilions, with the Palace of the Arts closing the end of the triumphal space. The monumental curves and square buttresses of the United Kingdom Government Pavilion and the sweep of the pillared Concert Hall already dominated the far spread of the exhibition site.

Holding his hard-hat on with one hand, Tait pointed to the left. "Did you see the spec' for the funfair?" he asked the others crowded on to the rattling platform.

Jack Coia nodded. "It'll be the largest in Europe – 16 acres." He looked across at his current projects, the Palace of Industry, North and the Roman Catholic Pavilion. "The show needs to be seen from this height!" he shouted as a rivet gun started battering the iron frame of the tower behind them, "but it's not a domestic environment, not at all."

"People would love to live at this height above the ground," said Basil Spence. "Glasgow would be the better for thoroughly modern appartment towers . . perhaps in the Gorbals . . ."

"You'll be sick if ye eat ony mair o' that, Alexander," said Mrs Dooley. "Yer mammy said see an' not eat too much at the Exhibition."

Alexander pushed the last of his toffee bacon and eggs into his mouth with a sticky finger and pointed towards the "Rocket Railway".

Mrs Dooley followed his gaze and shook her head. "Oh no . . . ! I read the wee book." She took the official guide out of her handbag and peered at it. "See," she said triumphantly. "A wall of death, 60 feet in diameter."

"Oh . . . pleeese!" wheedled Alexander, picking at her umbrella. "There's the water-dodgems then, or the Crooked House of Horror, and there's 50 'Brooklands Racers', the Magic Carpet Tower, Foster's Furious Loop-o-Plane . . ."

Mrs Dooley believed Alexander needed a firm hand. "Not today, mister blister," she said. "C'mon and see the nice Tele-Vision, whatever that is." She leafed through the guide book. "There's five underground stations pumping watter 80 foot intae the air frae 50 foot pylons. Whit aboot that, eh?"

Alexander sulked.

She straightened his school cap and took hold of his hand firmly. "Well ye'll do as yer telt!" she said with a frown. "'Mon and look at the nice show in the League of Nations place, or thae big battleships and bombers painted on the walls over there. Now THAT'S educational . . ."

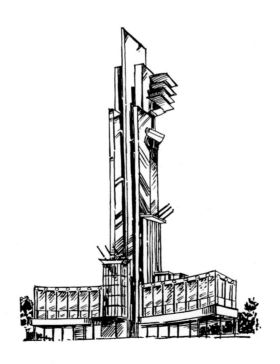

163

*It was only half-past ten in the morning, but the trams were full of people, mainly women on their way home. They had been queueing since early morning in front of the larger shops and the department stores in Sauchiehall Street, Renfield Street and Argyle Street to buy blackout cloth. Everyone on the trams and buses was carrying bales and bundles, so that the freak morning rush-hour looked like an immense double-decker funeral cortège, winding its way out of the centre of Glasgow in every direction. Over eight miles of black cloth were sold in one day.*

*Men who only went into a shop for "baccy", matches or a paper, were sent round to the local grocer's and butcher's shops to buy up everything that wasn't nailed down. Hoarding was frowned on, but tinned beans and peas, sugar, flour, anything that could be stored, was soon piling up on top of wardrobes and in garden sheds. Some people travelled out of the city to outlying towns and villages in search of provisions, plundering the general stores of Kilsyth and Kilmaurs, Bargeddie, Stepps, Drymen and wherever available transport would take them.*

*Another exodus began at 6.30 a.m. on 1 September 1939, when Glasgow chidren began assembling at 57 schools, 70,000 weans scrubbed and labelled for a bewildering adventure. Every child had a gas mask and a suitcase, or paper parcel. That night as the lights dimmed across the Clyde valley and the blackout curtains went up, the future of the great city of Glasgow, its children, tried to sleep in faraway beds on the other side of the darkened hills and starless lochs. Air-raid wardens in tin helmets watched the skies and silence descended on the empty streets.*

*It was 13 and 14 March before Clydebank, Dalmuir, and Yoker felt the full force of the German terror-attacks. On the night of the 13th, 237 German bombers dropped 204 tons of high explosives on the Bankies. The gigantic Singer's Wood Yard, site of the largest clock in Europe, blazed like a beacon, a tram full of people was hit, and as 55,000 struggled to escape, Scotland's first refugees trudged outward from the wreck of their blazing homes. Radnor Park, Mount Blow, the Holy City were blasted by incendiaries, and a solitary ME 109 flew up Kilbowie Road straffing the tram that stood on the swing bridge by the canal.*

*Earlier, in May 1939, No 602 (City of Glasgow) Squadron received its first spitfire, also becoming the first Auxiliary Unit in Britain to be equipped with the new 1000 H.P. 8-gun interceptors. The men of 602 were part of that group of young men who gave the greatest gift of all in 1941, when the Battle of Britain stopped the Nazi war-machine over the fields of southern England, the Scots accounting for 130 of the 175 enemy aircraft downed.*

*The reputation of 602 had gone before it. Within a few weeks of the outbreak of war, the Luftwaffe had a new name for the east coast of Scotland where the skies were patrolled by the young men of the City of Glasgow Squadron, and its leaders, Wing Commander Farquhar, Group Captain the Duke of Hamilton, and Squadron Leader Johnstone. The Germans called it "Suicide Corner".*

THE air war had started in Scotland. The first pilots to send Luftwaffe bombers spiralling down to crash into the sea were boys, auxiliary pilots who until a few months before had been flying antiquated Gloster Gladiators. They crossed the bridge of childhood's end on the afternoon of 16 October 1939.

About nine that morning a German pathfinder had been reported over the Firth of Forth. HQ realised that an attack was coming. The boys of 602, sitting at their camp tables reading *Picture Post* or playing chess were scrambled and their marker moved into the Forth Sector. Wing Commander Douglas Farquhar looked out of his cockpit window and down to the left. There was a shortage of Brownings, and his little flotilla of airborne cavaliers in their Supermarine Spitfire MK 1s, powered by 1,030 horsepower Merlin II engines, were only armed with four machine guns each. Far below he could see the lacework shadow of the Forth bridge on the glittering estuary and the long dark lines of the cruisers *Edinburgh, Southampton*, and further out, the destroyer *Mohawk*, under way for Rosyth after convoy duty. There were no further reports of enemy aircraft, and Douglas ordered his men to land in Fife and re-fuel.

The boys of 602 were on their second cup of tea and the "Spits" half-refuelled when a full-scale bombing raid, the first attack on Britain of the war, began out in the Forth. Twelve German HE 113s were bombing the Forth Bridge. The aircraft was known to the German Air Force, or *Reichsluftfahrtminsterium* for short, as HE 100 D, since the apellation "113" was considered unlucky. It was.

Douglas scrambled his men and they were airborne within minutes, roaring up into the cloud-flecked sky above the waters of the Forth. A train puffed steadily across the bridge as spouts and plumes of water stalked up the middle channel towards it from the sticks of bombs raining down. Tensely, the airmen looked below and saw the crowded train reach the North Queensferry side in safety. It was then they realised that the German target was not the bridge but the warships in the Firth of Forth. A bomb missed the *Southampton* by the breadth of the Admiral's Barge, and another showered the *Edinburgh* with shrapnel. The real fire-fight developed over the stricken *Mowhawk* which was hit several times and her captain R. F. Jolly, R. N. was fatally injured and a number of his crew killed.

Without warning, 602 and the Edinburgh Squadron pounced on the Germans, screaming down out of the sun and spraying the marauders with concentrated machine-gun fire. The battle broke up into a series of duels across the skies of Scotland, from Edinburgh to North Berwick. The Germans were also exploring the quality of resistance in the North, and looking on Scotland, with its coasts so close to Scandinavia, as a possible "soft option" for raids and attacks to the south. They were wrong.

The douce denizens of Edinburgh looked up in sudden amazement as a Heinkel thundered low across the rooftops beloved of Baillie Nicol Jarvie and disappeared beyond the hills, a spitfire hanging grimly on to its smoking trail and blazing away at it with all four guns. That same Heinkel managed to escape to the Firth of Forth, turn, and move back for another attack run. This time he was caught by Douglas Farquhar, the officer commanding 602. Douglas chased the German back over Edinburgh again for a second time, so low that "grannies" fell off chimneys and empty cartridge cases rained in back-gardens. A second spitfire came to Douglas's aid and the Heinkel was sent crashing to its doom in the water beside Port Seton.

The first raider had been downed only a short while earlier by Archie McKellar, who saw the attacker crash into the Lothians. Picturesque cobbled Crail was startled when a third Nazi attacker crashed on the coast nearby. A fourth was shot down by concentrated anti-aircraft fire.

The battle took a little over half an hour. The air war had started. Sir William Wallace would have been proud of them.

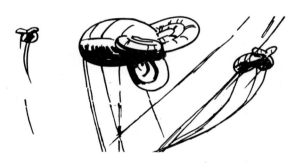

*Towards the end of the Second World War Glasgow became one of the busiest ports in the western world. As preparations moved ahead for the invasion of Europe, the American Army was landed in Scotland at the Gareloch and Loch Ryan. Churchill's "Mulberrys", the artificial harbours to be used for the invasion, were constructed on the Gareloch, and capital ships by the dozen, aircraft carriers, cruisers, battleships and destroyers – all lay off the coasts of the west or sailed into the Clyde. The Glasgow docklands area became a vast storage base with enough emergency supplies to feed the entire United Kingdom. The hundreds of thousands of letters sent "somewhere over there" were handled through the Port of Glasgow.*

*The yards were centres of tireless industry. Ships were built and repaired day and night; over 200 aircraft carriers, almost the same number of cruisers, 34 mighty battleships. In all, 25,000 ships were re-fitted and repaired, and almost 2,000 actually built from the keel up. The Clyde was alive with effort, delivering an unending tide of steel down the slipways and into the Clyde.*

*The city of Glasgow soldiered on. There were plenty of soldiers to help it. Every night the BBC played the national anthems of all the allied powers, and those under Nazi domination. There was the "Stars and Stripes", the "Internationale" the "Marseillaise", the Polish, Czech, Yugoslavian, Greek, Bulgarian, Rumanian anthems, and many more. It was a World War, and most of its nationals were in uniform. Sometimes it seemed like most of them were in Glasgow as well.*

THE jeep crawled along Argyle Street and turned right into Union Street by the all-night "Boots".

"Sure you know where we are Ben?" Corporal Riley was perched on the spare wheel at the back, "Looks like Brooklyn." He stared up at the taped and blackened windows passing slowly on either side. "Sure is dark in Glasgow!"

"Have I ever got us lost before?" The driver, a tall, Bostonian with a taste for Mahler and strong bourbon made the ideal paratrooper. "Rusty said the Central Station Bar." He pulled over to the kerb and struck a match, shading it with his hand. "Should be up here somewhere." The pencil lines on the back of the Lucky Strike packet that were supposed to represent the commercial heart of Glasgow, somehow didn't match up with the darkened canyon they were driving along.

"Say," said Riley. "Here's one of their trams. Maybe someone could tell us where we are. . . . if it stops."

Ben Gratzler, Harvard and Mullen's Bar at 29th on Dearborne, was a graduate of the School of Action. That's why they had given him his Wings. He waited 'till the tram drew abreast of the silent jeep and leaped on to the running board beside the driver. Ben Gratzler was trained to drop behind enemy lines, kill the signalman, and take over the running of a foreign railway system without stopping for breath. The No 18 tram for Springburn was not a problem. "Say," he asked the white-faced driver with a cheery grin. "You wouldn't happen to know where this here Central Station is, would you buddy?"

"Er . . . this is the . . . the front of the tram. Y . . . you get on at the back," replied the driver in a squeaky voice. Getting his breath back he took the handle from

Ben and stopped the tram gently. "You gave me a helluva fright," he said. "Ye canna' just stop trams in the middle of the street. You ARE on our side, aren't ye?"

Ben roared with laughter. "You Scotties are gr . . . eat. 'Our side . . .!'" He laughed uproariously and slapped the driver on the back. "Sure you haven't seen Central Station?"

"We are right in front of it," said the driver. "Nae lights. Ye get bombed in this country if ye show a light. Now will you either pay yer fare or get off ma tram!"

"Great, great," replied Ben, still laughing as he jumped down and rejoined his comrade in the jeep. The tram clanged its bell and rattled off angrily into the gloom. Several cars, headlamps painted deep yellow or with brown paper covering all but a central strip of the light, started up and resumed their journey in the wake of the No 18.

"Just queueing up," Riley nodded at the cars. "They waited while you were talkin' to that guy, Ben. These Limeys sure love queueing."

"Scotties," Ben corrected him. "Great little guys. Limeys ain't got no sense of humour. 'You on our side?'" He started to laugh.

"What was that?" asked Riley, endeavouring to keep up as the big man strode up the steps to the station concourse.

"Are we on their side?" said the giant, roaring with laughter. "That sure is rich . . .!"

Vladislaw Podgorny wanted beef.

"I'm tellin ye there's nane," Isa was adamant. "Come and look for yourself. There's nothin' 'under the coonter' here."

"Please?"

"Och give him a sandwich, Isa." Sergeant Morrison put his mug of tea down on the greasy bar and turned. "You wan o' the Czechs at East Kilbride?"

"I'm not supposed to say where from," said Vladislaw. He paused for a moment. "No. Not East Kilbride, Poland."

"Oh aye," said Sandy Morrison with sympathy. "Isa. Gie the man a sandwich. He's lost his country."

Isa reached up on tip-toe and took a white cloth from the top of the gleaming tea-urn. "Here." She used the cloth to slide back a hot glass plate and extract a rather tired looking object. "Sandwich," she said putting it on a plate bearing the legend LNER. "Tomato. Nothin' to do with me. All we've got. Winston Churchill widna' get any better."

"Ahh," said Vladislaw, happy to call anything that was edible, beef. "Thank you madam." He clicked his heels.

"Here, none o' that language," said Isa, narrowing her eyes. "This is a respectable Railway Station Buff-et, so it is."

"Don't be daft," grinned Sergeant Morrison. "'Madam' means 'Mrs' in Polish."

"I don't care if it means 'Your majesty' in flair Polish," sniffed Isa haughtily. "He needs tae watch what he says. There's enough o' these furrin' sodgers come in here and try it on. Here!" She turned towards Vladislaw who was happily munching his cardboard sandwich. "Where's yer money?" she held out her hand expectantly.

"P . . . ease," said Vladislaw, his mouth full.

"Money. Gelt. Ackers . . . a tanner . . ."

He looked puzzled for a moment, then turned towards Sergeant Morrison and winked. "No zank you," he grinned and clicked his heels again. "Polish officer not accept money."

Isa was trying to retrieve her jaw from the counter when the door opened and two Americans walked in.

"This is the place sure enough," said Corporal Riley as they walked over to the Bar.

"Americans," said Isa, slipping behind the tea-urn to moisten her eye-brows with her fingers. "Can I help youse boys," she smiled archly, the hand with the wedding-ring firmly in her pocket.

"Sure can, lady . . . how about a beer?"

"Make that two,"said Riley.

"Your a 'lady' now," Sergeant Morrison smiled at Isa.

Ben turned towards him slowly. "Say again?"

Sandy Morrison, only slightly over six feet, held out his hand."Welcome to Glasgow, pal," he said.

Riley looked up at the tall Scotsman and nudged Ben in the ribs. "Sure he's on our side?" he asked.

*Since the beginnings of the Glasgow Fair 1,000 years ago, the good people of Glasgow have been determined to enjoy themselves during the annual beanfeast. Gone were the days of dancing bears and "Wild Men of Java" when hundreds of steamers plied the Fair Fortnight waters of the Clyde at the golden turn of the century.* The Brodick Castle *and the* Ivanhoe, *the* Glen Rosa, *resplendent in the colours of the Campbells of Kilmun, the* Jupiter *and the* Jeannie Deans, *and the* Waverley, *last sea-going paddle steamer in the world, built for LNER.*

*Through two world wars, slump and revival, a diminishing fleet had followed the magic wake to Ayr and Saltcoats, the Cumbraes, Brodick, Dunoon, and of course, that name that is synonymous with the Broomielaw, a look at the engines, and the subtle aroma of chips and vinegar on a summer's evening beneath the palm trees of the Kyles of Bute, Rothesay.*

*After the war, Rothesay saw a revival of its fortunes with a contingent of naval ships based in the harbour, depot ships and submarine crews to augment the trippers and holiday makers who returned to their old haunts after six years of weary conflict.*

THE first sight of Rothesay Pier with its clock tower, the Skeoch Woods beyond, spelt two weeks of freedom for more mammies and daddies than there are spokes in the wheels of a paddle-steamer. Rothesay Pavilion, the Glenburn Hotel, slot machines and sunburn, and a new invention on an island granted its Royal Charter by the King of Scotland in the year 1401 . . . the Co-Op Holiday Camp.

"We're awfy fortunate in wir neighbours," Isa McGhee offered her companion a boiling. "On ye go," she urged. "That's what yer sweetie ration is for, I always say . . . holidays . . ."

"I won't say no, then," Masie Toal dug her hand into the paper bag. "Sorry!" she grinned awkwardly as her fingers searched the recesses of the paper and found nothing. "Poke's empty, Misees . . . Misees . . eh . . ."

"Oh sorry, Misees, eh . . ." Isa apologised. "That's me gassin' away. Never get the chance, normally speakin'."

"Oh, where'd ye work?" Masie Toal ducked as a seagull dive-bombed a passing matelot.

"Catering," replied Isa without looking up. She rummaged about in her brown paper carrier-bag for a few minutes more. "Sorry," she said. "Those bairns of mine are away with them."

Masie nodded sympathetically. "Mebbe it wis yer man."

"Him? The Thing? He wouldn'y take a poke o' soor plooms unless it had a pint o' heavy at the bottom."

"Mine's the same." Masie tucked her hair into her headscarf and turned away from the wind.

"They're aw' the same," Isa lifted her knitting out the carrier together with a badly printed pattern clipped from a copy of *The People's Friend* that she had found on the train to Wemyss Bay.

"They've been gone a good while." Masie looked up at the smoke belching from the red funnel. "Your weans were that keen on seein' the engines."

"Aw they'll be up to somethin', nae doot," Isa's needles clicked and the paddle-wheels of the *Jeannie Deans* churned on remorselessly through the grey waters of the Clyde, "Chunk . . . chunk . . . chunk . . ."

Behind them the shore was already a dimly glimpsed grey line, the individual details of buildings, or a car driving along the shore road, lost under the hazy shadow of hillside and moor beyond . The lithe vessel left a white wake that stretched all the way back to the long iron and glass walkway of the railway terminal, a thin cord of foam linking the crowded paddle-steamer to a solid world of steam trains, corner shops, and utility furniture.

"But darlin', the boys wanted tae see the engines," Charlie McGhee protested as he struggled on to the bus with three suitcases and an early afternoon hangover.

"So ye said," replied his wife, somewhere in the crush behind him. "Just get on. I'll see you later."

"Ye can see me now, more's the pity," he grumbled as he pushed his way to the back, treading on a few feet in the process.

"No' at the back!" Isa screamed over the heads of the struggling mass of men, weans, dogs, and luggage. "That's the bumpy bit."

Charlie remembered the assault on Monte Cassino with affection. "Canny move," he shouted back. "This is it."

The bus threw itself into gear, coughed, and started off noisily. Everyone still standing, and that was at least half the passengers, did a little backwards dance and righted themselves by the simple expedient of taking hold of the person or object closest to them. The engine of the bus protested bitterly and the close air filled with the heavy smell of petrol as they started up the steep brae. The holiday had begun.

*It was the year of the first 33 rpm long-playing record and the big hit was "Shall We Dance?" The United Nations had forces in Korea, the first H-bomb was tested with what was called "success", and a great plan was developed to divide Glasgow up into "Comprehensive Re-Development Areas". A model was exhibited in a basement near Byres Road that showed a garden Glasgow, green spaces and stands of trees punctuated by pretty towers and an ultra-modern sunken railway system. Models are not the real thing, and what looked like the something from the futureworld of Dan Dare on the cover of the new* Eagle *comic was to be and feel quite a different slab of concrete. The Gorbals re-development was not to be announced until 1955, but in the land of the prefab, the outside toilet, and the lobby-dosser, the world was long overdue for a change. In 1951 the population of Glasgow was 1,055,020 but new towns like East Kilbride, Irvine, Livingstone, Cumbernauld, and Glenrothes were to bring that total down to just under 900,000 by the early seventies.*

*The Glasgow of 1951 was still the old Glasgow. Anderston was a warren of narrow gas-lit streets, of tenements linked together by a spider's web of overhead tram wires, swaying in the wind above the cobbles.*

*Wilson's Zoo and its sad lion had given way to the brave attempt to create an early "Safari Park" at Mugdockbank. Calderpark Zoo in Broomhouse was building up a collection of small furry things and a few larger ones, and Easterhouse, Garthamlock and Ruchazie were still bramble-filled lanes between the Edinburgh Road and Stepps.*

*This was pre-Renaissance Glasgow, blackened with soot, full of heavy industry and shipbuilding, the park divided by the River Kelvin dominated by the grey gothic spaceship of Glasgow University Tower. Near at hand, on the other side of the Kelvin, the filigree pinnacles and spires of the Kelvingrove Art Gallery and Museum resplendent in its dress of Locharbriggs red stone outside and white Giffnock inside. The interior was paved with polished Italian, Belgian, and Norwegian marbles in a variety of designs, cool, full of an Aladdin's Cave of objects and pictures, entertaining and informing the Glasgow way. By 1951 the Art Galleries had been doing just that for 50 years.*

THE wee boy's best shoes clumped on the polished floor as his elder sister let go of his arms.

"I'll push it for you." She pressed the button on the side of the glass case and the cut-away wooden model of the steam engine began pumping its red and yellow striped piston up and down. They walked away, and the exhibit, full of intertia and its own importance, continued to slide and pump long after they had walked on into the next display.

The Art Gallery was a box of delights of heroic proportions. Samurai warriors of the Shoguns rubbed shoulders with Eskimos and headhunters. Pots and vases from the dawn of human history, armour for the "small man" of the middle ages, swords as long as a medium-sized lamp-post, delicately inlaid flint-lock pistols and hunting rifles, rooms and rooms and rooms full of dust-motes dancing in shafts of sunlight, the smell of wax and leather, the long shelves of dead things. Here lay the Siskin and the Lesser Redpoll, the Snow Bunting, the Roseate Tern, the Ptarmigan, white as drifted snow, the Raven, black as midnight ink.

"I want to see the animals!" the wee boy ran on ahead into the main gallery.

His sister followed reluctantly. "You know I don't like them," she said, standing behind her little brother and looking away.

"Interested in Zoology?" asked a tall, white-haired gentleman standing nearby.

"He loves them," said the girl politely. "They just look dead to me."

"Well, I hope they are," the man laughed and took his pipe out of his mouth. "I think the tigress and the lion mounted on artificial rocks are especially fine. It was Doctor Absalom, you know. He started the illuminated Habitat Groups under the arches." He looked at the displays with pride. Beneath the embossed title "Scotland", an unfortunate eagle flew "by wire" above a painted heathery hill, swooping over the cloth glen on some startled creatures clustered on the plaster earth. "Then there's 'Africa'!" Their self-appointed guide waved expansively at the huge panels of glass on the other side of the hall. The girl followed his glance and looked at those triumphs of taxidermy with distaste. She recognised the stitching that had been used on the elephant.

The old man recognised something of himself in the picture, stepped back and narrowed his eyes. The figure in the painting spoke of the human spirit and looked out at the world with a serene timelessness, and eyes that knew the great gift of being a master and an artist. Fur collar hunched round his shoulders, flat hat askew, he was surrounded by a background warm with a sense of movement, an atmosphere thronged with the memories and moments of a long life. Here was one of the finest pictures in the Art Gallery's collection, one of a life-long series of self-portraits by . . .

"Who's that picture of, an auld wumman in a fur coat?" asked Jim Jackson. "I often wonder, ye know."

"I see no one here but Rembrandt van Rijn," said the old man.

"Naw. Naw. The name's Jackson. Just come here for a bit o' peace and quiet. It's aye quiet lookin' at the auld pictures. Maist of them is in flats, backrooms and that. Best place fur them, ha, ha!"

"What do you mean?" asked the old man, curious in spite of himself.

"Aw," continued the worthy. "That Burrell things. They've nae room for it

here at Kelvingrove, so it's kept all over the west of Scotland hidden away.'' He tapped the side of his nose knowingly. ''Supposed to be worth a million pounds,'' his voice sank to a whisper.

''But that's shocking,'' said the visitor. ''Can't something be done?''

''Aw I don't know. Don't know anything about art, like, but I know what I like. No' that modern splashes oneywey. Mind ye, they've goat the money tae build anither Gallery, but yon Burrell said it had to be outside of Glasgow so the fog and smoke and that disna' get the pictures. You know,'' he nodded towards the Rembrandt self-portrait. ''I've often walked past that picter. Reminds me of somebody.'' He stared at the old man. ''You've been here before. I've a great memory for faces, great. I could go away and draw yer face for ye. Jackson the memory man. When DID I last see ye here in the gallery . . . let me guess now.''

''I must be going, perhaps another time,'' the old man excused himself and walked away quietly towards the Flemish Room.

''I've seen that face SOMEWHERE before . . .''

Rembrandt van Rijn, an old man in a fur coat made up of colours that breathed, looked out calmly from his gilded frame and watched the light change in the silences of the Art Gallery in the afternoon.

*The end of kisses and cuddles on the red and green divans of the Green's Playhouse, electric trains to Airdrie and Dalmuir, a mass-murderer loose in Lanarkshire, and "Rockin' Through the Rye". Change was in the air of Glasgow as surely as Bill Haley, his kiss curl hanging limply over one eye, was singing "Rockin' Through the Rye" and driving an entirely new breed of Glaswegian wild with frenzy . . . the teenager.*

*The Gartocher Bar had stood in Shettleston Road since 1688. "Modernised" in 1937 by architect William Ross, the charm that had survived Jacobites, Weaver's revolts, football fracas, and the decline of Empire, had been given a chic exterior of faience and rustic brickwork. It was only just getting over the shock 21 years later when an apparition sauntered past St Paul's School and round the corner of Gartocher Road into Shettleston Road.*

*The jacket drooped. It hung limply from the tubercular shoulders of its master like a wet rag on a cardboard donkey. Tailored for length, the jacket complemented trousers narrower than the art-deco drainpipes on either side of the "Gartocher" across the road. The toes pointed slightly outwards and so did the shoes, a pair of the finest winkle-pickers that ever threaded the eye of a needle. As for the wearer, or bearer of these tokens of the new age that was dawning in the East End of Glasgow, he was just a laddie. He had more cream on his hair than the Scottish Dairies, and sidelocks swooping down on either side of a pasty jowl. These had been brought up sharp in a mathematically exact line by one of those old-fashioned razors that the previous generation had employed for more antisocial purposes. He was a teddy-boy.*

I T was early evening in September, and the sky was already losing its lustre as Wully Gurk, the Ted of Balgair Terrace, made his way towards the café. The southern sky lit up as the Clydebridge works dumped its slag and the colours of fire and smoke drifted among the faint stars. Wully's grandad had been "lifted" down at Carntyne that afternoon. A crowd of eager "punters", and the illegal betting-shop on the waste-ground at the back of Budhill Avenue were also carted off lock, stock and blackboard. This meant that his grandad was temporarily unavailable for a "tap", but there was bound to be someone in the café who would stand him a coffee.

A group of teenagers sat, wedged in behind the fixed tables and seats in the alcove. The café was divided up by glass partitions, engraved with pictures of propellor-driven aeroplanes emerging from gigantic cloud banks, or simply rays of sunlight darting here and everywhere, right up to the edge of the bevelled glass.

Luigi bustled up to the group. "Two coffees, one milk-shake, one sundae. The bananas have ran out," he said apologetically.

"Hope they paid first!" said Sandy brightly, and the girls laughed.

"What you say?" Luigi opened his purse and searched for change.

"I was saying, if the bananas have ran out, I hope they . . . aw, forget it Luigi. How much is that?"

Luigi looked at the order on the table, nodding his head and moving his lips silently. "Four and six," he said. "Please." He held out his hand.

"We'll all just pay for our own." Meg, a brunette with a little too much make-up on, pushed her coins towards Sandy.

"No. That's all right," he brushed the money away with the back of his hand, his heart sinking. "I can manage." He handed the four and six to Luigi. "Not goin' to bite the half-crown, are you?"

"Eh?" asked the little man. "Why?"

"We thought that Italians always tested the silver to see if it was real."

Luigi pretended to cuff him across the ear. "Good thing I know you are cheeky," he smiled. "I was in prison here in the war because I was an Italian."

"You've told us," replied Sandy wryly. "Often."

"He's only joking, Luigi," said the smaller of the two girls, a red-head. She leaned across to pat his hand and her foam petticoat burst out of its confines under the table. "We always come here."

"I know this, I know this," muttered Luigi, bustling away. "Now I'm busty."

Shocked giggles and sniggers ran round the company. "He means 'busy'," said Sandy, blushing.

Sarah shook her red curls and leaned across the table. "You've gone all quiet, Rob," she said to the boy sitting beside Sandy.

"I'm thinking," he said.

"Looks like it hurts," laughed Sandy, wresting the straw away from Meg and drinking her milk-shake noisily.

"Oh you be quiet," Sarah slapped him on the arm and he spilled some ice-cream on the table. "I like to have a good conversation with a boy."

Luigi appeared out of the woodwork and mopped up the spilt cream. "Now no carry on," he scolded, ". . . or outa you go."

"We could talk about the meaning of life," continued Sarah, encouraged.

"Oh no we couldna'," said Meg. "Here's Wully Gurk comin'."

Wully Gurk sidled up and squeezed himself on to the end of the seat. The girls groaned.

"No' crowdin' you cats, am ur?" he asked pleasantly. "OK, baby?"

Meg looked at him angrily. "I'm no' a baby!" she said.

"Suit yourself, doll," replied Wull, picking a speck of dust off the velvet lapels of his jacket. "Hey Luigi!" he called out, half turning. "Gies wan o' yer frothy bopper stoppers and make it snappy pappy."

Luigi continued polishing his new coffee machine.

"Hey!" Wull produced a comb out of his breast-pocket and slicked his greasy hair back in slow sweeps. "Gies a 'spresso-presso, daddy-o, you dig?"

Luigi walked across to the little group. The rest of the youngsters were having problems trying to contain their laughter.

"You speak to me?" said Luigi, flicking his dishcloth like the tail of a bull. "What a' you want?"

Wull jerked his head to one side and looked menacing. "Get with it!" he said, slipping his comb back into its holster with panache.

Luigi looked across at Sandy and winked. "What he say?" he asked.

"He wants a coffee Luigi," replied Sandy, choking.

Luigi looked down at the teddy-boy. "How do you say in English 'Have you got any money'?"

Wull raised his eyebrows. "Ur you daft or somethin'? Ye just said it."

"Can you pay?" Luigi was remorseless.

Wull leaned across and pulled back the sleeve of Sandy's jacket. "Got a watch on?" he asked. "Naw. Any of youse cats got the time?"

"Naw. 'Cause you haven't got the money," said Meg poking Sarah in the ribs and giggling.

Wull pulled his own sleeve up and down very quickly. "Oh!" he said in surprise. "Look at that. I've tae meet the gang at Kenmore Street the noo. Nae good if the boss is late!" He laughed heavily, stood up, squared his non-existent shoulders, and walked towards the door. "See ya later alligator," he waved his hand and pretended to be chewing something.

"Nota if I see you first, crocodile," muttered Luigi, patting his new espresso machine affectionately.

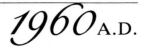
*I remember 1960, long before Glasgow was locked in the grip of a Renaissance. Renaissances do happen occasionally. They descend on Glasgow whenever a few people with talent appear. The cultural revival has been planned for years by members of the good old Council, members that prefer to stay in the background, having achieved the astounding feat of legislating and pedestrianising their way through the licensing laws, to an atmosphere of continental cultural* Bonhomie *from Blairdardie to Baillieston. It is only too easy to forget that there was a time when the fragile flower of Glasgow culture might just as easily have been swept up by the great philistine scaffy man of indifference. Glaswegians are many things, but they are not indifferent.*

*A Renaissance had last happened in the days of the "Glasgow Boys" and the other artists, architects and the like at the turn of the 20th century, and one of the stars of that re-birth of style and innovation, was the late, great son of a police superintendent, Charles Rennie Mackintosh.*

*There was a man at the bottom of Sauchiehall Street. Andrew was a cross between Dennis the Menace and Jean Paul Sartre, and in the late forties and fifties his flat was full of the aroma of coffee made with milk and boiled in a saucepan, and the company of people like Davy Donaldson, Alfie Avella, Bill Henry, Bet Low, Ernie, a motorbike philosopher who pre-dated Jack Kerouac by 1,000 years, and various other artists, and literati, who were encouraged by Andrew to give up their jobs driving buses or whatever and accept the roving hard-luck life of the creative. This was in a city still grey with rationing and demob suits, but it was a beginning.*

ANDREW put down his binoculars and moved away from the grey lace that hung from the curve of the curtain-wire in front of his window.

"Come in, boy, come in," he waved to a comfortably dusty easy-chair beside a pile of books and papers. Andrew Taylor-Elder was an enigma with many variations. He was said to have had a family in Belgium at one point, known Janke Adler, met Gauguin in a park, scribbled all over the statues at *L'École des Beaux Arts* when a student in Paris, and lost all his money when the Japanese had the bad taste to conquer his rubber plantations sometime during the confused struggle for Manchuria during the opening stages of the last big one. He was, in fact, a Socrates of no mean accomplishment, and had given his life over to making people think, never an easy or popular task. The flat, just across the corridor from the School of Modern Languages, was something of a crucible for the variety of aspiring hopefuls and creative folk who occasionally called on the recluse. Few emerged from Andrew's company unchanged.

Some loved him, others hated him, but everyone respected what little they ever found out about this strange "refusenik" who was part of no group or establishment, yet managed to affect so many people's lives.

The visitor sat back and watched the alchemy of the coffee take shape as the slightly stale odour of boiling milk permeated the room and steamed up the windows that looked down into Sauchiehall Street.

"Well boy?" Andrew asked. It was the kind of question that demanded an answer.

"Been up at the School today," replied the visitor.

"He's been up at the School!" Andrew raised his eyebrows and confided in the corner of the room. "The boy's been at school!" he laughed.

"We set fire to it," said the visitor, anxious to make some kind of philosophical statement.

"Oh yes?" Andrew yawned, decanting the stewed milk into a heavy mug, granules of coffee bean floated on the surface. " . . . But did you LEARN anything?"

"I said . . . "

"I heard you the first time, boy." Andrew sat down on the corner of the bed, his aged and baggy trousers flaring about him like the leggings of a geriatric Zouave. "We used to do that sort of thing in Paris. Climbed over the railings when the place was shut and did all sorts of things to the statues and the balconies. So. Set fire to the place! Nobody will notice. If there was a helluva crash along the road and 19 buses fell off the bridge into Queen Street Station nobody would notice."

"I know," said the visitor, nodding agreement.

"Ah." The eyebrows shot up again. "Know, do you? If I said to you, 'I saw a chair going down the road yesterday and . . .' you would interrupt and say, 'That belongs to Mr So-and-So, 316 Carphalute Quadrant North, Lesmahagow, AND his dog has the croup, and last year he lost his . . .'"

"I don't know everything!" protested the visitor, sitting forward in his chair.

"Glad to hear it," Andrew smiled. "What else have you been doing?"

"Well, I climbed up on the roof through the window of the ladies' toilet, and hung a string of underwear from the Mackintosh Bird . . . for charity."

Andrew roared with laughter. "Good! Good! There's hope for the boy yet!"

"Yes," the boy continued. "You should see the roof. Nobody ever goes up there. The rest of the Mackintosh building is beautiful, the corridors twisting inside it like a folded castle in coloured stone, the light from the stained glass in the inch-thick doors . . ." He became excited. "But Andrew, the roof is marvellous! It's like Gaudi in Spain. Mackintosh has covered the place in arches and ceramics, what Benno Shotz would call 'Kerramiks', and there are little twists and spirals of metal and stone. It's a sculpture garden above the eye-level of the birds. And when you look about, there is the city, grey on grey, flowing outwards in every direction. The only green is the green of the copper domes, and . . ."

Andrew interrupted him . . . "Something else was 'set fire to' today."

The boy ignored him and continued, enraptured. "I climbed into the little turret down from the Bird. They had to get old Mr Letham in his green coat and brass buttons to struggle up and get the flag of clothes down, but up there, the last name carved in the sandstone right up there on the corner looking down over Glasgow, was in 1910. Now there's mine in 1960 . . . 50 years later."

"Nobody else mad enough to crawl over the rooftops for 50 years!" Andrew complained to the ceiling. "I said that something was set on fire today."

"So did I."

"No, I said it next, boy. You were."

The visitor sipped his coffee and looked at the impish old man with his goatee beard.

"If I was a person who believed in such things . . ."

"What things, and do you?" interrupted his visitor.

"Not telling," said Andrew, *l'enfant terrible* to the last. "But you are, boy. You are telling me that up there on the stone face of Glasgow your soul was set on fire."

*Tollcross and Parkhead, Scotstoun, Cowcaddens, London Road, the voyage of discovery to Auchenshuggle, and "The Land of Oz" at the Roxy, Maryhill. Nights of fog and days of rain, cobbles and kerbs, and bagwash in a pram, land of the hard man and the wee hauf, the upper cottage flat and the fossil groves of tenements, where ships sailed by the end of the street, and the closes echoed with the cries of skelped weans and the rumble of passing trams.*

*When the last tram ran through Glasgow in September 1962, and two days later, the Burgh of Clydebank ran its last tram, it was like the loss of some favourite place and time, a vision of childhood vanishing down the sink in the wash-house. Men, women and children of all ages, wept openly at the going of the blues, and the yellows, the white and the green and the orange, the last of the "Standard Bogies", the Cunarders, the "Coronations" and the single-decker from Dalmuir. They were all there on the last day, even down to the original horse-drawn trams, rattling or gliding past in stately line-astern, a fleet from decades gone, past the Central Hotel and the "Mal", up Hope Street, and bidding farewell to Argyle Street under the gateway of the Hielan' Man's Umbrella.*

TEENY McGuire shouted from the kitchen, "Gonny turn that aff! I canna' hear it with this watter runnin'."

"It's no' you that's watchin' it, anyway. I'm waitin' for my results to come up."

The tap in the kitchen was turned off and there was a moment's silence. Teeny appeared in the doorway, wiping her hands on the dish-towel. "See you and yer coupon!" she said. "Are we goin' out the night or not?"

"Aye darlin'," her husband clasped his knees and leaned closer to the flickering grey screen. "In a minute."

"No' in a minute. You didna' hear a word I said, did ye, John McGuire? Well, I just hope it comes up, that's all I can say."

"The boys in the work won last week," he replied, reaching for the "coupon" and the picture on the screen faded to be replaced by strident music.

"Aye, alang with about 10,000 ither folk. How much did they get again?"

"Twelve pound sixteen and eightpence."

"Fine, fine," snorted Teeny. "We can go and visit Senga and thaim in Southern Rhodesia. He's daein' fine now. Livin' off the fat o' the land oot therr. No' like Porkheid, I kin tell ye." She turned and vanished into the kitchen. The sound of running water returned with renewed violence and John leaned forward and turned up the telly.

"And now for the football results . . ." the announcer said in perfectly modulated Standard English. "Scottish League Division One . . ."

Several miles away in Queen Margaret Drive, a BBC technician knelt down beside a music stand and gently pulled a strip of card aside revealing some names and numbers.

In Parkhead John McGuire watched the black and white screen with a tense fascination that would not have been unfamiliar to Christopher Columbus when he first saw the West Indies float over the Caribbean horizon.

"Cowdenbeath 6 . . . St Mirren 4. Queen of the South 0 . . . Airdrieonians 2. Third Lanark 2 . . . Partick Thistle 2. Celtic 1 . . . Rangers 1."

The voice droned on and John scribbled "X"'s or "O"'s frantically, occasionally muttering to himself. "Home, Away," or "Bugger".

"It's out!" the voice floated through from the kitchen with a smell of fresh chips and hot beans.

He continued scribbling.

Teeny appeared in the doorway. "I said . . . your tea is out, John McGurie. It'll get cold."

"Minute . . ." he replied without looking up.

"I said . . ."

"Teeny!" he shouted standing up and knocking his packet of cigarettes and lighter on the floor. The dog ran under the table.

Teeny opened her eyes wide and gaped. "John . . . John" she said in a whisper. "John. Ye . . . havna'?"

"Naw," he replied angrily, crumpling up the pools coupon and throwing it at the television set. "I havna'."


It was Sunday, and dead as the proposal to market a can of "Diet Guinness". John McGuire was slightly the worse for wear after his night out with his wife. Nothing moved in the entire length of Westmuir Street. Beardmore's loomed like a sleeping giant over the hill, and down towards Shettleston Road a break in the clouds painted a fleeting blue on the topmost windows of the tenements. A cloud of steam crawled slowly upwards from the chimney of Wellshot Baths. They were cleaning the steamie. John walked down the hill, on his way to meet some of the lads in the town. To have a drink on a Sunday, he had to be a "bonna-fide traveller", and had to go at least three or four miles before he would be served.

He walked on manfully, cutting down Springfield Road towards London Road. In the distance he could hear a familiar rumble growing louder. A "Coronation" tram, No 1174, swayed into view and he began to run for the stop. His feet and his heart pounded faster and faster on the pavement and he found himself racing neck and neck with the tram as it approached the fare stage. Without stopping, the double-decker tramcar, its lights blazing, whined away into the distance. John stood, leaning against the upright, panting noisily.

"Missed the tram, did ye?" asked an old man leaning against the close mouth.

"Looks like it," gasped John.

"Last wan, that," the old man tapped out his pipe on the wall where the railings had been taken away to make munitions and never replaced.

"There will be anither in a while surely?" John was getting his breath back.

"Naw. Yer wrang there," the old man smiled. "Nae mair. That wis the last wan ever."

*There were changes. Re-development struck the city like the depredations of an invading army. Great bald patches of earth appeared among the clustered wynds and courts, and people woke up to find themselves negotiating a strange wasteland where familiar street patterns and haunts had vanished overnight. Bulldozers dug their way through the huddle of single-ends and 100 years of Galsgow's story, closely followed by the bonfires that incinerated the more combustible remains of homes, hearths, and memories.*

*Gable-end art began with the first gable-ends, the torn halves of tenements left open and bare to the sky with a strange pattern of part-staircases and broken rooms, hanging crazily from the edge of a roof or a wall, four or five storeys up. The ends of tenements, shorn as if by a giant scythe, were a patchwork quilt of wallpaper and the ghosts of fireplaces. A kitchen cupboard, still with its shelves and lining paper stained by the tobacco smoke of three generations, might stand out from the wall of a lost room high up in the air. Curtains flapped from empty windows, rubble grew like a fresh fall of boulders from Heaven, and slowly, by painful fits and starts, a new Glasgow began to emerge from the wreck of much of the old.*

*People were "decanted", or moved out, to the housing schemes or new towns. Gone were the corner shop and the familiar pub, the bustling life of the stair where every door was unlocked and neighbours chatted or fought, shared their problems and their gossip, borrowed a cup of sugar or a bag of flour. Gone also were the backcourt kingdoms of the armies of weans who had risen to grubby adulthood running up and down closes, playing peevers or "stot-the-ba" and then grown up and away and made new lives in London, Canada, or Australia by the thousands.*

*In the heart of the city ancient veins and arteries like the Parliamentary Road disappeared entirely – the debris drifted citywards, wreathing the Royal Infirmary and the Cathedral in a pall of dust. Buchanan Street Station, the "Station of the North" was axed, together with the Gaiety Theatre where the bar had been full of the memorabilia of the Boer and First World Wars. The terminus of the Monklands Canal was replaced by a new motorway driving remorselessly towards Edinburgh and the East.*

*The Tramcar Vaults lost its tramcar, which found its way to the People's Palace via sundry back-gardens and hallways. Dairies and butcher's shops, glazed by time like huge windows of Edwardian life, shops signs, lamps and doorways, all fell victim to the march of the "knock-doon" men.*

*The skyline in Glasgow changed day by day. Towers and high-rise flats sprouted up everywhere, from the Red Road, where the highest steel frame flats in Europe scraped the sky over Barmulloch, to the Gorbals, where no mean towers sprouted, spread, and covered the old legends with a newness that was to be harshly judged by those who were but weans in their push-chairs at the time. It is easy by hindsight to say that these developments were wrong. What they replaced was wrong. A hundred years of bestial dunnies and cramped living conditions gave way to houses with plumbing, proper kitchens, and some hope for the future, which is all any generation can ever give to the next.*

*Georgian houses behind Allen Glen's School bit the dust, and "bison-built" schools, colleges and offices erupted in the four corners of the city circle . . . and in among the change, the upheaval, and the good intentions, there lingered on in out of the way corners, a few of the old ghosts, and some of the newer ones.*

THE drizzle did nothing to dispel the smell of gas hanging heavy in the evening air. Somewhere on the waste ground a pipe had been ruptured and there was a slow seepage of sweet smelling fumes from under the piles of rubble. On the far hill, the enormous cylinders of the gasometers telescoped gently into each other as a thousand kitchens heated their pies or boiled their kettles. One gas lamp, looking more like the first than the last, had, unaccountably, been lit. It stood, tilted slightly to one side, with its tapering glass windows smeared with the dying light of the flame flickering in its gauze mantle. Towering overhead a line of new dry orange fluorescent street lights marched away over the hill. Far off on the Cathkin Braes at Burnside, a similar line of orange crested the hill, winking where they passed behind some trees nodding in the wind a long time ago.

Sandra and Chuck waited outside the chip shop. The cinema had been full and nobody felt like an evening in the pub. None of them had enough money to risk meeting their friends and start "standing rounds". It was beginning to drizzle and George was in the queue so they looked at one another in unspoken agreement, and went inside.

George was next, after the bus driver at the head of the queue. As they warmed themselves against the polished metal frame in front of the little piles of batter and curling fish, the driver, shift over and jacket open, was already making for the door, tearing open his steaming parcel as he went. He popped a piece of white fish in his mouth, making a large "O" with his lips as he tried to perform the feat of swallowing and spitting at the same time. He elbowed his way out of the door, already chewing happily. His glasses were spattered with rain.

There was a magnificent sizzling as a bucket of fresh raw chipped potatoes were dropped unceremoniously into the bubbling cauldron of hot fat. The sunburst of mirror shapes shining above the cigarettes, the jars of mussels, and the puff-candy South Vietnamese tank-destroyers, steamed up in an instant. Like links in a chain the queue moved forwards a little.

"Nex'?" A Cantabrian face peered across the fish-fryer at them. She had the red hair that had terrorised the last of the Romans when their city was being sacked and burned a wee bit. "Chips'll no' be a meenit, n'that."

"We're with somebody," Sandra nodded towards George, struggling to wrap his short arms around a fish supper, a single white pudding in soft batter, a single smoked sausage with brown sauce, and a wee wet poke with three onions, or "pickles" as they were universally known by the banks of old River. They followed him out of the door.

*185*

The queue edged forwards again. "Nex'?" demanded the girl wiping her brow and tearing yesterday's news in half.

"Never see shopping-bags these days," said George, juggling with a sausage.

"Sorry?" Sandra had suggested that they look for somewhere out of the rain to eat their food.

". . . Never see shopping bags these days," George continued philosophically. "You used to see wee boys and women, men sometimes, with the shopping bag at the chippy, getting the tea for the whole family, you understand. Not now. It's after the pub, now."

"Or instead of," replied Chuck, a thick set heavily-bearded American, studying in Scotland at his own expense. "If I don't eat I'm gonna go ape."

"There's The Priory up the hill," Sandra nodded, holding the hood of her duffel coat tight under her chin to keep off the rain. "Cross over after the MacLellan Galleries and we can nip in there."

The Priory was deserted. It was under the threat of the hammer, or the ball-and-chain, or whatever the demolishers were using that week to smash buildings like pyramids of damp sand. It had last been used as a school, but it was known simply as "The Priory". There was something unpleasant about it, and the students who daily crossed Renfrew Street or made their way to Charing Cross by Garnethill tended to avoid it.

This evening it was "any Priory in a storm", and the three friends were happy to squeeze past the corrugated iron nailed in front of the door and make their way into the dark but dry interior.

These were the days before vandals. It was easy to walk the silent shop-floors of vast empty factories, pick up an abandoned disconnected telephone, watch pigeons swoop through grey openings overhead like holes in the sky, enter the passageways and sculleries of the houses of yesterday's life.

The priory was a Scots Edwardian school in the dark. They climbed to the balcony that surrounded the first floor and went into a classroom.

"Rain's still on," said George after a minute or two, licking his fingers and plucking a chip from the greasy paper.

The rain pattered against the window, driven in every direction by furious gusts of the night wind.

"What are we whispering for?" Sandra stood up, wiping her hands on the seat of her jeans. "It's just an old school." She crumpled up the paper that had held her supper and threw it high in the air.

The classroom was divided by partitions that could be folded back to make a larger space. The panels that made up the wall in front of her stopped short of the ceiling by a good two feet. As they watched, the crumpled ball of paper soared up and over the top of the partition and into the dark, silent room next door.

Sandra stepped back and produced a packet of cigarettes from her pocket. She held them out to Chuck but, before he could speak, the crumpled newspaper she had thrown over the wall, was thrown back. They stood looking at it, lying in the dust at their feet.

Chuck bent down, retrieved the missile, and winked at them. "I bet that's Donald," he said in a stage whisper. He tiptoed across the floor in his National Guard boots and threw the paper deftly over the top of the partition again. Back it came. They looked at one another in silence. Chuck took hold of the paper again and threw it up and over the wall at a different angle, the far end by the rain drenched window. He grinned. He was enjoying himself. They were not the only ones playing soft-ball with a chip poke in the empty school. Back it came. It lay at their feet in the same place as before.

186

Chuck drew them together. "Somebody's at it," he whispered, his beard bristling. He pretended to roll up his sleeves and moved slowly towards the door. Either the army, or the night he and his brother had stolen a parking meter in New Jersey and buried it in the back garden, had taught him stealth. He stealthily opened the door, tip-toeing out into the dusty corridor. There was silence, apart from the soft tap, tap of the rain. The wind had died away.

Sandra and George waited. The blackboard had the last lesson scrawled on it. They had been studying poetry, Stevenson. "Give to me the life I love . . ." said the words scratchily, grey on the dim surface. The last part of the quotation had been smudged by a careless hand, and a trail of drunken characters faded towards the edge of the wooden frame.

Suddenly the silence was pierced by a sharp curse, trailing upwards to a scream. George and Sandra stood still, frozen in time for the flicker of a heartbeat, then ran out into the corridor and next door.

Chuck was standing, or rather, leaning into the open doorway. His arms spread wide, his hands gripping either upright. The fingers and knuckles were white. They looked past him into the room next door. It was empty. There was the other side of the partition, the far wall, the window, the floor . . . there was NO floor, all the way to the basement, two storeys below . . .

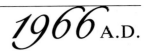
*Doctor Zhivago and the Cultural Revolution, the dream of a land fit for the elderly brave and their dependants, 20 years after the war. Anderston–68 per cent, Kingston–94 per cent, Gorbals–68 per cent . . . not percentages of the votes cast for Harold Wilson and his pipe in the General Election . . . the numbers of people lost to the inner heart of old Glasgow. They were sent out, like wagon trains on a voyage of discovery, to settle the new lands that grew, like Topsy, spreading across the hills that ring a city of seven hills, Drumchapel to the north, Castlemilk in the south, and eastwards to Ruchazie, Garthamlock, Barlanark, Easterhouse, and Cranhill.*

*The second wing of the flight of fancy that was the enormous C.D.A., the Comprehensive Redevelopment Plan, was a network of roads and motorways cutting across and encircling the city. It was intended that the new web of motorways would carry Glasgow into a new era in the seventies and eighties. Where there had been 100,000 ramshackle tenements there would be a gleaming super-city of modern offices and industrial developments. That was before the bottom was kicked out of the bucket by the oil crisis, but the controversy of which way the roads should go still rages on, 25 years later. But great works were in hand. Parts of Glasgow seemed like the bed of the Panama Canal when Paul Gaugin was still digging it. The roads arrowed through the middle of the town and left the Cathedral and the Garngad Howe stranded like islands. The tide of inside lanes swept out of the city, north, south, west to what is now Glasgow International Airport, and east, lapping about the islands of concrete planted in the wilds.*

*There had been a time, not very long ago, when the hill that rises beside the old Edinburgh Road near Queenslie Industrial Estate had been rich brown earth. It was farmed by the monks of the Monklands, then riven by Victorian engineers with their hundreds of thousands of navigators, or "navvies" as we used to call them. Their railways and canals spread to every point of the smoke-filled compass.*

*I remember looking up at that hill from Springboig and seeing a team of horses pulling a plough. Sillouetted against a sky still heavy with snow, remote, and yet immensely solid, they moved slowly away from the present. I can see them now. Then one morning instead of rooks and trees, the hill became a vast lumberyard, built of wood that must have cost an entire forest its life, huge disordered heaps of planks nailed against the sky, forming the outlines of the new housing scheme that was to stretch back towards the piggery and the Monklands Canal, now in its turn the bed of the M8. The wood spilled over in a log-jam of direct works, over the lanes, past the quarry and the wee country shop where we bought tomatoes and lemonade. Sometimes a man with a bright red flag would jump out of the hedge and warn of forthcoming explosions.*

*The real explosion took a few years, but when the dust had settled, the landscape that sloped towards Steppes had changed its shape. In place of the copses, fields, and barns, there stretched mile after mile, street after street of strangeness, a new colony of Glasgow. Fresh concrete and balconied tenements, carefully designed to withstand the rigours of a Mediterranean climate, marched back to Hogganfield Loch where once the Bishops of Glasgow had culled the best swan's feathers for the scribe's quills as if grown from some strange alien seed. Like a crop of giant pre-stressed tatties, there was the world of the roof and the close, complete with buses , but never a pub as far as the Campsie Fells. Vans roamed the asphalt braes and banks, harbingers of the double* nougat slider and the single oyster, their clarion bells ringing out "Chapel in the Valley" or "Be My Teddy-Bear" as 1,000 curtains drew back in the face of the new cliffs ringing the valley.

Of course there were gangs. More Byzantine, convoluted, daft, viscious, than the Montagues and Capulets in their prime, better graffiti-scrawlers and battlers than "The Jets", children of television-land surviving on a diet of crisps and "ginger". They haunted the bus-shelters and the sterr-heids like trolls in sneakers. The shallow grassless dells and dunnies echoed to the cry of "Y.Y. San Toi Kill, OK?" or "Tiny Monks RULE!" or "Mental Badgers RULE, OK?" There was always a question before or after attempted murder or pillage. "OK?" There was always a question. If they had seen the apocalypse approaching, they would have said, "Here's ra end o' ra world comin', OK?"

SMADGER pushed the wee boy back against the wooden door. "Don' MESS! Aw' right?"

"Aye. Sure thing, Smadger," Bundy whimpered, snivelling slightly. The whimpering was fear, the snivelling was habit. In any case he didn't have a handkerchief. He was wearing it.

"Aye, well," continued Smadger remorselessly, his brown hair falling forward in front of his eyes. "If'n ye dae, ye'll get THIS!" Smadger produced a second-hand comb from his back pocket and waved it in front of the unfortunate Bundy's glowing nose. Bundy sidled along, his back to the wall, 11 years old and bound for no "Highers".

"Didna' mean it, so I didna'!" He edged back, tripped, and sat heavily. Smadger looked down poised for the kill. Far off in the chill haze of a late summer evening the sound of the "Cake and Ginger" van echoed through the chasm of the close like the call of some lost and lonely animal.

"Aw' right , well." Smadger pocketed his weapon with a flourish, the tension broken. "No' gonny stick the heid oan ye oneywey, Bundy. Jist checkin', OK? Yer a Badger, so ye are. Jist watch it, OK." The last "OK" was not a question.

Bundy stood up shakily and eyed the rampant Smadger. "Aye, Smage," favouring him with a glutinous sniff. "Yourraman, by the way gnaw this."

Smadger nodded regally, acknowledging the tone of deference in his subordinate's voice.

Tommy bit the cushion speculatively and looked pathetic.

"Now jist you stoap that. Ye'll get yer walkies in a minute." Mrs Flanagan looked away from the television set and over the top of her glasses. Tommy looked crestfallen, an elderly Scotty with a blue collar and rhinestones.

". . . following the catastrophic floods in Florence," droned the newsreader, "Glasgow has agreed to send tons of blotting paper to the stricken city."

"That's a damp't disgrace." Mrs Flanagan reached for the lead lying on the low table beside the Spanish dancer made out of plastic shells.

Tommy left off dribbling on the cushion and leapt to the floor, wagging his tail. "That's the van anyway." His mistress stood up. "Ma' slippers'll dae."

"Woof!" agreed Tommy helpfully.

The queue at the van was growing longer as Mrs Flanagan and Tommy shuffled out together. To the right of Startpoint Street by the secondary school the ground sloped sharply away to the park, or what would be the park if the trees took and the grass grew. As she approached the van the little knot of people waiting at the lighted window suddenly moved away and across the road, looking down past the railings into what should have been the empty school playground at this hour.

"'Mon boy, whit's aw' this?" She ambled across the road. Tommy looked nervously right and left, but the long road was deserted.

A group of about 30 boys and girls, none of them older than 14, were shouting and waving at another similar group standing by the far wall near the park.

"Is that no' terrible?" Mrs Flanagan spoke directly to Tommy. He was lost for words. As the crowd that now ranged along the railings looked down, two motor-scooters broke from the opposing camps and drove directly at each other. They passed and one rider, wielding a knotted rope, lunged at his opponent with a flourish. His adversary appeared to be waving some sort of stick. The riders passed, turned, and rushed at each other again. Again an impasse.

"Jist like in that film *The Sword O' Robin Hood*," said a wee boy standing beside Tommy.

Without warning a blue van appeared through the open gates of the playground beside the Edinburgh Road, and the cry of "Here ra polis!" rose from half a dozen throats beside the railings.

Several large and extremely healthy looking specimens of Glasgow's Finest leaped out of the back of the van before it had quite stopped and began to shovel the tiny rebels towards their waiting pokey wagon. There was a surge and several girls ran forward, thumping on the side of the van with their fists and shouting, "They've goat the KING! They've goat the KING!"

"That's them huckled," an elderly man snorted with satisfaction.

"Aye," agreed Mrs Flanagan with feeling. "They should send them tae clean up that Florence place, no' blottin' paper . . ."

*Those were the days my friends. Man walked on the moon and there were weddings on Glasgow Green. A phenomenon called the Beatles were sweeping the Mull of Planet Earth. A man from Neilston invented Carnaby Street, and skirts were shorter than ever. Danny the Red's agents had been and gone to the London School of Economics, speaking through broken microphones with "jaws of iron", and taking their paving stones with them. The midnight cowboys of Glasgow donned flowery shirts and round steel-rimmed spectacles, and the Clydeside changed again.*

*Glasgow was passing through a long night of post-industrial doldrums, preparing itself to become the first city in Britain to pass through that tunnel of old sooty bricks that linked the end of Empire with the present. Glasgow was on the edge of a Renaissance.*

*It was a good year for jobs. Banks, the police, insurance, nursing, machinists and engineers, all were in demand. Long articles in the papers lured school-leavers into hundreds of different paths in life. There were uneasy rumblings in the city about the problems already arising in the Red Road flats. Housing Associations were born and for the first time, after demolishing almost 80,000 tenements, the suggestion was made that it might, after all, be more sensible to renovate the old buildings and modernise their surroundings, than take a bulldozer to the lot.*

CHARLIE had a club. It was called "The New Explanation", and he was very proud of it. The top rooms of an old flat on the corner of Buchanan Street and Dundas Place, it was never going to be in direct competition with the Grand Old Opry in Finnieston, but it was packed, and it was Saturday night.

A girl emerged from the cloakroom and looked around at the jumping, shoogling mass of long hair and flaired trousers. The air was sweet with the smell of burning rosemary, or joss-sticks, or something. Marianne Faithful trembled on the edge of "Those Were The Days".

The girl walked across the dance floor towards him. She was tall and thin, and wore a blouse with beads or beads with a blouse, the psychodelic pattern and the winking strobe lights made it difficult to see her for the camouflage of fashion, swirling among the twisting bodies thumping and stamping on the old wooden floor. Her hair was long and beautifully unkempt. The glasses, large and covered in hand-painted flowers, looked as though they had been extracted from the wrong end of a telescope. Her skirt, a more extreme example of the genre, was hardly there at all.

Charlie, a man of the world, waited for her to break the ice. "This your place right enough?" she asked with a smile.

"That's what I was tellin' you," Charlie put his arm round her waist and propelled her towards the far wall.

"That's great."

"So it is."

"You tryin' to chat me up?" she smiled again, her body swaying in time to the music.

"Dance?" asked Charlie, rolling a small cigarette in liquorice paper with one practised hand.

"You askin'?" She looked coy.

"... yesterday I saw you in a tavern!" bawled Marianne Faithful.

"What?"

She put her lips to his ear. "Are you askin'?" she shouted. The music chose that moment to hit a quiet stretch.

"Askin' what?" he screamed back. Everyone looked around.

"Nothin'," she frowned, taking a step back. "S'cuse me. This is ma' song."

She whirled off by herself and began drifting around the dance floor. Charlie shrugged and walked to the front of the hall for a breath of cool air from  the well of the close. Fred was standing there looking at the door. Charlie and Fred were old friends, but Fred had been away making a fortune or a fool of himself in the heart of swinging London.

"What a racket!" Fred gestured towards the warm chaos of the dance floor. "Going good?"

Charlie glanced over his shoulder. "Provided there's no more trouble like last week, yes. How was the smoke?"

"Not bad," Fred leered at him in the shadows. "Not at all bad. I barely survived. Last week I passed a guy playing a grand piano on the waste-ground at Battersea. It's all happening down there."

"That's the scene," Charlie nodded. "Still taking pictures?"

"Apple are making a new full-length cartoon."

"Oh yeah?" Charlie kept half his attention on the cacophany inside, dreading the sound of breaking glass. "What's that about?"

"*The Yellow Submarine* . . . Pepper Land is invaded by the Blue Meanies . . ."

"Sounds like Glasgow."

"All the old gang are down there. You should come down Charlie." Fred gestured vaguely towards the South, away over the rooftops of the Buchanan Hotel, dimly glimpsed out of the top-floor window.

"No thanks. I like it here," Charlie leaned far out over the iron railings and looked down the stairwell.

"I met her you know," said Fred, joining his friend and peering downwards, the pair doing a joint "hing" over the stair heid.

Charlie glanced over his shoulder nervously. "Not that bird with the beads?" he asked. Charlie was choosy.

"No, no." Fred toyed with the ring he had bought at the down at heel market in the Angel Islington, a slum district of London. "Her. Marianne Faithful. Went to the Television Centre with an actor I met in 'The Eagle' in Camden Town. She's OK. Likes the Stones," he laughed.

"The wee man still living at Brian Jones's place?"

Fred smiled. "Who isn't? I'm tellin' you. It's the scene down there. Went to see *Hair* though. It's great."

"So what brings you back here?" Charlie asked with the aggression permitted between friends. "Beatles, pubs, actors, what's here for you?"

Fred turned round and leaned back against the railing. "You know," he sighed. "I don't rightly know. I was nearly hired as a Russian soldier by Paramount when a

pal discovered I could speak a few words at the "Kismet Club" one night. What's here? I might get married, if anybody'll have me. I might . . . I might just stay . . . I LIVE here . . . !"

# THAT'LL LEARN YE!                    *1972* A.D.

*The true purpose of education is for living. Education is about making wee Scots and Scotesses true captains of their own puffer, able to cope with anything, from performing the tasks of the workaday world, to scaling the face of tenements, and you'll find out how!*

*Scottish education, always very different from that of England, had the reputation of being "the best in the world", but by 1972, the system was under a fair amount of unfair pressure, not the least in the new large comprehensive schools, some with rolls between 1,700 and 2,000 pupils. There was a chronic shortage of teachers, and a special inducement of a hale £200 was offered to lure staff to the outlying areas. These were the days of the belt and the raising of the school leaving age, or ROSLA as it was known to the war-torn warriors of the staff-room who survived the great upheaval. The age for leaving school was to be raised from 15 to 16, only one year, you may say, but because of birth dates and "intake points", some third-year classes ended up with very reluctant 17- and 18-year-old pupils. The huge schools, many like small towns, were also preparing their pupils for a world about to undergo an incredible revolution.*

*In 1972 there were no pocket computers, no desk-top PCs, no video games, no compact discs; video-recorders were monsters using reel-to-reel-tape as wide as your socks, and colour television had only just barged into the Glaswegian living-room. It was the dark ages. The spin-off from the great American Moon Project was about to filter down to the market place and make many aspects of learning and leisure virtually obsolete overnight. The new technology was going to make redundancy seem a way of life, and before industry and society could adapt, throw up an entirely unforeseen rash of problems. 1972 was as different and as far removed from this last decade of the 20th century as it was from the days when James Watt had a bright idea that changed the world. And that's where education came in. The greatest natural resource of any country is not oil, or gas, or electricity, it is original ideas, and the trick is to legislate so that weans of all ages can be encouraged to have them.*

A BOY at the back of Class 3B fingered his moustache and looked out of the window.

"... and furthermore," the Headmaster's voice boomed over the tannoy, "furthermore ... I wish Vannamore Fibbs in 3B to report to my office immediately."

Class 3B looked at the empty seat third from the front in the second row of desks.

"And ... and ... " The speaker shook as the announcer coughed directly into the microphone. "There is too much running going on. I spoke about it at this morning's assembly. I do not want to have to speak about it again. Keep to the left ... left, always the left. The left is the right side ... "

Mr Trainer and his pupils waited.

"Sir! Sir!" a hand shot up in the front row.

"What is it, Geekie?" Mr Trainer looked myopically over the top of the boy's head.

"I think he's stopped, sir!"

"I'll tell you when he, I mean the Headmaster, has stopped, Geekie. It's for me

*195*

to say and you to do, boy. Rivet!'' He pointed cryptically at the desk, boring a figurative hole in the open jotter. ''Rivet your attention on your work.'' He cast a piercing gaze over the motley collection of glazed expressions in front of him, children of the seventies, minds waiting to be fed. The heads bowed and silence descended on the classroom.

Next door a small uproar stepped into the breach. ''Naw. Naw I wullny!'' shouted a small, anguished voice.

Mr Trainer scowled at his charges. ''Pay no attention. Carry on with your work!''

''Sir! Sir!'' Geekie waved at the ceiling again. ''Sir, whit page is it?''

Before his teacher could answer there was a loud ''CRACK!'' followed by another, also next door. 3B drew in its collective breath sharply, but continued to peer at their books.

''Page 35,'' said Mr Trainer, pretending along with his class that murder and mayhem were not taking place next door.

''Sir, that student canny draw the belt!'' Geekie smiled innocently up at his tutor.

''No, but I can,'' replied Mr Trainer, wishing death and damnation on uncertificated students and life in general. He reached inside his jacket and produced a heavy strap of leather, inherited from a now sadly departed colleague. His belt was habitually carried tucked over his shoulder inside his jacket so that it could be ''drawn'' instantly, like a gunfighter making a play for the marshal's job in Tombstone, Arizona. He laid the belt on the desk in front of him. ''Just carry on, Geekie.'' Mr Trainer was a merciful man.

Geekie carried on.

''Now then,'' said Mr Trainer brightly, the tension safely bottled and corked. ''We were looking at the troubled history of our own country, Scotland. When the Covenanters fought at Bothwell Brig . . .''

''Sir, I know about that wan!''

''Do you, Geekie?'' asked Mr Trainer with a tired sigh.

''Aye, sir. The Bothwell Boys and the Holytown Boys got lifted at Bothwell last Saturday and . . .''

The door opened and Mr Gunn, the Headmaster, walked into the room unannounced as Geekie was dangling by the collar from Mr Trainer's trembling hand.

''Class STAND!'' said Mr Trainer mechanically, forgetting to let go of the squirming Geekie.

''Girl Fibbs not here today?'' Mr Gunn cast an enquiring glance about the room.

''No, Headmaster,'' replied Mr Trainer. ''Apparently she is 'under' the Dental Hospital.''

The Headmaster smiled grimly. ''I understood the usual excuse was 'absent because of diarrhoea through a hole in the shoe?' Perhaps I might also speak to you at the interval about your climbing club and the Duke of Edinburgh Scheme. However . . . I shall leave you to your er . . . discipline matter . . .'' The door closed quietly.

''You haven't got anything

wrong with your shoe, have you?'' Mr Trainer demanded, holding the unfortunate Geekie as far away as possible.

Davie Trainer drank his lager with gusto and looked at the climbing gear spread across the living-room of Bob's flat, together with an assortment of Glasgow University students.

"So did they find her?'' Bob asked, buckling and unbuckling the harness as he spoke.

"Vannamore Fibbs? Oh yes.'' Davie wiped some froth off his chin. "She'd fallen in the canal, as well as having hysterics.''

"That bad?''

"Well, you see the girls had had a new biology class in the morning, and when Vannamore fell in the water she swallowed some frog spawn, or something like that. She thought she was going to have a frog.''

"As distinct from a prince,'' nodded Bob. "She would have more than a frog if she saw James.'' The door opened and a gorilla walked in. James, a rebel with a cause, believed that he couldn't be killed, and was preparing to raise ''that wee bit extra'' for charity come the bright morning.

"I'm ready,'' said the gorilla, turning round.

"Are you sure?'' said Davie, looking at the climbing harness strapped round the gorilla's middle. He was not that drunk, not yet.

"Oh yes,'' the gorilla gave a muffled chuckle and tugged at the rope secured to a table leg. "Absailing down a tenement is a mere bagatelle compared with the north face of Paisley Town Hall.'' He had done both.

Somebody slid the window up and the gorilla climbed out into the night. Lights twinkled in the dark sky beyond Jack Coia's Kelvindale Church. The London shuttle swooped low on its way to Glasgow Airport. The rope uncoiled itself slowly as the gorilla vanished over the edge. Suddenly there was a smell of burning as the rope fled down into the darkness below. It was pulled up short with a jerk by the table, the table shot across the floor, and from below came the sound of a roar followed by the crash of breaking glass.

Mrs Grant was a polite old lady, and since her husband's death, she had settled into a life of happy memories, surrounded by the bric-a-brac and souvenirs of a married life that spanned two great wars, and countless holidays on Arran, days of strolling along the beach in an age when the fastest thing in the world was a hungry seagull and Glasgow was the greatest shipbuilding city in the world, and her late husband's employer. She sat back, stroking the plump feline grace of Molly, her cat, and watched Dan Dailey dance down the steps of old St Louis.

With a violent crash that sent the cat at least five feet in the air a gorilla was catapulted through the window, hung there for what seemed like the merest flutter of an eyelid, muttered something that sounded like "Sorry!" and vanished out of the window again, and flew upwards with a jerk.

The polis were apologetic when they called at the top flat. They were duty bound to answer the old lady's call, and somebody, vandals, had broken her window. The young men sitting about the front room talking and discussing rugby and university sympathised with the big bobby. "She says a gorilla flew in her window and then flew out again," he said. "It'll be boys, likely. I blame it on their teachers . . . ''

197

*In the good old days "foreign parts" started just down the street where the cart-track turned the corner and vanished into the Caledonian Forest. Up the road where thon ruined temple marked the gateway to Bogle Land, things were said to get nasty on dark afternoons and rainy nights, and people tended to stay very much in the area of their own rigs. This was usually because part of the privatised investment in land included the people, neffs or nyaffs, serfs, huddled together with the chickens, and with no reason to travel, and nowhere to go anywhere anyway.*

*The equitable distribution of wealth shifted down the years, and by the 20th century package holidays had made substantial inroads into people's travelling habits. The Glasgow Fair, originally a market fair, was not a holiday of the "travelling" variety as we would understand it today. Then heavy industry invented the annual exodus of the Ferr in Victorian times, and the Clyde coast blossomed with boarding houses and chip shops, fed by an armada of steamers sailing from the Broomielaw. Nobody realised, as the age of aspidistras drew to a close in the early years of the 20th century that within a few decades, legions of punters and their wives and weans would grow wings, fulfilling man's age-old dream of flight. Flight, soaring above carpets of cloud castles, essentially the same folk who watched the dancing bears of the Middle Ages, paddled in the bay at Port Bannantyne and read about the South African War . . . Clydeside, off on holiday but taking its miracles in its stride, buying its marvels at the souvenir stand next to the bingo.*

*Destinations varied and sleepy little Spanish fishing villages were transmuted into cities full of lidos, and millions of unfinished holiday appartments. General Franco died, the same Generalissimo that hundreds of Glaswegians had fought against during the Spanish Civil War, and Spain had its first free election. Down in Tenerife, the gulf-stream warmed the bikini-bottoms of the fancy free, as Glasgow took to flying down the coast of West Africa in search of a wee bit of diversion.*

IF there were flowers on the moon, they would be made of stone. There is a stone flower in Tenerife, a great rose of basalt, high up on the slopes of el Teide, the mountain that the ancient Greeks and the Carthaginians called "the Pillar of Heaven".

Night drew close, a cloak spread across the sky from the vastness of Africa to the east. Stars flickered into life in the high blue above la Esperanza, the forest called "Hope" that clothes the long slopes of the volcano to the north, sweeping down towards the university town of la Laguna with its square fortress of wooden towers, and the white streets and portside bars of Puerto de la Cruz.

On the western slopes of the sleeping giant, a black tide of old lava falls 3,000 feet sheer to the Atlantic. It covers the old town of Garachico in a blanket of iron hard rock that was poured 400 years ago. Beside it terraces and houses form steps of pink and pale grey all the way down to the endless ocean.

A dusty road ran out and forward, a springboard for the last heat of the day, as lights snapped on in country *bodegas*, and the chill, noticeable this far up the mountain, touched the shoulders of old men sitting in the doorways like the ghost of the sinking sun, reminding the villages that night was drawing close.

Far below, in the tropical bay that forms a part of this land of many climates, the town of Puerto de la Cruz was coming to life for the evening. Shops would be open for a long time yet. Along the sea front by the Church of Sant Elmo and the gross café named after Christopher Columbus, the tour buses were returning after a hot day touring the island. It was said that Columbus stopped in Tenerife on his way to America. He probably did, as had every other explorer and pirate for 500 years. It was said that Columbus spent his latter years cruising up and down the coast of the land that was not named after him, since he did, after all, only discover the West Indies, flogging any man who would not admit that Florida was India. Dreams are very hard to give up, but Tenerife was not a dream, at least, not all of it. Most visits only lasted ten days, airports permitting.

One post of responsibility I have occupied down the years that outshines all the others, was that of Captain of the Donkey Safari. Another was as a guide, but then, I have always been something of a traveller. On this particular stage of the journey, shepherding the denizens of old Glasgow around the base of the Dragon Tree, conversing in measured tones with a friend who had given up East Kilbride for the life of a hang-glider, in spite of the fact he had a pacemaker, I came across news of the Thing with Big Lugs that dwelt in the forest and still, according to some reports, scared the pants off almost everybody.

It was Fat Sanchez and Willy the Scooter, the Evil Kneevil of el Botanico who first told me about the Monster of Taganana. Actually, the monster was dead, but it seemed the son was the living image of his father and had set himself up in business terrifying the tourists like his dear old dad. My pal, the portly Sanchez, had the part-ownership of a bar called "The Sloping Palm Tree" with a Señor Dorta, an ex-traffic policeman with a wooden leg, who had lost his leg while trying to collect a speeding fine. Willy the Scooter was a bit of a monster himself. He had earned his nickname during the Spanish Civil War when he travelled to Santa Cruz, found General Franco in the act of leaving for mainland Spain, and escaped into the mountains on a borrowed motor scooter. He had spent some time driving round the island in first gear, settled in the garage underneath his mother's flat, and never moved since, except for a nightly bottle of the old *Vino Tinto* and a nibble of octopus in the "Palm Tree". The monster had to wait. This was my night for the night clubs, part of my onerous duties as a travel guide.

It was a warm summer's night in the foothills of the immense mountain, the air heavy with the scent of flowers and rich green things in the dark. The ridges and steps that climb the cliffs were lit by the blossoming fire of a fiesta, and accompanied by the distant sound of a tinny band playing a samba in fast tempo under the trees. Paper plates and streamers were lying on the benches. A cigarette stand was open late, women hovered in doorways, and I could smell hot stones cooling in the tropical night. A telephone ringing on a balcony and a face in the crowd swirling past, glimpsed, and still not forgotten.

Those were the days when Glasgwegians first thought of buying property abroad, something that would have made many a pre-war granny go and white the step in disgust. Many were travelling to foreign parts for the first time, a generation that had made sugery watter and run around with the seats out of its collective breeks when Sir Stafford Cripps was rationing everything and you only saw a car at weddings and funerals. One nice lady from nether Clydeside had to be sent home after only one sultry tropical night. She was that upset that people spoke another language. The remarkable thing about foreign countries is that even the local children get very good at it.

Cameras and ferocious sunburn, chicken in a basket, it was all a far cry from

the days of Jacobites and sailing ships . . . and the Monster of Taganana . . .? He was really a man in a mask, like so many, and keeping abreast of the times. He has parted his curly locks and is selling timeshare.

But horizons get wider and the world gets smaller. Here was the sun and the sea, the Southern Cross glimpsed over the curvature of the earth, a magic Glasgow Fair on a hillside in the night, with stalls, and sideshows, and longing kindled in enough hearts to make the difference. Glaswegians have always travelled the world. The newness of it all is that nowadays they come back again.

*When St Mungo spent his first Christmas in Glasgow, Christmas Day fell on 9 January according to the old Julian Calender. Mistletoe, holly and other pagan symbols were regarded with horror, and robins were a welcome winter morsel.*

*Christmas as we know it was not celebrated in Scotland, but 1,000 years ago some remembered the Norse Goddess Harta who brought gifts down the chimney or through the hole in the roof, and the fir tree, used in ancient Rome at the December Festival of Saturnalia, was still a symbol of birth and of sacrifice. The "wassail bowl" of hot ale and spice arrived from England about 1400, and cheer was needed. If anybody did decide to celebrate the season with a meal there were no forks, and even the Earl of Lennox, Lord Provost of Glasgow, had no glass in his windows. In the year 1800 Christmas Day in Glasgow was a working day like any other. Queen Victoria's husband, Prince Albert, introduced the Christmas tree from Saxe-Coburg, and well-to-do Glaswegians began to stiffen plum porridge and turn it into plum duff. Those who could afford it ate goose or beef, while candles from the Candleriggs and yule logs, symbols of fire and light, blazed merrily, and merchants' families crunched duck and starling, even eating the beak.*

*The Victorian Christmas didn't really take off in Glasgow until after the Second World War. Until quite recently newspapers were published on Christmas Day and 25 December was regarded as a purely religious occasion. The real party was at New Year. Yuletide was a time for celebration of the birth of Christ in the middle of winter, but Santa and his wee elves, Christmas trees, cards, and all the rest of what is now known as a "traditional" Christmas were late coming to the Clydeside.*

*Whatever happened in the time before this? One way of driving out the winter chill was "Glasgow Punch", a heady mixture of black-heart Trinidad rum, sugar, and acetic acid, with a fresh lime, if available, sliced and dropped in the middle of this early form of rocket fuel. In the 18th century people stayed at home and made their own entertainment. The streets were far too dangerous, whether the peril be footpads or thin ice. In the late 18th and early 19th centuries there were a series of mini-ice ages, when the Clyde was completely frozen over for weeks and the Toll Bridge Company nearly went bust, what with all the carts, horses and people trudging across the frozen river.*

*In 1934 Glasgow schools stopped for the holidays on Christmas Eve and went back on Boxing Day, but they had eight days clear at New Year. In those days the Clyde Valley Electric Company was responsible for lighting displays in shop windows, and most children could expect little more than an apple, some nuts, and a polished penny in their stockings on Christmas morning.*

*New Year was an entirely different plate of black bun. A man had the right to kiss any woman he met on the streets of Glasgow between midnight and 1 a.m., if he had the nerve and there were no polis about! The* Northern Looking-Glass *wrote: "All await the coming year, and on hearing the bells, all of Glasgow gives a great cheer that can be heard in distant parts as far as Rutherglen."*

*By 1981, the "great cheer" and the good cheer began somewhere in September, and Christmas was here to stay in a big way. But behind it all, unchanged, there remained the real Christmas. It had always been there even in the long ago, and is not very hard to find if you look for it.*

*201*

THE skylights above the gym hall were hung with paper decorations, made by the children themselves. The rostrum at the end was prepared for the Christmas show, when a legion of small children, even smaller than elves, would sing carols, "be" a variety of things from ducks to camels, and perform the dual function of celebrating the end of term and the advent of that special holiday. This morning, the library and the television room where deserted. Clusters of children stood crammed in their doorways expectantly. Santa was coming to the First Infants. Even the older ones, on the brink of secondary school, waited with excitement. The strident clanging of a bell drew nearer and, walking confidently across the white lines drawn on the lino of the hall, Santa appeared around the corner from the direction of the Head Teacher's office.

"That's not old Mr Maclean," said one of the seniors, slightly puzzled. "Maybe he's not well." Mr Maclean had "been" Santa since they themselves had been toddlers fresh into the village school.

"Of course not, it's Santa," said their teacher with a grin.

"Ohh . . . MISS!" they all chorused together. They were, after all, 12 years old.

Santa sat down in front of the little row of faces. First Infants were very small. Some of them were rascals, others quiet as mice, but in a small school where sometimes hard words and a rich and varied educational experience was underwritten with an old-fashioned principle called love, they were among the most fortunate of children. Santa smiled, handing out a little present from his sack to every child. Even the two teachers sitting nearby were not forgotten.

"Please Santa," said a small boy, puting up a hand just big enough to pull a cracker, "Jim isny here, Santa."

"I've got a present here for him," Santa held it up. "Will you give it to him?"

"Please Santa," the wee boy continued, hand still up, "He's off with a measle."

"Well I'll give his present to teacher then, and he can get it when he comes back."

Half an hour later the Head Teacher and her staff were having a cup of tea and discussing whether the angels were to come on before the ducks, oxen and asses, or if the piano was close enough to the stage for this evening's performance. There was a timid tap on the door of the staff-room.

"Yes," asked Miss Lane, looking down. The herald was clad in a track suit bearing the words "Boston Red Sox".

"Please Miss," said the Yankee elf, pigtails tucked in at the back. "That's the Santa you asked to come waiting at your office. He says he is sorry he's late."

203

*In 1973 the name "Strathclyde" was re-written on the map of Scotland. Missing for almost 1,000 years, since the days of St Mungo, it was only fitting that Glasgow should be the headquarters of the NEW Strathclyde. The new region, vast by the standards of St Kentigern, and with the District Council at its ancient heart, was just another "founding" in a millennium of charters and great deeds.*

*By 1975, Glasgow, 800 years on from the Charter granted to Bishop Jocelyn, was still going strong. The occasion was celebrated with plays and pageants, religious processions, all manner of events and souvenirs. It was also International Women's Year. Mrs Margaret McKay of Castlemilk was 103 years old. Glasgow bus drivers were learning Kung Fu. About £1,700 a year, or £35 a week was a respectable wage for a married man with a family. By 1983, the year of "Pride for the Clyde", the required figure was more than four times that. In 800 years plus Glasgow had turned into a metropolis, Second City of the Empire, passed through two terrible wars and become, with its motorways and its huge housing developments, new bridges, tunnel and airport, a city of the eighties, smiles and many many miles better. But while some things had changed, in many ways the people who dodged the traffic, payed for things with plastic money, riveted and wrangled, were no different from their distant cousins, far down the stream of time.*

D AVIE tucked the goose under his arm and turned left, taking his usual shortcut up behind the Sang Scule towards the top road. The wind changed and the reek of wood smoke grew stronger. A group of serfs were reluctantly chopping down the hawthorn bushes growing behind the Brothers' House on the hill. The hedge was no longer required with the wall going up about the extensive herb gardens, but the country folk believed the tree was sacred to the Lady Who Rode on the Moon, the May Tree, *sgitheach* in the old tongue, and *uath* in an older still. The fire crackled merrily.

"Aye, Davie!" Clevwen the Senechal leaned against the half-built wall and grinned toothlessly. "The Merket Fair's the ither way, man!" He laughed and squared his shoulders, a barrel of a man clad in grey cloth and leather, a shapeless fustian bag he called a hat crammed down over his large, red ears.

"Don't give me 'Markets'," Davie replied ruefully. "They are all a pack of thieves down there. Trying to get an honest piece o' siller is like askin' the Blessed Lady, beggin' Her pardon," he crossed himself, ". . . for a miracle."

"Better watch yersel' man," Clevwen frowned slightly and gestured with his thumb. "There's Brother Anselm in ahint thae whins."

Davie looked out of the corner of his eye without turning his head. Russet brown, like the ferns that covered the bank sloping down toward the Cathedral, the habit of the Brother could be glimpsed through the branches, still as a fox.

"He likes to keep an eye on things," said the Senechal in a whisper, walking across. "He says the masons are shirking. Not that he disna' roll up his sleeves and dress a block o' stane himself with a will. It was him that mastered the new Port down at the Gallowgate."

The branches rustled, and plucking a twig out of his hood, Brother Anselm struggled out of the thicket. An "Eminence Grise" in brown, well read in Greek and

Erse, Brother Anselm could crack a walnut with his fingers, and took hard decisions without flinching. "Well this garden will provide herbs for the apothecary, and some peace for contemplation, so I don't want this scrawny herd to slack, man. My Lord the Bishop is aware of all that goes on in His city." He blinked myopically. There was nothing in the growing city of Glasgow that escaped the secretive Brother.

"Er . . . fine day, your Worship," Davie changed his goose to the other arm.

"Fine day for work. We could do with your aid, David Farulfson, goose allowing."

"Oh, er . . . this is for an old lady that's ill, her that lives up beyond the Meikle Cowcaldanes. I mun tak it there now, Master." He moved away.

Davie took his accustomed short-cut up MacLeod Street off Castle Street. The parcel under his arm was heavy and he shifted it, digging his hand into his pocket to give him more purchase.

"Oh aye?" said Craigie, leaning against the low sandstone wall of the school. "Daein' the shoppin' now?" He raised an eyebrow scornfully.

"Oh, the wife's mither is stayin' with us, and they've taken the weans to some procession or other in the Square. I had to get to the butcher's afore it closed." The parcel slipped again. "Mince," he added apologetically.

The smell of wood smoke came from the bonfire on the waste ground, and the workmen repairing the low wall in front of the school looked forward hopefully to their tea-break.

"Fixin' this up as an Adult Learnin' Centre," said Craigie the ganger helpfully. "I hear there's goin' to be a lot of work doin' up old buildings, restoring tenements if ye can believe it!"

"Can't think why," said Davie, balancing his parcel on a pile of red sandstone, waiting to be replaced. "Our new flats up the back are grand."

"Aye, used to be the Parly Road, that," Craigie nodded sadly. "That Collins's a Library for the Uni' now."

205

"Strathclyde? Aye, we've got two Uni's. Never had a chance when I was a boy. University o' Life, me."

"Watch yersel'," said Craigie, pretending to find something interesting on the ground. "Here's Andrews comin'. Clerk o' Works."

"Time to dilly dally have you?" said Mr Andrews, his rimless glasses reflecting the orange light of a street lamp somebody had forgotten to turn off. "This job's to be finished this week coming after next. We had better get on."

"Hullo Mr Andrews," said Davie politely. "Been to see any of the '800' celebrations with your good lady?"

"I'm afraid not, McLeish," replied the little man haughtily. "No time for all that . . . and it seems to me as if we have been at this job for 800 years as it is . . .come away now, Foreman. Glasgow is supposed to be 'Smiles Better'. We had better get on with it." He walked away, peering at the pointing work going on at the back of the old stone wall.

"Disna' miss a trick, him," Craigie nodded after the departing tropical lightweight business suit. "I'm beginning to feel as if I've been around here for 800 years myself . . ."

*Glasgow is Exhibition City. It has been since 1888, again in 1901, in 1910, 1938, and by the time 1988 came round, the old town was ready with its pennants and pavilions to write another story of fun, glitter and patter. Admission to that first exhibition, back in the era of the Second City cost all of one shilling; £5 for a day's visit in the year of Grace and Renaissance 1988 also seemed reasonable, given the fact that a fair amount of water had flowed under Glasgow Bridge.*

*That first exhibition covered 60 acres in Kelvin Park, and had been resplendent and munificent, full of sandstone fantasies and fylfots, a Fairy Fountain, a Café for Bachelors, a complete reconstruction of the Bishop's Palace from the days of cobbles and carthorses. Not far from the Women's Industries Hall, there was even one of the very latest and newly invented telephones.*

*At 120 acres and about £15 million the jamboree of 1988 was all it promised to be. Sited on the old Princes Dock area, it brought colour, life, glass and millions of people to an area that had once been part of the busiest port in the western world. For a few months the view from the majestic sweep of the Kingston Bridge during the rush hour, always something to enjoy at your leisure, was of a futuristic panorama of brightly col-oured towers, tall masted ships riding at anchor, pavilions like prismatic pyramids of twinkling light, and the hustle and bustle that millions of Clydesiders gave to the great Flower-Plan of the layout. The Garden Festival was, of course, a market, and Glasgow has a long history of those as well . . .*

THE boxed Dutch Blue Willow Pattern toureen and finger-bowl set shone in the Saturday sunlight.

"See you, misses, that's no' china, that's a present, by the way!"

"I'll take it as a present then, mister," the wee bachly wumman with the headscarf waved her battered purse at the auctioneer.

"Come on now, hen, whit ye think yer oan, yer daddy's yacht?"

"You said it," the lady replied boldly. "Aw these ur witnesses!"

The crowd began to drift away.

"Right, now, a PRESENT at that price!" the barker bawled at the retreating punters.

"It's cheaper in the shops, hen," said a passing shopper, her miniature poodle surfacing from the shopping bag to see what all the commotion was about.

"I know that," said the lady in the headscarf. "It gets me oot the hoose, though."

The air was split by a vaguely stereophonic crackle and hiss. Up the street towards the cast-iron arch bearing the legend "Barrowland", backwards from their point of view, a strange apparition was setting up shop. A diminutive figure in a crumpled tuxedo was jumping about as if something had escaped from the petshop round the corner and had found sanctuary in his baggy second-hand breeks. White-gloved hands waved about in an uncontrolled fashion and the face of a middle-aged Glaswegian without a bunnet was liberally smeared with Kiwi boot-polish.

"Aw rerr Al Jolson! Owerrerr . . . he's rerr!" She pointed and held her dog up to see the antics. "They say it's no' him pentin' his name oan the walls." There had

been a rash of ''Al Jolsons'' all over the centre and East End of the town of late, and the phantom publicist was yet to be spotted in the act by the polis, or anybody else. ''They say he's loaded.''

''Swaneee . . .'' he wailed breaking into a mimed whistle, sticking gloved fingers into the corner of his mouth.

''Been to the Garden Vegetable yit?'' the dog-holder asked the lady with the headscarf, who had now lost interest in the barker since he had actually started to sell things.

''No' yit. Good, is it?''

''Oh aye. It's a great day out . . . 'Out of this World' so they say.''

''Maybe I will then,'' the old lady tucked a stray wisp of white hair into her headsquare. ''Jist tae be different for a change.''

Bell's Bridge swung back slowly to allow the Lighter through. It sailed along close to the embankment past the amber glass of the half-completed hotel struggling upwards beside the Scottish Exhibition and Conference Centre. The Water-Patrol roared past. The driver, a young girl with fine red hair, was making up for pulling a body out of the water that morning, and showered the spectators with a generous helping of the old River Clyde. With a ''toot'' the steam train drew its brightly-painted carriage packed with visitors round a tight curve and vanished behind the giant teapot. The Japanese Garden, built in anxious competition with the Chinese Pavilion, sprouted bonsai trees like dots in a Paisley Pattern, and over by the Marina, the platform of the Clydesdale Bank Tower, stuffed to overflowing with eager and apprehensive faces, spiralled slowly up into the Glasgow sky.

''We'll just stop at that wee clock,'' said Gran. ''My, my dogs are barkin' right enough.''

''We'll need tae find a toilet for Thomas, Mammy,'' the young woman looked about her at the milling crowds. Half a British Rail locomotive, bright as the nose cone of an abandoned spaceship, loomed to the left beside the Bank of Scotland fountain.

''I like that wee tower.'' Granny sat down on the wooden bench and sighed. ''Oh ma feet! 'Merchant City Clock Tower','' she read. ''Where's the Merchant City?''

''I don't know Mammy,'' her daughter was becoming impatient. Thomas was getting desperate.

''Mammy,'' he whined, pulling at the tail of his father's shirt, his mother's favourite ''jacket''. ''Mammy! Me need . . . ''

''Come on then,'' she dragged him off along the path beside the river. Gran followed slowly.

Clanging towards the ''Tower of the Four Winds'', a title once given to a building in Athens, but that was about 2,488 summers ago, a bright red Paisley single-decker tram drew up to the terminus. It had the word "Tennent's" emblazoned along the side.

"Is that a pub?" asked Granny, but her daughter, propelling Thomas along in front of her didn't hear.

High up in the sky at the peak of the gravity incline, the thrill-ride car stopped for one awful moment. Briefly, the prisoners looked down and saw the wee yellow headscarf that marked the weary granny and the white shirt and coloured dot that were her daughter and grandson. With a slight lurch that left several hot dogs behind in the firmament, the car swooped down towards the hard earth, screamed through a curve, and met its own shadow on the upside-down return journey.

"Now they havna' got THAT at the Barras," said Granny, looking at the white-faced fun-lovers with a critical eye.

*Since the beginning Glasgow and Scotland have traded with the world. In earliest times the world was France, Flanders, and a few points south. Sometimes trade relations soured and on paper at least, Berwick is still at war with Russia!*

*In Victorian times the wide world was Glasgow's market, often a two-way influence as in the case of the Indian inspiration behind Paisley Patterns, but goods, knowledge, and muscle went from the banks of the Clyde to all the continents. Glasgow helped build up the plantations in the southern states of America, fought for and against President Lincoln, settled, named and tamed large swathes of the great nation of Canada, voyaged to the time-locked Empire of the Shogun, brought Christianity to western Africa, found a second home in Australia, began a "colony" with Dunedin in New Zealand, and all from what was once a few huts by a shallow salmon-river.*

*Towards the close of the 20th century Glasgow has built on the changing pattern of maps and principalities, and twinned itself with cities like Rostov on Don in the Soviet Union and Turin in Italy. Designated European City of Culture for 1990, the old town found itself part of a select European Club that included Athens, Florence, Amsterdam, Paris, and in 1988, Berlin.*

STUDENTS clustered like pigeons round the base of the ruined Gedachtsnicht Kirke on the Ku'damm and the photographer from the *Evening Times* walked round the white taxi and took the lens cap off his camera. Lord Provost Susan Baird was concerned.

"Careful of the traffic!" The Lord Provost, a lady who cared about the life and limb of press photographers from her beloved home town, looked up apprehensively as a double-decker bus careered towards them past the cafés and the cake-stalls.

Jim Young was a professional. He had faced worse things than buses. "Don't worry, Lord Provost," he said , giving his picture an extra f-stop. "I wouldn't be the first Scottish Soldier to die in Berlin." The bus passed by and his hair blew back. "Click" went the camera. "One more please," he stood up, walked back on to the pavement, and framed up a picture of the Provost and the white taxi. "Glasgow's Smiles Better" wound past the cheery round face painted on its side. "That's it," he said, smiling as curious passers-by stopped to see the smart lady with the bright gold chain step inside the chunky vehicle and speed off along the busy Kurfurstendamm. Glasgow was in Berlin.

Jim had spent the morning at a photo-call in the big store where there was a trade display of native goods from the good old Clydeside. He had walked past the wooden sheep that said "Baa . . . Bonnie Schotland", and taken his quota of pictures of the "Gnomosapiens" people, the blonde lady who was painting flowers on glass, the kiltmaker, mobbed as usual by Berliners eager for a Saturday-night plaid. The Highland dancers looked rather shaky, but they had been under a lot of pressure. The Tourist Board display was a forest of pamphlets and leaflets, together with a snappy little video presentation. He had acquired a print showing almost 100 of Glasgow's buildings, delicately tinted in watercolour and illustrating some of the other cities that were "up there" with Glasgow on the European scene. He was on his way to meet the artist, "inventor" of the Glasgow poster, who was currently working on a similar print of

Berlin. Jim's editor had asked him to try and get some pictures of the new work in East Berlin as well. A rendezvous had been arranged at a notorious café called "The Kranzler" with a colleague, Vic Roderick, a kenspeckle journalist whose father-in-law was a flamenco singer. Glasgow was very definitely in Berlin!

Jim and the artist looked out of the window of the train. Vic had had to stay behind because he didn't have the correct papers, and nobody was taking any chances in the land of "The Wall". The "S" Bahn ran directly across the wasteland separating the two Berlins, and as they watched, a panorama of desolation unfolded beside the banks of the Spree. A rather bored looking guard was taking his Alsation for walkies beside the concrete watch towers as the train pulled into the Friedrichstrasse Station.

The checkpoint was a series of metal doors, each with a beady-eyed official seated behind bullet-proof glass. Long queues wound back from each of them, mainly elderly Germans visiting relatives, with a sprinkling of tourists from Europe and America. The waiting area had the aura of a bomb-shelter, bare concrete, and television cameras poking out of holes in the wall. This was the point where East met West, two conflicting systems that had divided the planet for nearly 50 years. It was a place where ordinary people completed a journey of a few feet and it took them a lifetime, patrolled by soldiers and guards with machine guns. A high ranking official emerged from a side door, sharing a joke with another uniformed guard. It all seemed very relaxed. Then the cameras moved, and everybody looked down.

The artist was working on a picture which showed the principal buildings of Berlin as it had been, and had decided to take an eraser and rub out the wall. This meant going to East Berlin frequently to draw there. The guards had become used to the improbable kilted figure, and when he explained that he and the photographer were visiting the East for "Cultural Purposes", they were waved through the barrier with a look of amused tolerance. Lunatics and photographers were clearly not regarded as a threat. Jim tried to get a special stamp on his passport to show his wife, but when it was explained to him that this was only given to criminals and dissidents, he declined the honour. They passed through the control, changed their money for freshly minted little bits of green paper, and entered East Berlin.

It was like stepping back into 1950, or even 1930. The streets were wide and clean, and largely empty. Tiny cars with motorcycle engines roared past beside one of the loveliest sights in the world . . . trams!

They made their way to the Unter den Linden. This broad street used to run as a great processional boulevard across Berlin but was now divided by the forbidding line of the Brandenberg Gate. Jim and the artist strolled together down towards the wall from the eastern side. Halfway down the boulevard a head popped out from behind a tree, pointed a camera at them, took a photograph, and vanished again.

"Don't crack on," said the artist out of the corner of his mouth. "They do that all the time." He sat down on an iron bench under one of the last of the linden trees and posed for a few shots with his half completed painting. It started to rain.

"Is there anything else we might get a good picture of?" Jim asked buttoning up his camera bag. The artist had been wandering about East Berlin for days.

"The Protestant Cathedral up by the canal," the painter pointed past the dome of the Soviet Embassy. "That's in my picture."

They turned round and marched back up the avenue, pausing by the Russian War Memorial. The Russians lost more soldiers and citizens in the last war than anybody else, and they take what they call "The Great Patriotic War" very seriously. The artist and the photographer stood outside the little shrine for a moment in the rain. A bright red flame flickered in the depth. Two guards carved out of steel stamped up and down, clicked their heels, and turned smartly. One of them caught sight of the kilted figure, and for the briefest flicker of an instant, a smile touched the mouth of that rigid Red Army soldier. Discipline, never really absent, returned, and even a kilted figure with a woolly jacket on and a wet painting under his arm, could no longer break that icy calm. Having refused to buy Czechoslovakian film from an East-German wide-boy by the canal, they turned and headed back towards the Alexanderplatz and the train.

Vic was still waiting in the café "Kranzler", eyeing the matronly ladies ranged round the wall nervously. "They allowed you out?" He ordered another coffee.

"Well, I suppose so," said the artist with a grin. "What I like is the way here in the West they have glass cases full of valuable furs, antiques, jewellery, all along either side of the Ku'damm, and nobody steals them. In the East they have the same thing, but their cases are all full of wellies, thousands and thousands of wellies."

"Would you say that was the high point of your visit to Berlin?" asked Vic, opening his note-pad.

"Oh no." The painter became serious and emptied his brandy into the last of the coffee. "I like East Berlin. I've been all over it by tram, 'drawn' to them, you might say. No, the high point of my visit was emerging from the big store where we have our show, a few nights ago, the night of the big demonstration when all the windows were smashed. Great fun. I walked into the Wittenberg Platz station dressed in my full Highland regalia, kilt, dirk, jaiskit, brogues, the lot, and was laughed at by two guys dressed as parrots."

*It was the year of Green issues. Some said the climate was getting warmer, the "Greenhouse effect", and that there would soon be sharks and crocodiles in the Clyde. Others said there always had been. The Tramway Theatre became the place to be if you could stand the draught, and an international bicycle race hurtled through Glasgow in the rain. Theatres and galleries sprouted up across the city, television crews from all over the world began to pop out of closes or perch themselves on the concrete planters in the pedestrian precincts. Princes Square and the St Enoch Centre with their glass lifts, the elegance of Glasgow's Harrods, Frasers, the Candleriggs Market – Glasgow was no longer "The best kept secret in Europe", it was THE place, subject of international newspaper stories, the skyline of the city centre punctuated by busy cranes building and restoring, a Renaissance place, a mecca for art-hungry dealers from California, a haven for retiring double-base players from Russia.*

*Folklore was not dead in Renaissance Glasgow. Mayfest, Scotland's premier popular arts festival, Street Biz, the Jazz Festival . . . the plans and schemes of a unique partnership between the City Fathers, Government and business was bearing fruit in a spectacular way . . .*

*Batman arrived and multi-theatre cinemas overflowed. More curry was eaten in Glasgow than in Bombay, and satellite television dishes began to appear, like a giant tea-set scattered across the roofs of pubs and clubs. The Garden Festival site was no more, except for a bridge and a wee tower. Eight inch giant gerbils were advertised at £8 each. A few cars could run on unleaded petrol, and a part-time woman was required to manage a bar in Nitshill. Some folk got upset because Mo Johnson signed for Rangers. During the First World War Constantine McGhee, a Third Lanark player and a Catholic, had played for Rangers as a full-back. As he ran down the wing he always said that one mighty voice stood out in the heart of the Celtic roar. The voice was that of big Mick Cassidy, a giant of a man whose son left Hamilton Accies' to play for Rangers "extra" team during the temporary Southern Region League during the last war. There is nothing new under the sun. The truth is that Glasgow is really only ONE team, made up of all the men, women, and weans who are the Glasgow story. There is no city in the world that can put such a smile on its face, and for those who had left the Clydeside and made new lives for themselves in lands afar, a return to the blossoming Cultural Capital of Europe only reminded them of that.*

THE cat walked daintily along the top of the fence, paused to judge the distance, and leaped on to the roof of the garden shed. A thrush flew off, complaining bitterly.

"There's that Tibby there again, John. It'll be in your sweet peas next. We should get a dog."

John glanced up and busied himself in the sink again. "I'd rather have a dishwasher."

"We've got one," replied his wife, stirring her cup of tea. "John! There's enough sugar in this to sink a ship!" she complained. "You know I only take one."

He put the last saucepan on the pile on the drying-board. "I forgot," he said, wiping the suds off his hands and arms on the dish-towel. "It's been quite a rush to get it all ready."

"Well leave the dishes then," replied Mrs Maxwell. She sipped her tea and pushed the cup and saucer away in disgust. "Och . . . I canna drink that."

"Is that the time?" her husband looked up at the Habitat clock on the wall beside the diet chart. "I've to be at the airport by ten. It's the back of nine now. What about the sitting room?"

"Now don't you worry," she said, relenting. "The place'll be nice and tidy when they all get here."

"It's just that I haven't seen my brother for over 12 years."

"It's ten, dear. He went to Canada in 1978."

John sat down and stood up again. "I suppose I'd better get my jacket." He rushed out of the room and could be heard rummaging about in the cupboard under the stairs. He stuck his head round the door. "Are my glasses in here?"

"You're wearing them, darling," said his wife, running her finger over the "clean" dishes. She elected to say nothing.

"Oh. Oh aye. So I am. Imagine that! Well . . . " he paused. "I suppose I had better be going then."

She turned him about gently and propelled him towards the front door, closing it after him and putting down the snib. She stood silently in the hall looking at herself in the darkened mirror until she heard the car drive off. Humming a tune to herself she busied herself untangling the knots in the vacuum cleaner flex.

He drove over the Kingston Bridge. To his left the river curled through the heart of the city, the spires of the Tolbooth, the Tron Church and St Andrew's marking the older original heart of the city, while close at hand the offices of the Scottish Development Agency, mastermind of change, BP, and the Ministry of Defence sped past as he put the car into overdrive and raced for the airport. Past Hillington Estate, the disused Electric Light Bulb building, a prime example of the architecture of the Empire Exhibition awaited an interesting future, and away over to the right beyond Clydebank the long line of the Campsie Hills marked the edge of the valley and the beginning of the Highlands. An aircraft appeared suddenly out of the low cloud beyond Renfrew, circling to approach. He put his foot down.

The voice echoed through the airport. John ran up the stairs, two at a time. "British Airways announce the arrival of their flight No 135 from London Gatwick." There was a sizeable crowd at the arrivals gate past the tie shop and the stand selling teddy bears.

"John! JOHN!" A tall bronzed figure strode through the mass of people towards him. He had a momentary vision of a wee boy throwing a cardboard glider out of a bedroom window in Carntyne, 30, more, years ago . . .

"How's my little brother?" The stranger dropped his bags and flung his arms around him.

"Mike!" his eyes felt moist, in spite of himself. "I'm that glad to see you. Welcome home."

Mike smiled down at him. "Home? Well I guess it is, at that . . . old place looks the same," he glanced around him at the hurrying throng.

"No it's not," replied John, picking up his brother's case and bag. "Wait 'till you see . . . but it's still home."

214

# A MERCHANT CITY

*A few years ago there was an area of Glasgow that could properly be said to BE Glasgow, but was sadly in need of repair. Roughly bounded by the High Street, Argyle Street, Queen Street, and Cochrane Street, it was a part of the city which had seen the tide of years flow past for more than eight centuries. The Black Friars had had their orchards there, Bonnie Prince Charlie had marched through it on his way down the Back Cow Lone, and the Ramshorne Kirk had known the nightly raids of body-snatchers more terrible than any Burke or Hare. Doctor David Livingstone and "Paraffin" Young had lived just outside its boundaries, the other side of the High Street had been the home of the ancient college, Glasgow University, before it moved to newer, more expensive premises on Gilmorehill. In its heyday, it had also been the location of some of the darkest, most noisome streets of the Thieves' Kitchen, the Havannah Wynd, and the rest. Wars and revolutions, proclamations and battles had all been fought out or drunk over at Glasgow Cross. When the Tolbooth Tower, Town House and Jail were attached, the occasional execution was not unknown, the hangman striding up to the gibbet in his white gloves to do his office. The Tontine Hotel and Coffee-house had been the favoured meeting place of scheming tobacco barons, who also strutted proudly along the "plainstanes" on the other side of the street, resplendent in their scarlet capes and gold-topped canes.*

*By the middle of the 20th century the area had been forgotten, a dusty lily lying at the bottom of a dry pool, but the magic that really lies at the heart of what might seem like a very down to earth sort of people, was not dead, nor even asleep. Plans began to be laid to bring a new kind of life to a city within the city. The Merchant City was about to be reborn.*

*The restoration of the old warehouses in the heart of the area, the Houndsditch Building, Montrose Street, Glassford Street and Miller Street, were part of a grand design that was to be one of the pivotal keys of a new city, stretching down and along both banks of the Clyde. The former Sheriff Court, designated as a Museum of Fashion with its splendid Classical Greek portico, Hucheson's Hospital Hall, headquarters of the National Trust in the West of Scotland, already gleaming white like an American colonial church, the Italian Centre. It is small wonder that the area was given a prestigious European award as the best and most imaginative development of its kind. Life and leisure was part of the plan, and an Adam house, little better than a faded ruin, was restored to all its former elegance as the Babbity Bowster. Rab Ha's, named after the incredible Gleca Glutton of the same name also preserved the character of the 18th century.*

*The Merchant City is only the beginning. The whole of Glasgow is a Merchant City, and always has been, but the old heart of Glasgow has a special character which only history, a plentiful supply of ghosts, and a few modern merchants and characters could give it.*

L IVING in the Merchant City meant that when everybody else was going home, you were already there. The presses thundered in preparation for the morning edition as I turned the corner into Albion Street, stepping out into the road to avoid the huge lorry unloading bales of paper. Newspapers kept a different time from the rest of the world. It was the world's time, and although it was already

dark in Glasgow, tomorrow's headlines were being made in the afternoon sunshine of Los Angeles or New York, or the early morning fog of Azerbaijan. News was now, anywhere and anywhen, and walking on, I crossed the streets by the Ramshorne Churchyard to avoid walking over the graves that are under the pavement. The lights of the Strathclyde University Halls twinkled down the Georgian facade of Blackfriars Street as I skirted the old City Hall with its cornucopia of polychromatic stone fruit and the BMWs parked outside the "Café Gandolfi". The little courtyard in front of The Babbity Bowster, one of my "locals", was full of people. There was live music on, and the place would be packed.

"Well you see," he said slowly, putting his white trilby on the bar with care. "What is this City of Culture all about, anyway?" A columnist with a controversial streak to his wee nature, who was a past-master at putting the moggie among any set of pigeons that crossed his word-processor, drained his glass.

His face wrinkled in disgust as I ordered a fresh orange juice and pointed at the posters on the wall. There was drama and music, dance, exhibitions, events, all pasted up together, obscuring those from the weeks before.

"That's just paper," said the columnist. He was a friend, and really a quiet sort of chap underneath the Diogenes-like exterior.

"I know that," I played along with the game and sipped my orange juice. "That's just a part of it. Culture is people, no, more than that, THE people."

"You can't just make a Renaissance."

"Aye you can, we are. It's about tourists and the local economy, not just pictures that might as well be hanging upside down. People place an estimation on you largely equal to the one you give yourself. The same goes for cities. Glasgow knows it's good, and it's getting better."

"Is this intellectual chatter, or can I join in?" Wull wasn't anything to do with the theatre or the arts, he was just Wull.

"Aye. We're talkin' about the City of Culture."

"Oh that!" said Wull eyeing the hat suspiciously. "Saw a man in a film with a hat like that once," he said, "either a gangster or an Irish poet or somethin'."

*216*

"Why not both?" I said. "The Medicis didn't achieve power and money by being polite. Read *The Prince*. They had no principles whatever, vicious."

"Sound like artists to me."

"It would. Anyway, these 'gangsters' of Renaissance Italy were the patrons who payed for some of the most sublime works of art ever created."

"But is Glasgow better than Edinburgh?" asked Wull.

"Paisley's better than Edinburgh. You can't place a price on Culture." I leaned forward. "Look, the Glasgow Renaissance is nothing new. It's been here all the time. Too many people couldn't afford the time before, that's all. The people are the same. Painters, dramatists, poets, musicians . . . people, that's what Glasgow is famous for. Glasgow people have been creating, inventing . . . "

"Conquering and pillaging."

"A bit of that too," I agreed. "But they've been doing all those things around the world for centuries. Now they are doing it at home, without the 'pillage' bit. Glasgow isn't just the Clydeside. Glasgow is worldwide, and another thing," I said, picking up the hat to make sure there was, in fact, nothing hiding underneath it, "Glasgow always has been a City of Culture . . ."

*Glasgow is not just a city, it is a story, a story begun in the centuries when today's streets were woods, when today's Clyde dried up in the summer and got lost in the reeds and rushes somewhere about Bridgeton. Through all the changes of nearly 2,000 years, the tales and times of the city by the banks of the Clyde have one constant theme running through them – the humour and the special strengths of the people of Glasgow. The crest of the city shows a bird, a fish, a bell, and a tree, and that bell, which the first Lord Provost of the City, John Stewart of Minto "caused tae be rungen lood", is the bell of liberty and of laughter. Its peals have survived war, famine, flood, plague, riot, and rung out the great achievements that have contributed so much to the making of the modern world. The great days of Second Cityhood have passed by, but another, newer Second City is being born. The same fires burn in the deep valleys of the Clyde, and new explorers and engineers, artists and scientists, will take the place of the shadowy legions of the past in whiskers and wigs, leather aprons, armour and wool, lined up like sentries at the gate of every day before today. The story of Glasgow is essentially a tale of tomorrow, of what men and women, faced with the unknown, can really achieve, and just how loudly they can ring . . . THEIR "Bell in the Tree".*

*Lasers struck out across the valley, coherent light, undiminished by distance, downwards from the high ranges of the night sky. Red-gold, greens ranging through blue, a rich dark violet that could almost be tasted. The light touched the pinnacles of the churches and towers in a city of towers, washed its rainbow way along Park Circus, danced on Trinity Towers, flowered on the crest of the Greek Thomson Church in St Vincent Street. Quick as thought the criss-cross fingers of colour found the Tolbooth Tower with its Imperial Crown, reached for the Tron Church, St Andrew's, the Merchants' Steeple, darted across George Square to St George's Tron, played the pinnacles of the City Chambers with the music of light. Glasgow was Cultural Capital of Europe.*

*A procession of children moved through the trees, the paper lanterns lighting their upturned faces, tracing a soft glow about the "Ohs" and "Ahhhs" as fireworks burst in splendour over Kelvin Park and rains of silver stars fell glittering into the river to vanish with a soft "hiss".*

*The carillon of bells in the Tolbooth, usually rung to honour Cameron of Lochiel, who saved Glasgow from Charles Edward Stuart's Jacobite army, pealed out across the city, lit like a great ship riding at anchor in the darkness of the surrounding countryside. Other bells in other steeples took up the sound and the clamour and the lights joined together to celebrate the rebirth of Glasgow, the coming year and the coming millenium.*

JIMMY had slept all the way home on the back seat of the car, the tartan blanket his mother usually wrapped over her knee tucked around him and under his head. He opened his eyes sleepily as his father carried him upstairs and his mother pulled his shoes off and unfolded his nightshirt.

"That was great Daddy," he said. "I'm glad I got one." He opened his hand to show his parents the little blackened cinder in his palm, a fallen star, caught just as it bounced about on the damp grass beneath the trees in George Square.

"I'll put it beside your bed for the morning," said his mother, taking the treasure from him gently.

He turned his head towards his star. "Can it shine again? Can we go again?" Jimmy asked, yawning. "Go and see the lights in the sky."

"Shhh, now," she said, folding back the covers. "There'll be lots of other days and other times. You've never been up this late before."

He clambered into bed and closed his eyes. His parents shut the door quietly and went downstairs for a while.

Jimmy was high up in the air, looking down. He was not afraid. He thought, and moved where he thought, watching the curving curling spires approach as he glided over the city. A cockerel, strutting proudly about on its perch on the great spire, watched him drift past, and spread its iron tail-feathers with the arrogance of all weathervanes. A copper galleon near at hand, beached on the pinnacle of a green dome, broke free and drifted past, its metal sails forever full of old trade winds that blew across seas long vanished from the world. He seated himself comfortably in the prow and watched as the panorama unfolded beneath him.

Kings were there, and horses, children playing happily among the rich cloths that hung on either side of the knights, riding stiffly beside their squires, each with a lance ready to hand. Men carrying exciting-looking sacks of rough cloth or bundles of twigs, the green leaves and bright berries still clinging to them like strings of burning pearls wreathed in dark green ivory. There were tall cloaked figures in scarlet capes and washerwomen, pushing and jostling, laughing as they made way for a tight little group of grey-clad figures with bright lamps shining on their helmets. Dogs with long soulful

faces and chickens, haughty cats with eyes green as ice, solid, serious Clydesdales, big as mountains, ridden by small boys in rags, all laughing, all going somewhere with a sense of purpose. He sailed on through the sky and the procession fell away below him until it was a tiny ribbon of colour threading its way through an undulating landscape.

His ship sailed up and over a bank of cloud, laced with lines of coloured light, like ribbon wrapped round an enormous parcel. The light was tied in a knot. As he watched the knot began to unwind itself, as if a huge invisible hand was untying it. The cloud was a parcel, and inside was the world, turning slowly, glittering blue-green the way he had seen pictures of it taken from orbit. Only this world had clouds around it and beyond it. The ship sank lower and below him he could see flecks of white, the crests of waves racing towards the shore. Ahead of him, waiting on the shore were the people and animals he had seen in the procession. The ship stopped, not quite touching the water, bobbing in the air as light as a dream. With that thought the bright throng on the shore seemed to recede, back and back into yesterday. He knew then that he was part of their story and they of his, but they were yesterday. He was still part of tomorrow. Drawn upwards by a thread of silver, the bright copper ship set sail for the morning.

"Still sleeping," said his father in a whisper as he looked round the door into the bedroom. "I wonder what he made of it all?"

He closed the door quietly. In the dimness of the bedroom Jimmy's face was lit in sleep by a brief pale glow. On his bedside table lay the precious cinder. Only dreams can kindle a fallen star.

*The eastern sky was laid out in a neat geometric pattern of squares. They were faint, they were several miles high, but they were there, or at least they seemed to be. Davy admired his hedge and took no notice. Do you looked surprised because your house has walls? You know it has. Well then, the world had Stringers. Same thing. He leaned across and re-arranged a leaf.*

*Between 1880 and 1980 the world had leapt ahead several thousand years in technology. By the closing decades of the 20th century the pace of change and development was accelerating at an ever-increasing rate. It was exponential. It was getting a wee bit faster all the time.*

*Somewhere between 2035 and 2036 a research student working in Kelvin Collegium, the unified body that had replaced both Glasgow universities and many of the major colleges, made a crucial discovery. It was nothing unusual for great discoveries to be made in Glasgow. Professor Black and Lord Kelvin had both changed the lives of Glaswegians and a wider world more than almost anyone realised then, or later. The student, a native of Bute, was determined to get the best out of his studies, and was actually aiming at a secure long-term career with the South of Scotland Energy Conservation Board. He was soon to put them out of business.*

*It had been theorised during the eighties that there might be a cheap way of producing power from water, but there was some missing key, some alchemy that made fusion perpetually elude the best minds who believed in it. A few scientists knew that they were getting close to regions where anything might describe matter, words, grunts, even a line drawn in the sand with a twig tied to a cigarette packet. The closer you got into things the less it seemed to be held together by anything but faith, charm, spit, strangeness, or whatever words popped into unpoetic scientific brains. It had also been thought that there might be ''lines'' of energy crossing the universe, incredibly dense, or words to that effect. Stringers were narrow channels into an alternative universe where energy was being created all the time. It was a giant fishnet to catch the power that created galaxies and started hearts ticking. It was easy. Davy MacLean discovered it. The Stringers were not actually there, their* effect *was. He had worked it all out in his head one afternoon in Kelvin Park once again green with elms, grown from the cloned seeds developed by Kelvin C's own laboratory facilities on the Amero-Soviet space station, now several kilometres from hub to antennae. He had retired from active research, to a small house in the forest that surrounded the city, content with his garden and his collection of late 20th-century compact discs.*

*The first years of the millenium had been difficult ones for the older nations of the world. The formation of a common market between the United States and the Soviet Union that excluded Europe had led to a series of brief thinly disguised wars in Central Asia and Southern Africa, but the offer by the Japanese to buy Europe outright had been the signal for greater co-operation with the Amero-Soviets, and Europe had been saved from privatisation. The world was now administered by a central authority which did little more than bow to the rugged individualism of states growing increasingly tiny within an interdependent framework of common concern for a ravaged environment.*

*The temporary isolation of Europe had given birth to the City-States Movement, led by Glasgow, Hamburg, Gdansk, and Marseilles, and throughout, Glasgow had*

*maintained an integrity and individuality that had been a reality for centuries. The early establishment of the Media Ville Europe headquarters in Glasgow meant that the city, the natural centre for the interchange of goods and information between North America, European Russia, and Central Europe, had given a fresh impetus to a cultural Renaissance that had already been evident during the late 1980s.*

*The elevation of all living things, including trees, to the status of "protected species" and the introduction of severe penalties across the world for damage to the environment had halted the rapid escalation of the "greenhouse effect", but not before the global temperature had climbed by two degrees. Large areas of the coastline were flooded by the melting of the arctic ice, and Glasgow was now virtually an island surrounded by a graceful fan of 36 bridges and two tunnels. The Channel Tunnel found itself emerging under water at either end and had to be abandoned. The seas had stopped receding now, and grape-growers of the Clyde valley were beginning to complain as frosts became more severe year by year. Some people were never satisfied, and some things never changed . . .*

McGHEE tapped on the door and looked about him furtively. The pavement outside the block of Victorian flats, tucked between an Earthcom Relay Station and a transit tube, looked neglected. Weeds grew in cracks in the kerbstones, and a quaint old neon lamp, still with a few scraps of dark green paint adhering to it, tilted darkly towards the banks of the river where the new embankment ran along Argyle Street.

"Aye, what is it?" A panal slid back, revealing an eye, unblinking in the darkened opening.

"I was telt to see if you were in, that is, if anybody was . . . "

"Who telt ye? Who sent ye?" said the voice with deep suspicion.

"Sandy, down at the Recycling Office. He gave me this." McGhee held a grubby piece of real paper, the kind made from wood pulp and rags. "That proves I'm here with his say-so. He said that wis the passport."

"Let's see it then," a scrawny hand emerged from the depths and snatched the paper away. "Aye, it's real right enough. OK." The panel slid shut with a "bang" and opened to reveal a flight of steps descending into the gloom.

McGhee stumbled after his guide and found himself in a long, low basement. It was poorly lit. A single old-fashioned electric light bulb dangled from a frayed wire. There were no glowpanels anywhere. The place had a stale, musty odour and small groups of men and women sat about in furtive knots of whispered conversation.

"Well?" said the guide. "What do you want?"

"Er, what have you got?"

"The very best, if you have the Ecus to pay for it. Genuine canned lager, pre-Flood bottled beer, cigarettes, not the kind made in the Kingdom of Cornwall, neither. Real ones. Look." He held out a small box with a badly printed label. "Cools" read the label. "Product of the Commonwealth of Australia."

"I'll take those," said McGhee eagerly. "And two cans of lager and a bottle of that brown stuff."

"Expensive."

"This do?" he slapped a thick bundle of metallic banknotes down on the dingy counter. "Any . . . whisky?"

The little man looked puzzled. "Whisky, what's that?"

"Just asking, because if you had . . . that would be a capital offence!" He produced his badge and a thin wicked-looking needle gun. "You are all under arrest!"

Somebody shouted, "Proctors! It's a raid!" and the pathetic denizens of the cellar stampeded towards the wall as heavily booted City Proctors thundered down the stairs and started to turn the tables over methodically.

"You are charged with managing an illegal cigarette and canned beer shop."

"I've a right to representation," protested the barkeeper as he was spread-eagled against a wall.

"For the crime of 'Off-License' we can hold you for three days without," said McGhee harshly.

"That's the lot," the sergeant stamped over and waved his stunprod about. "MacClure has gone down, sir. His nose plugs fell out and the tobacco smoke was too much for him."

"There must be whisky in a place like this somewhere," said McGhee, casting a professional eye around the cellar. "It's getting harder to come by, I mean find."

"Sir!" the sergeant clicked his heels together and saluted.

Outside the night sky darkened through pink to black. The white disc of Amero-Soviet Station One, almost as big as the moon, drifted across the zodiac. Like a chess board drawn across the heavens, the net of Stringers spread upward from the northern latitudes, catching the raw bouts of fire that drove another universe. There were still fishermen by the banks of the Clyde.

223

# SELECTED BIBLIOGRAPHY

Berry, Simon and Hamish Whyte, Ed, *Glasgow Observed* (John Donald, 1987)

Fife, Hugh, *The Lore of Highland Trees* (Famedram, Gartocharn)

*Glasgow Herald/Evening Times* archives

Gomme and Walker, *Architecture of Glasgow* (Lund Humphries, London, 1987)

Greenwood, Cedric, *Glasgowtrammerung* (Heritage Press, 1986)

Hale, Reginald B. FSA Scot, *The Beloved* (University of Ottawa Press, 1989)

Holmyard, E. J., *Alchemy* (Penguin Books, 1957)

Hope, Iain, *The Campbells of Kilmun* (Aggregate, 1981)

Hume, John and Michael Moss, *Beardmore* (Heinemann, 1979)

*Jones's Directory for 1787* (Republished William Love, 1868)

Kenna, Rudolf, *Glasgow Art Deco* (Richard Drew Publishing, 1985)

Kinchin, Perilla and Juliet, *Glasgow's Great Exhibitions* (White Cockade, 1988)

Mackie, J. D., *A History of Scotland* (Penguin Books, 1964)

Marzaroli, Oscar, *One Man's World* (Third Eye Centre and Glasgow District Libaries, 1984)

Nancarrow, F. G., *Glasgow's Fighter Squadron* (Collins, 1942)

Oakley, Charles, *The Second City* (Blackie, 1967)

Phillips, Alastair, *Glasgow's Herald* (Richard Drew Publishing, 1982)

*Scottish Firsts* (SDA Publications, 1985)

Smart, Aileen, *Villages of Glasgow. Volume 1* (John Donald, 1988)

Stewart, Ian, *The Glasgow Tramcar* (Scottish Tramway Museum Society, 1983)

Teggin/Samuel/Stewart/Leslie, *Glasgow Revealed* (Heritage Books, 1988)

Tuchman, Barbara W., *A Distant Mirror* (Penguin Books, 1978)

Tweed, *Glasgow and the Clyde a Hundred Years Ago* (Molendinar Press, 1979)

Walker, Frank, *The South Clyde Estuary* (Scottish Academic Press, 1986)

Worsdall, Frank, *Victorian City* (Richard Drew Publishing, 1982)